THE GODDESS SPEAKS

Myths & Meditations

THE GODDESS SPEAKS

Myths & Meditations

Dee Poth

SIBYL
PUBLICATIONS
PORTLAND, OREGON

Published by **SIBYL Publications** • a division of Micro One, Inc.
123 N.E. Third Avenue, Suite 502 • Portland, Oregon 97232

Grateful acknowledgment is given to Merlin Stone for permission
to use the prayer to Ishtar from *Ancient Mirrors of Womanhood,*
© 1979 by Merlin Stone.

Illustrations by Rene McCullough

Graphic design by Design Studio Selby

Library of Congress Cataloging in Publication Data
Poth, Dee.
    The Goddess speaks : myths & meditations / Dee Poth.
    p. cm.
    Includes bibliographical references.
    Includes a deck of meditation cards with illustrations of 25
goddesses.
    ISBN 0-9638327-2-7

    1. Goddess religion. 2. Mythology. 3. Women–Psychology.   I.
Title.
BL473.5.P58 1994   291.2'114
                                       QB194-21095

Printed and bound in the United States of America

CONTENTS

INTRODUCTION

$\mathbf{T}$he Goddess personifies the oneness of creation, the unity of all life. She creates from her body and with her spirit and energy. Her manifestations are life-centered, embracing a cycle of birth, nurturing, death, and re-birth. The Goddess provides an embodiment and focus for the concept of feminine spirituality.

Our earliest evidence about the Goddess is from the Pale-olithic and Neolithic periods (35,000–3000 B.C.E., that is, Before the Current Era). Though there are no written records from these eras, her story is told in the physical characteristics of figures and artifacts and the varied symbols depicted on them. These symbols have left an enduring mark on Western consciousness. The spiral and snake represent energy and the life force. The V is the symbol of birth, the crescent the symbol of becoming. The head of the bull symbolizes the womb, the horns the Fallopian tubes. The butterfly signifies rebirth and new life.

Her attributes are personified in the postures and func-tions portrayed in her images. Early figures are of pregnant nudes and of mothers depicted in the act of giving birth, signifying abundance and fertility. Huge breasts and protruding buttocks suggest nourishment. As a bird goddess, her associations with the heavens are illustrated. The presence of a lion or panther proclaims her royal power.

The Goddess was the supreme deity of the planet from at least 30,000 B.C.E. until the beginning of the Bronze Age, about 3500 B.C.E. With the shift to patriarchal power, the Goddess was eventually subsumed by the gods. Legends of the gods tell of power and strength, of control and domination. Without the balance of the feminine, masculine dominance over the last four thousand years has led to the separation of humanity and nature, of male and female.

The Goddess ruled under many names and manifested herself in many guises, but fundamentally she is the Earth itself, the energy of the planet. She reveals feminine creative energy through her many roles. She presents the positive, the life force that energizes the world and brings joy, dance, and song, as well as fertility, birth, and death. Death in the goddess myths becomes an avenue to rebirth, to a new cycle of life. According to this ancient wisdom, life, not death, is the primary energy of the universe. These varied functions have been described throughout history with numerous names, diverse stories, and changing images that appear to be different goddesses but are in fact one.

From the psychological view, we have become increasingly aware of the lack of feminine form and spirit in the prevailing religions of our day. Many feel this yin/yang imbalance has led to much of the mental, physical, and spiritual abuse to the life forms on our planet. The recognition of a universal need to nurture and be nurtured is being answered with the development of the feminine aspect.

The resurgence of the idea of a goddess who personifies the oneness of all life has been aided and accelerated by new findings in physics. Quantum mechanics points out the interrelatedness of all. Images of the Goddess as weaver illustrate the connections of life forms and reflect this concept. New physics theories describe the effect of the observer on the observed. The world that ancient peoples observed was seen as friendly, not threatening. Life was viewed in a positive way. The result of this view, which does indeed suggest that the observer affects the observed, was a peaceful society. This proposition is supported by archeological finds of early goddess-centered cultures that show no evidence of warfare, of defense structures, or of institutionalized violence. These findings lend authenticity to the Goddess movement.

The rise of the women's movement was a response to the political and social problems experienced by women. However, it did not address women's spiritual needs. As women have become aware of these needs, a focus on spirituality and the

Goddess image has emerged as an answer both to feminine spiritual hunger and women's need for spiritual validation.

What the human family has not experienced is a true partnership of God/Goddess attributes. Both talk of love. What is needed is the empowerment of the loving, nurturing principle that will result from a merging of masculine/feminine energies. Then the possibility of a vigorous, peaceful world filled with abundance and love becomes a reality.

Observing the images of the Goddess and reading her stories bring these ideas back into our consciousness. Though many myths were grievously distorted and changed by the patriarchy as it rose to power, sifting through the tales and filtering the basic ideas will bring women a new source of strength and pride, of authenticity and validation. Men, too, need the nurturing, feminine side of their psyche unveiled so that together in feminine and masculine balance, the God/ess can touch our lives with life-affirming messages. And so we welcome the return of the Goddess, not to replace a god, but to unite in equal partnership.

HOW TO USE THE
GODDESS CARDS

Use the Goddess Cards to absorb the essence of her multiple images and stories. Handle the cards often, imbuing them with your energy as you contemplate the images that have represented feminine spirituality since ancient times.

Start your day by drawing a card. Read her story in the accompanying book. Center on the attribute named on the card during your meditation. Explore, experience, and demonstrate this attribute throughout the day. Realize that you are part of the bringing forth of the earthly expression of the Goddess. You have a share in today's realization of a feminine spiritual presence.

Though we have lost sight of the Goddess through the ages, focusing on her myths and on the gifts she has brought to the world is important. How she can relate to you and your life will heighten your awareness of the presence of a feminine spirit of love, nurturing, and power.

ALA
(A̲h-la)
Africa

WATCHFULNESS

Impart to me your attribute of watchfulness that
I may see where I must review and revise my
attitudes and actions. Guide my daily life
so that it reflects your nurturing love.

Africa myth is directly con-
nected to daily life. The sacred does not just permeate life, it is
life. It is all that constitutes the everyday. Everything has a purpose, objects and possessions as well as acts and intentions.
Myth provides the correct forms to follow, whether one is planting
seeds, making love, or taking part in a ceremony or ritual. Though
the stories may change over time, vary from tribe to tribe and
from one geographical area to another, there is an underlying
unity in the sacred and the profane.

The Mother Goddess of the Ibo tribe of Nigeria is called
Ala. She rises from the distant past and is still worshiped today.
Rather than a solemn rite or ritual, she is honored by the act of

building a small house surrounded by a porch. These houses are called Mbari and are built by a group of men and women when the priest or diviner calls upon them to do so. When he receives what he considers an appropriate sign from the Goddess, which could be as slight as coming upon a snake in his garden or as major as a crisis of famine or plague, he gathers the group of men and women. They will live together in celibacy until the Mbari is built, which may take weeks or may take years.

A figure of Ala is placed in the center of the Mbari. From this vantage point, she looks out at the village and observes all that goes on. She considers all the villagers her children. Surrounding Ala are mud sculptures of people involved in village life: a farmer, a woman at her sewing machine, a policeman, water spirits, mothers, and children. They are painted with bright color and pattern.

After the house is completed and a festival or celebration has been held, the Mbari is left to disintegrate. Neither the house nor the sculptures are ever repaired. The Mbari represents concerns and aspirations of the village that must be discarded so that new needs and cares may be addressed.

Ala is the caretaker of the Ibo tribe. She is the Goddess of fertility and birth, provides laws for the living, and receives the dead so they can be reborn again. She is often honored with a tree that is central in the village. Whether in a house or a tree, she is always where she can see the villagers and all they do. Ala, in turn, can be seen by the villagers and is there to be turned to for guidance.

The concept of a mother goddess who watches over us is found in many myths and legends. Her presence functions as a guardian of morality and as a loving, caring presence that is always there for us.

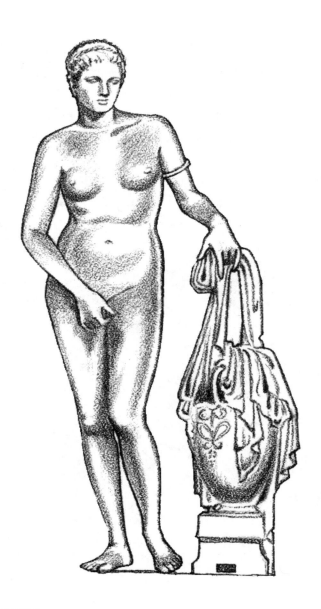

APHRODITE
(Af-ro-<u>di</u>-tee)
Greece

LOVE

You personify not only the love of woman for man but the love of friendship, of nature, and of a just cause. May I share your beauty and joyousness and your giving of self to all expressions of love.

Aphrodite is said to have risen from the sea, born of the union of the Sky God and the Sea Womb. She rode on a mussel shell to the island of Cyprus, where she shook her long hair and watched the falling drops of water turn to pearls at her feet. She had journeyed from Canaan, where she was Mother Goddess, to Greece, where she became the Goddess of Love. The powers of the Canaanite Mother Goddess were downgraded by the Greeks, but Aphrodite, even though considered demoted, became a powerful symbol.

When she arrived at Cyprus, she was greeted by the Horae, who became her attendants and priestesses. They lamented with

Aphrodite as she honored her memories of Adonis, who had been her son/lover in Canaan. In her rituals, the Horae wove poppies and myrtle leaves into wreaths for their heads and planted seeds that died before maturity as Adonis had.

Aphrodite elevated the definition of the Goddess of Love to represent every kind of love humans are capable of: the love of friendship, of woman for man, of caring for a cause, of nature, and of life itself. She was associated not only with grand passions but with simple joys. She was married to Hephaestus, the God of Smithcraft, who was crippled and ugly, but made beautiful things. She was the lover of Ares, the God of War, and the mother of Eros, or Cupid.

Aphrodite is the only Greek goddess to be portrayed nude. Her sculptures show her unself-conscious acceptance of her beauty and body. As an archetype of love, beauty, and joy, Aphrodite offers a positive symbol to women today.

ARTEMIS
(R̲-teh-miss)
Anatolia/Turkey

WHOLENESS

As you personify the many aspects of womanhood, be
with me in my many roles: in the home, in vocation,
in relationships with others.

Artemis is an enduring presence
in the Goddess pantheon. Her beginnings can be traced to ancient Turkey, then called Anatolia. She was adopted by the Greeks
when they conquered Turkey, and she acquired many personas.
The twin of Apollo, she established her role as a midwife by
aiding her mother, Leto, in Apollo's birth immediately after she
was born. As a goddess, she cared for women in childbirth.

Artemis was the Goddess of the hunt and protectress of
the animals. Her blessing was required for a successful hunt;
many images show her with bow and arrow in hand. She embodied the ancient idea that the animal who was hunted must
be a willing victim or the hunt would not be successful. Early
man blessed the animal before killing it, honoring the gift it gave.

Artemis personified both hunter and hunted. In offering homage to her, one showed respect both for the victim and for the action taken. She is often depicted as a friend of the animals, sometimes pictured with lion cubs or bears. Stags draw her chariot, dogs accompany her through the forest.

The Goddess permitted no deviation from the responsibility one owed her. The story of Actaeon is an example. Actaeon was a hunter who, while walking through the forest with his dogs one day, happened upon Artemis bathing in a woodland pool. He hid to watch the beautiful Goddess. When she discovered him, she was furious and turned him into a stag. His dogs no longer recognized him and after a rigorous chase, leapt upon him and devoured him.

Her dark side is also evidenced in the classic Greek story of Iphigeneia. Agamemnon was hunting in a grove sacred to Artemis. There he killed a stag and announced that Artemis could have done no better. The Goddess did not like his comparison of their hunting skills, so she calmed the winds to prevent his fleet from sailing to Troy. He could appease her only if he sacrificed his daughter Iphigeneia. At the last minute she was saved when Artemis allowed a doe to be substituted. Iphigeneia was taken by the Goddess to become her priestess.

Artemis personifies both the dark and the light and is

therefore a stern taskmaster. Still she is known for her role as a caretaker of women and as both a virgin and fertility symbol. Her role as a fertility symbol is evidenced in the statue found at the temple in Ephesus. The base seems almost like a tree trunk; the upper portion of her torso is covered with what some thought were multiple breasts and others considered to be the testicles of bulls, which could represent the completeness of male/female fertility.

For women today she brings together in one figure many desirable and varied attributes of woman: sense of self-worth, beauty, strength, and power.

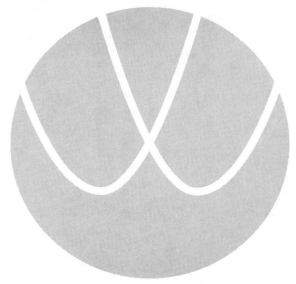

ASTARTE

(A-star-tee)
Syria/Palestine/Canaan

ASCENSION

*As you descended to Earth as a blazing star, allow me
to ascend to the heaven you left, strengthened
by your power and your wisdom.*

Astarte is the daughter of El, the
god whose name is used interchangeably with that of Yahweh
in the Book of Genesis. Her mother is Asherah, the Hebrew
Goddess called the Queen of Heaven, and her brother is Baal,
the God of Thunder so feared by the Hebrews.

Astarte was not born in the usual way. She descended
from the heavens as a falling star. Her fiery mass was cooled at
the Lake of Aphaca and a great temple was built to house the
holy stone. The stone was believed to heal those who touched it
and foretell the future for those who could understand it. Sometimes the names of Astarte, Asherah, and Anath were used as
though for the same personage, representing the maiden, mother,
crone trilogy.

Women were the chief worshipers of Astarte. Their ceremony is described in the Old Testament by Jeremiah. During his time, goddess sites and statues were being systematically destroyed by the Hebrews. The women rose up in protest and said they would continue to offer incense and libations to the Goddess. They baked cakes in the shape of the Goddess, and the family ate them together to celebrate Astarte. Some believe this was a forerunner of the Eucharist. A goddess mold, dating from 1600 B.C.E., that could have been used for this purpose was found in Israel.

The Book of Jeremiah in the Old Testament (44:11-19) contains a description of the rituals used for the worship of Astarte/Asherah. Jeremiah had told the people that the God of Israel was angry with them because they burned incense and served other gods. "Therefore … says the Lord of hosts … I will set my face against you for evil … I will punish those who dwell in the land of Egypt … with the sword, with famine, and with pestilence." But a great assembly of people gathered to answer this message from God that had come through Jeremiah. "We will not listen to you. But we will do everything that we have vowed, burn incense to the queen of heaven and pour out libations to her, as we did … for then we had plenty of food and prospered, and saw no evil. But since we have left off burning incense to the queen of heaven and pouring out libations to her, we have lacked everything."

Astarte represents abundance, healing, a relationship with the stars, and a respect for all stages of life.

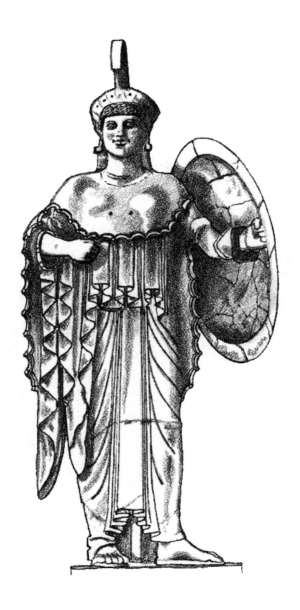

ATHENA
(Aa-<u>thee</u>-nah)
Ancient Greece

POWER

*Weave with me a fabric of life that will combine for me
your power as a warrior, your skill as a
craftswoman, and your love
as a goddess.*

Known as the Great Weaver,
Athena's ancient description discloses her origins as a goddess
of women. She is thought to have originated in Minoan Crete as
a household goddess ruling domestic crafts, especially weaving.
After the patriarchy gained power, she was established as the
patron of Athens and assumed a more masculine, warlike de-
meanor. Her early associations with the moon, snake, and owl
would have revealed her initial affiliation with women. Therefore, they were stripped from her so that she could assume her
aggressive role.

The new legends woven round Athena declared she was
born from the head of Zeus. They introduced the idea that, at

least for the gods, a woman was not necessary for creation. Zeus could produce Athena by himself. She sprang forth fully armed, acquired a new warlike personality, and was often depicted with helmet, shield, and sword.

However, many of Athena's early attributes could not be made to disappear. She was a symbol of responsibility and of fairness. She considered a deed before embarking on a path of action. In many myths and legends, she came to the aid of Greek heroes. One of her titles was Goddess of Wisdom. She was a supporter of good government, a civilizing influence. Though depicted as a warrior, she was associated more often with defense than aggression. Always practical, she invented the chariot and the ship and planted the first olive tree on the Acropolis.

Her early attributes could not be eliminated, even with the power of her new position as protectress of Athens. Athena never married or had children and was usually portrayed as rather austere and forbidding, but her deeds tell us of her love for humankind. In her rituals, her statue was taken once each year from the temple to the sea, washed, and adorned in a new robe woven by the women of Athens.

She speaks to us today of giving attention to the practical needs of life, of thinking before acting, and of supporting what we believe in.

BIRTH GODDESS of
ÇATAL HÜYÜK

(Cha-tall Hoo-yuk)
Çatal Hüyük, Turkey

BIRTH

Be with me as I birth new paths to follow and new
directions in my life. Strengthen me
to do this with love.

One of the most fascinating
finds in recent archeological history is the town of Çatal Hüyük
in Central Turkey. Estimated to be nine thousand years old, it is
the oldest urban center ever found. Çatal Hüyük, excavated from
1961 to 1965, contains much evidence of a sophisticated form of
goddess worship.

Houses in Çatal Hüyük were flat-roofed and were entered by a ladder through an opening in the roof. Platforms
were built in for sitting and sleeping. The bones of the dead were
buried under the platforms. The city based its economy on trade
and agriculture and was apparently quite prosperous. No evidence of warfare or institutionalized violence has been found:

no weapons, no destruction, no signs of aggression. It seems to have been a remarkable and inspiring society.

Many shrines dedicated to the Goddess were found at the site, giving us some idea of its rites and rituals. The male principle is represented by the bull; the Goddess is often portrayed in the act of giving birth. One shrine, which appears to have been a birthing room, is painted red, the color of life and blood. In another, the figure of the Goddess is suspended on the wall, legs spread over three bull heads. A fourth head is emerging from her body, suggesting that the Goddess is always in the act of giving birth. Maiden, mother, and crone appear.

One of the most notable sculptures found at the site is a small figurine of a birthing goddess flanked by leopards. She sits on a throne, her arms resting lightly on the felines as the head of a baby emerges. The cats symbolize royalty; she has the posture of a queen. This image of the Goddess honors the birthing process as the birth of new life, of expanded vision, and the rebirth of the self.

BRIDGIT

(<u>Bridge</u>-it)

Celtic Britain

COMMUNICATION

Light the fires of inspiration in my heart that
I may speak with words that reflect
your healing wisdom.

Bridgit rises from the ancient British past as an early example of a triple goddess. Triune goddesses assumed three roles, representing youth and renewal as the maiden, fertility and nurturing as the mother, and the wisdom of age as the crone. As a triune fire goddess, she gave people three examples of the sacred flame: the gift of inspiration in writing, the magical alchemy of metal craft when the metal is melted with fire and the molten mass is fashioned into something beautiful, and finally, the warmth of compassion and healing.

Bridgit is often depicted with a flame rising from her head. She was tended by nineteen priestesses, who kept her sacred fire burning at all times in her shrine. These women would take

Bridgit's messages of healing and advice to the people of the village. Bridgit's shrine was secluded behind a hedge of bushes where no man was allowed to enter. If he did, it was said he would burst into flame and disappear.

There are stone circles in Britain made up of nineteen stones and a space. Each stone represented a priestess who was in charge of one day; on the twentieth day the open space was said to be filled by Bridgit herself. When Christianity adopted the old goddesses into its pantheon of saints, Bridgit's fires were cared for by nineteen nuns. This custom was in practice until 1220, when a local bishop decreed her fire to be pagan and caused it to be extinguished.

There are many wells of healing in England established by Bridgit. Those who were ill could come to these wells to be cured. One of her best-known legends tells of a man who had leprosy. The Goddess cured him, then asked him to cure his leprous friend. Now that he was well, he refused, repulsed by his old disease. Bridgit, seeing that he had no compassion, gave him back his leprosy and cured his friend.

Bridgit's feast day is called Imbolc and comes at the first of February. Even today, women make a "Bridgit's cross" to honor the celebration. Shaped like a swastika, it is made of straw or barley stems. The swastika is an ancient symbol representing the turning of the sun and the earth.

Bridgit in her three guises strengthens us today. She lights the fires of inspiration in the arts, her gift of writing symbolizes the skill of communication, and her sacred wells represent compassion and healing for all who seek her wisdom.

CHALCHIUHTLICUE

(Chawl-chee-<u>oot</u>-lee-cue)

Mexico

JOURNEY

*Enable me to journey across the rainbow bridge to a
level of loving consciousness. Here, let my spirit
be energized so as to return to daily life
revitalized and empowered
with love.*

The Aztecs, whose power was established by the thirteenth century, C.E. (Current Era), believed that four worlds existed before ours came into form. Each of these civilizations was destroyed by a cataclysmic event. The first was devoured by tigers, the second by wind, the third by fire, and the fourth by water. Ours is the fifth world. Chalchiuhtlicue was the Goddess of the fourth world, and her legend echoes the Bible stories of the Old Testament.

She became aware of the wickedness of humankind and sent great floods as punishment. Therefore, she is also known as the Goddess of the Waters. Before she sent the floods, however, she acknowledged that some people on Earth were good. For them, she built a bridge of many colors. The bridge is so bright and beautiful it is thought to have been the first rainbow. This bridge enabled the righteous to travel from the fourth world to the fifth. We are the descendants of the righteous. However, it is predicted that this world too will be destroyed, this time by earthquakes.

Those she had saved remembered Chalchiuhtlicue with great festivals and honored her with gifts of jewels and incense. She is often portrayed with a crown of quetzal feathers, signifying a relationship with bird goddesses and a connection to the heavens. She wears turquoise discs in her ears and a skirt of blue to reflect the water she represents.

According to the Aztecs, the worlds were destroyed because they were imperfect. The Aztecs considered that every day the world survived was a triumph. But the knowledge of this history of destruction can serve to keep humankind alert, always aware that this world too is being tested.

DEMETER and PERSEPHONE

(<u>Dem</u>-uh-ter and Per-<u>sef</u>-fo-nee)

Greece

EMERGENCE

As Persephone descended to the underworld,
I descend into my inner self to reaffirm my own
truth and my own feeling of self-worth.
Then I rise again to the outer world
to put this knowledge
into practice.

The story of Demeter and Persephone tells of the love of mother and daughter. It combines tales of rebirth and regeneration with the love of parent and child. Demeter is a goddess of agriculture and growing things, and her daughter, Persephone, is the virgin, the maiden who represents youth and springtime.

As mother and daughter, Demeter and Persephone lived on an earth that was perpetually in summer. They lived happily in a world of abundance. Hades, God of the Underworld, saw Persephone and desired her. With the full awareness of her father, the god Zeus, Hades abducted her. As they descended into the underworld, her cries were heard by Hecate, the crone aspect of this trio of goddesses. Hades, with Persephone, reached his underworld kingdom, where he raped her and kept her. Demeter was bereft. With the help of Hecate, she searched the world for her daughter and ignored her duties. The earth was barren and, reflecting her sorrow, produced nothing. Finally, prompted by the plight of the world more than husbandly and fatherly concern, Zeus took pity on Demeter.

In order that Persephone be released from the underworld, Zeus required that she eat nothing there. On the assumption that this requirement had been met, Hades released her, and mother and daughter had a joyous reunion. Then Demeter discovered that Persephone had eaten a pomegranate seed. Therefore, Zeus ruled that she must return to the underworld for a part of every year. Demeter, Goddess of growing things, mourned during this period and the earth became barren again. Thus, the story provides an explanation for the seasons. When Demeter and Persephone are together, the earth rejoices and blooms. When they are apart, the earth rests and nothing grows.

In very early goddess stories, there is often one goddess of life, death, and rebirth. Later the myth was divided into three parts with separate personalities to explain the three stages of life: the maiden as Persephone, the mother as Demeter, and the crone as Hecate. Stories of descent and resurrection figure in religion throughout time.

On the personal level, the descent represents an inner search, a subconscious exploration; the ascent represents the return to life with a greater understanding of self and a renewed sense of purpose.

GAIA
Classical Greece

ABUNDANCE

Mother Earth, renew and restore my knowledge and respect for you. As my awareness of you as a living being and of the necessity to care for you grows, strengthen my knowledge that I am part of you and you are part of me.

Gaia was first among goddesses, the first form to emerge from Chaos. Her reality gave shape and substance to the void, which had been limitless. Thus she brought the possibility of order and purpose to Earth.

Eros, the God of Love, came next, to provide the energy to power creation. Gaia experienced love and so created Uranus, the Sky. She mated with him and gave birth to the Titans, the Titanesses, and the Cyclops. The last of her Titan sons was Cronus, the God of Time. All these children were compelled by Uranus to stay deep within the earth. Gaia vowed to retaliate and asked Cronus to take revenge for her. She gave him a sharp knife and with it, Cronus castrated Uranus. Drops of his blood fell on Gaia, and, out of her extreme fecundity, she begat another series of gods and goddesses that figure in the Greek pantheon. These stories serve to remind us that life is abundant and all comes from Mother Earth.

Temples to Gaia were usually established where there were fissures in the Earth. Delphi is one of these sites. Homer described Apollo's efforts to slay the Goddess, whom he called the she-dragon. As Apollo smote her, she lay on the ground, writhing and screaming in pain. He covered her with a mountain and built a temple to hide her from view. It is a graphic description of the patriarchal destruction of the Goddess and her sites.

The reemergence of the idea of the earth as a living organism is being viewed seriously by modern science, fostering a new attitude toward the needs of the earth and an increased awareness of our personal responsibilities. As the story of the Goddess Gaia is told once again, it becomes easier to conceptualize the earth as a living being.

After thousands of years of exploiting the earth, humans are unfolding a new consciousness of Gaia. This awareness is a healing force for our planet and for ourselves as we honor the source of life and abundance.

HATHOR
(<u>Hay</u>-thor)

Egypt

JOY

*I honor my body with the gifts of Hathor: music,
song, dance, touch. In joyous celebration
I exult in life and honor
your bequest.*

Hathor was worshiped in an-
cient Egypt as early as 2850 B.C.E., and her reign as a goddess
continued for more than three thousand years. She is a goddess
of joy and sensuality, a life-affirming presence. She is sometimes
portrayed as a cow, sometimes as a woman with the sun disc on
her head. She gave lovers to the lonely, and dance, song, cos-
metics, and art to all. She explained to mortals how new life is
made. Bringing happiness and honoring good, she was celebrated
with rites of pleasure and beauty.

Feminine energy was still considered so much a part of
reality in early Egypt that very often, goddess images could slip
in and out of focus, first as one name, then as another. Some-

times the stories and images of Hathor and Isis overlap. Both are daughters of Ra, the Sun God.

Hathor cared not only for the living but also for the dead. She lingered in the sycamore trees at the edge of the desert, where she would offer bread and milk to the newly dead to welcome them to the underworld. She was sometimes portrayed as a cow half-emerging from a mountain to welcome the dead to the afterlife. She would carry them from the land of the living to the land of the dead on her back.

The Temple of Dendura in southern Egypt was associated with Hathor. In rites celebrating the Goddess, her statue would be carried from the temple to the outdoors to catch the rays of the rising sun. She would be placed on a ship of gold to float down the Nile to the Temple of Edfu to visit her husband, the god Horus.

Hathor speaks to us today of the legitimacy of joy. She enables us to exult in her gifts of song, dance, and the delights of life, just as she did.

HECATE

(<u>Heck</u>-a-tee)

Greece

TRANSFORMATION

*Be with me at the crossroads of life so that my
decisions will be guided by crone wisdom. As
I age, let me turn to ancient wisdom, honor
that which has gone before, and accept
what life brings at each stage on
the journey to cronedom.*

Hecate is queen of the night,
Goddess of the dark of the moon. Though an important goddess of the Amazons, she is most often associated with the Greek
goddesses Demeter and Persephone. She completes the triad:
maiden, mother, crone. Hecate was the only one who heard
Persephone's cries as she was abducted into the underworld,
and she helped Demeter in her search for her daughter. Though
she was a moon goddess representing the three days of the dark
of the moon, the association with Persephone also placed her in
the pantheon of the underworld goddesses. Hecate could keep

the spirits of the dead from invading the land of the living and was often called upon for protection.

Hecate has a strong connection to the number three. She was frequently depicted with three heads; she was found at the three-fold crossroad; at Hecate suppers the cauldron was circled three times and stirred in the moonlight.

Hecate has an association with the Dog Star, Sirius, re-confirming her place in the night sky. As she walked the ancient roads and crossroads of Turkey and Greece, she was accompanied by her sacred hounds. It was at the crossroads that transformation could take place. Offerings of food were placed at these junctions or left in front of houses. Sometimes they were eaten by the poor, but it was felt Hecate would approve.

Small figurines of Hecate were placed in niches in the front of houses to bring protection to the house. Sometimes they were placed at the crossroads so that when she roamed at night, she would bring good magic and offer protection from the spirits that walked at night.

With Hecate as part of the Demeter and Persephone story, it becomes complete. The Moon Goddess is bonded with the earth mother, the maiden, and the underworld. As the crone in the triad, she is full of wisdom and offers us the opportunity for transformation.

HERA
(Hair-a)
Greece

DIGNITY

*Bring to me a respect for all stages of womanhood:
maiden, mother, crone. As the ritual waters of
old restored your youth, let my consciousness
of oneness with all be restored through
the flowing energies of life.*

Hera is a goddess whose story
has been undone by the later patriarchal legends. The earliest
evidence about her describes her as Queen of Heaven, great
Mother Goddess, ruler of the people. In these images she is associated with the bird, the snake, and the bull, suggesting connections with water, earth, and life energies. Even in later sculptures, the image sometimes depicts her as more powerful than
her husband, Zeus. In a Greek relief dated about 680 B.C.E., she
is crowned the Great Goddess, hands held high in the gesture of
blessing, flanked by two lions, symbols of power.

When the Acheans, a tribe from the north, invaded Greece

about 2000 B.C.E., they realized Hera was too strong to destroy. Their successful solution was to marry her to their Sky God, Zeus. The many tales of Zeus's sexual exploits and Hera's thundering jealousy may be the Acheans' effort to empower a god image while destroying the power and respected position of the regional goddesses. Whether disempowered by the rapacious Zeus or destroyed by the new portrayal of Hera as a jealous shrew, the same result was achieved. The local goddess was forgotten or became an object of derision, and Hera was portrayed as a vengeful, cruel, jealous Olympian wife.

In spite of the slanderous tales about her, she would emerge at festivals in her honor as a goddess who cared for women. It seems the women refused to give her up entirely. At these festivals, called Herea, she represented women in each stage of life. She was the virginal maiden, virginal not because she had no lovers, but because she had no responsibilities. She was the mother, representing the mature woman who accepted and discharged her responsibilities. Finally, she was the crone, the woman who has fulfilled her obligations and can live unto herself again. Women competed in races at these festivals in three age groups to reflect her three aspects: maiden, mother, crone. At the end of the games, there were three winners, one from each age group. The image of the Goddess was then ritually washed to represent her rebirth as a maiden and reinforce her association with water as the source of life.

It is satisfying to restore dignity to this ancient Goddess. She has survived ages of abuse to her reputation and to her myth but is reemerging today as an inspiring figure of strength and dignity.

HESTIA

Classical Greece

GENTLENESS

*Bless the house I live in. May the fire of love
and tranquility burn brightly in
my house and heart.*

Hestia was the first-born of the
Olympian goddesses, the daughter of Cronus and Rhea, the
granddaughter of Gaia. The ancient Greek proverb "Begin with
Hestia" meant one would begin at the beginning. Hestia is the
gentle goddess of home life, keeper of the hearth flame offering
domestic happiness. She had few temples or statues in early
Greece but was considered to be part of the fire at the center of
every home. She was honored and worshiped in private more
than in public. She blessed family unity. In spite of her role as
goddess of the hearth and home, she was revered as a virgin
goddess.

As she was the center of the home, Hestia was also the
personification of the center of the town or village. Each com-

munity built a Hestia sanctuary, a public hearth with a constantly burning flame. Those seeking refuge could find it in this shelter, and the government received official guests here.

Though there are few stories about her in Greek mythology, Hestia appears to be the sweetest and mildest of the Greek goddesses, never taking part in the Olympian quarrels and battles. Rather, her concerns are with happy homes and stable relationships. She reminds us that life is made up not so much of grand and great deeds but of the small daily concerns of the private and personal.

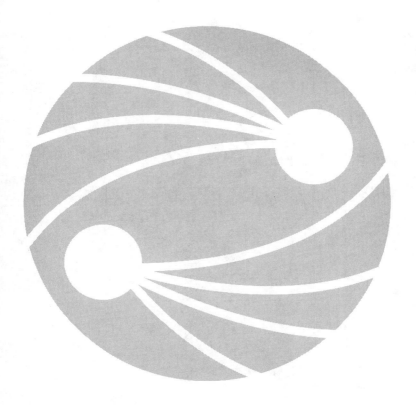

INANNA
(Ee-<u>nah</u>-nuh)
Sumer/Middle East

DESCENT

*Show me the way to shed all preconceptions, to drop
the burdens of life as you dropped all your
possessions on your descent to the
underworld. Then enable me to
rise restored and ready
to live life fully.*

Inanna's tale, often intertwined
with that of Isis and Ishtar, began in the mist of ages past but
was not recorded until the patriarchal takeover had begun. She
was called Queen of Heaven, signifying her association with the
sky. She was a vegetation goddess, signifying her association
with the earth. As patriarchal powers increased, the sky was
given to the male god and the earth was placed under his
dominion.

Inanna was also a goddess of descent and resurrection.
She made two descents. One was from heaven to earth to bring

humankind the gifts of civilization and the arts. The second was to the underworld, where she gave up all, died, and rose again to bring new life to the earth.

After Inanna had tricked the great god Enki into giving her the gifts of civilization and she had presented them to the people, she realized she needed a consort. She wanted to marry a farmer but was told by her brother that she must marry the shepherd Dumuzi. This is symbolic of the nomad invaders who were taking over the land. She agreed to marry Dumuzi, and at first they were ecstatically happy. The poems describing their passion are among the world's most beautiful love poetry, considered by some to have been an inspiration for the Songs of Solomon.

Inanna cut down a great tree to fashion a marriage bed. This tree/bed whispered the secrets of life to Inanna and Dumuzi as they lay upon it. The result of their love was not just children but abundance for the earth. She gave to Dumuzi all her symbols and powers and made him the king, revealing the Goddess' submission to the new male gods.

Inanna's story of descent to the underworld was recorded three thousand years before Christianity. She went to the underworld to visit Ereshkigal, her sister, her dark side. She was required to discard each symbol of office, each article of apparel as she descended. At last, naked and with nothing to offer, she stood before Ereshkigal, who condemned her to die and to hang upon a hook. In this way, Inanna completed a full cycle of learning about life. From sky to earth to underworld, her understanding of herself and the totality of life's meaning was accomplished.

The priestess Ninshubur, who had been told to find help for Inanna if she did not return quickly from the underworld, went to Enki, the God of Wisdom. He agreed to help so that civilization would not be lost. So after three days, the three days of the dark moon, Inanna rose from the dead. Ereshkigal allowed her to go but required a substitute in her place. Inanna chose Dumuzi, since he had become so engrossed in his role as king that he was not even aware that she was gone. "Dumuzi … was dressed in his shining garments. He sat on his magnificent throne; (he did not move) … . Inanna fastened on Dumuzi the eye of death."* As a vegetation god, his absence meant that the earth would be barren until his return. Thus the cycle of the seasons was played out.

Inanna's story illustrates the necessity for a personal descent in order to understand the inner self. Then, with better understanding, we may accept and use well the gifts of creation brought by the Goddess from the heavens.

*Wolkstein, Diane and Kramer, Samuel Noah. *Inanna, Queen of Heaven and Earth.*

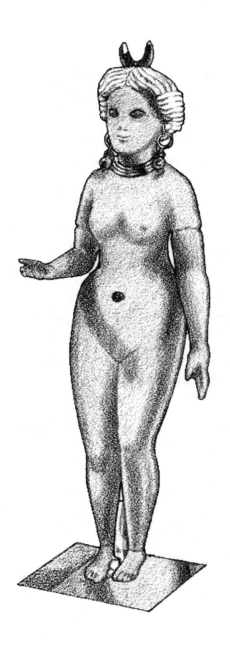

ISHTAR
(Ish-tar)
Babylonia

RENEWAL

May I allow the joyful power of Ishtar to move
through me so I may celebrate my place in
the world with confidence
and strength.

The mighty Ishtar, a goddess of
descent and resurrection, was worshiped in Sumer and Babylonia.
She ruled over life and death and rebirth. Each year she married
a god of vegetation who died and descended to the underworld,
only to rise again with the spring. Ishtar's son/husband was
Tammuz, who died when he was still very young. He descended
to the underworld. Ishtar and her priestesses mourned his passing, so Ishtar decided to go to the underworld to search for
Tammuz. She was required, as was the Sumerian goddess Inanna,
to discard all her worldly possessions, shedding her garments
and jewels one by one as she went. Ishtar did not go meekly. She
pounded on the door of Hades, demanding the return of Tammuz.

Each year, she symbolized his return as she chose a new partner to play the role of Tammuz and share her couch and her pleasures until it was time for his ritual death and a new god of vegetation.

Ishtar celebrated sexuality as the source of life. In her temples, her priestesses took lovers to demonstrate that sexuality was sacred. An ancient prayer to Ishtar speaks to us of her exalted position:

> *Woman of women,*
> *Goddess who knows no equal,*
> *She who decrees the destiny of people,*
> *Highest Ruler of the World,*
> *Sovereign of the Heavens,*
> *Goddess, even of those who live in heaven.*[*]

At a later point in time, after the patriarchal takeover, Gilgamish made his entry in the story of Ishtar. She used all her wiles to entice him to be her husband, but he did not want a year of kingship followed by death. He led a rebellion against her. However, he and the kings who followed him recognized that they could not dislodge Ishtar totally. Once a year, the king would ritually cut his hair, discard the robes of office and his jewels, and allow himself to be struck seven times in the face

*Stone, Merlin. *Ancient Mirrors of Womanhood.*

with a cord of knots. Then he would descend into the river, rise from it, and walk about for three days dressed in sackcloth. With these ceremonies, the king demonstrated that he represented Ishtar on earth and brought her wishes and decrees to the people. Though her priestesses were still consulted for advice, their power had waned and the mighty Ishtar's throne no longer represented the powers of the heavens.

Though her story takes us into the patriarchal era, the record of her rituals demonstrates the power of early goddesses, the sacredness and the celebration of sexuality, and the sureness of renewal.

ISIS
(Eye-sis)
Egypt

RESURRECTION

*Bring to me the assurance that when I have lost my
way, the path will be restored to me and
whatever is broken can be
made whole again.*

Isis, the Divine Mother, ruled in
Ancient Egypt from about 3000 B.C.E. to 200 C.E. Her story cen-
ters on death and resurrection, and encompasses the concept of
the trinity. She was the daughter of Nut, Goddess of the Sky, and
Geb, the Earth God. Her elder brother and husband was Osiris,
the first king of Egypt and giver of civilization. His story cannot
be told without Isis.

It is said they fell in love while they were in the womb,
where they were together even though they were not twins.
After they married, their brother Set became very jealous of the
power of Osiris. Set built a beautiful coffin and said it would be
given to whoever would fit in it. Since it had been made to

Osiris' measurements, he fit perfectly when he lay down in the box. Set immediately had the coffin sealed with lead and flung it into the Nile. It floated to sea. When Isis found out what had happened, she searched the world for Osiris' body. The coffin floated to a far shore and rested against a tree trunk, where the presence of Osiris made the tree grow so fast it enclosed the coffin. The queen of the country, Astarte, ordered the tree cut down to be used as a pillar in the palace. Its fragrance was so sweet that when Isis heard of it, she knew it was Osiris. She recovered the body and took it back to Egypt.

When Set found out, he stole the body again, chopped it into fourteen pieces, and scattered them throughout the world. Isis once again searched relentlessly until she found all the parts, save the genitals, which had been eaten by a fish. Isis fanned Osiris back to life with her great wings and with the art of embalming, which she bequeathed to the Egyptians. Once resurrected, she and Osiris resumed their relationship and conceived Horus. The concept of consort/son is completed. There are many images and reliefs of Isis with her son, Horus, on her lap.

Isis was important to the Egyptians because she was the Mother Goddess who could restore life. She represented the unity and ongoingness of life.

The narrative confirms that there is one who will search

for the lost, restore them to their homeland, resurrect them from the dead, and bring new life forth. For women today, she offers the assurance that what is lost can be found, what is torn asunder can be brought back to wholeness.

KALI

(Kahl-lee)

India

FEARLESSNESS

*Give me the strength to look my faults in the eye and
to allow you to strike my fear with the dagger of
annihilation, so I may find my true self
and reside in the comfort
of your blessing.*

Devi is the name of the Great
Goddess in India. However, many of her aspects have separated
themselves from her and become goddesses in their own right,
taking on form and personality. Kali presents the most frightening image of these personifications.

Kali began as the beautiful Parvati, who was married to
Siva, the great God of the Dance, the energizer of the universe.
He assigned her the role of dancing the cosmic dance and they
began to sway together. As her dance became wilder and wilder,
she assumed the role of Kali, Mother of Death. As her dancing
and spinning increased in intensity, the world began to shake. In

the midst of her spinning gyrations, she realized that Siva lay beneath her feet and she was dancing on his body. She stopped the dance just in time, but it is written that one day she will begin again and dance the world to death.

Kali is often portrayed as bloody and knife-wielding, wearing a necklace of human skulls and earrings of dismembered bodies. She is known as the terrifying Goddess of Death. However, careful readers of her story consider what it is she is destroying. Her necklace of severed heads represents mankind's faults: vice, lust, jealousy, aggression. She offers to attack each evil practice, to destroy them one by one until we have faced them down and found our true and loving selves. In most of her images she holds one hand in the traditional posture of blessing.

Once Kali is confronted and understood, she releases us from fear and becomes a goddess of comfort. Vivekananda, the Indian yogi, said that we should adore the terrible one. In Hindu tradition, it is considered that we are living in the Age of Kali, the time when feminine spirituality rises again.

KUAN YIN
(Kwan Yin)
China

COMPASSION

*As I receive the gift of compassion from Kuan Yin, it
transforms me and enables me to be compassionate
in turn. She comes to my aid when I am in
need and teaches peace and
patience to all.*

Kuan Yin, like the Virgin Mary
in Catholic societies, is often more popular than the male deities
in China. Her reputation for gentleness and her sweet nature
allow people to accept her presence when they are troubled.

It is said that she lived on earth as Miao Shan, the youngest daughter of a cruel father. Her two older sisters married at his
command, but she asked to enter a temple of women. He ar-
ranged for the women to treat her cruelly so that she would
agree to marry, but the animals came at night and helped her
with her tasks. Her father was so enraged that he set fire to the
temple, but she was not harmed. He ordered her head cut off,

but the sword broke. So the executioner strangled her. In the land of the dead, she sang chants of goodness and mercy to relieve the suffering of those who were there. The king of the dead was so displeased, he banished her. She refused to transcend the human state and she returned to earth to help those in need.

Many symbols are associated with Kuan Yin. The willow branch she sometimes carries represents spring and also repels demons. The peacock symbolizes beauty and dignity and drives away evil. A fish often seen in her basket suggests wealth. The Chinese word means abundance. A pearl in the center of her forehead represents the third eye and signifies purity and preciousness. The lotus is the symbol of life-giving waters.

Kuan Yin chose to forego life in heaven to stay on earth and answer the needs of humans until each one of us attains enlightenment. The stories of her compassion inspire us to appreciate the joy of service to others.

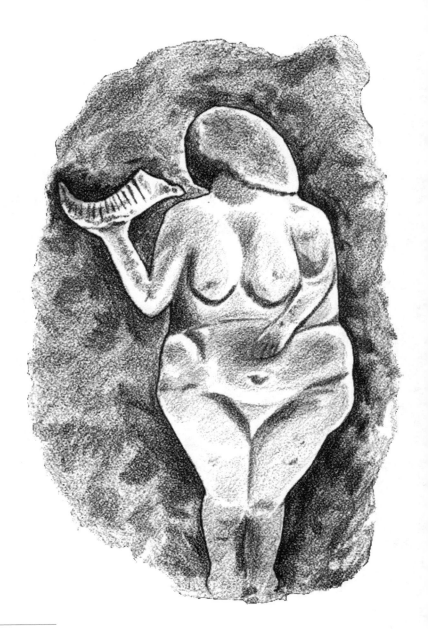

GODDESS of LAUSSEL

(Low-<u>sell</u>)

France

CYCLES

*Raise your horn on high, honoring the cycles of
woman and the force of the maiden moon. As
you guard the entrance to the cave, so guard
and guide the cycles of the feminine
within me.*

The Earth Mother, or Goddess
of Laussel, honors the mysteries of the female body. She is carved
over the entrance to a cave in the south of France near the caves
of Lascaux. The caves were used for ritual and ceremony. Though
only seventeen inches high, she presides at the cave gateway
with great dignity and presence. The carving was done with flint
tools and utilizes the undulating shapes of the rock. As guardian
of this gateway to the spirit, she was honored by all who entered
there. Her form is a tribute to the fertility of the feminine: body,
mind, and the spirit of life.

In her right hand she carries a bison horn shaped like the

crescent moon. The horn is incised with thirteen lines equaling the days of the waxing moon cycle and the thirteen months of the lunar year. Her left hand rests lightly on her pregnant abdomen caressing and welcoming new life. Traces of red ocher, a sacred color representing the blood of life and birth, can still be seen on her body.

The carving dates from 25,000 B.C.E. It combines much of the known symbolism of these early times. The horn of the bison/bull suggests the life force, the crescent form is that of the rising moon, the mathematics of the incised lines speak of astronomical sophistication, and the pregnant figure, ubiquitous in cave art, represents fertility.

This Goddess personifies abundance and a relationship with the earth, the moon, and sky. Her symbols pay homage to the cyclical nature of life as her upraised hand confers a blessing on those who enter her portal. We respond to her today because her message is eternal, uplifting, and validating.

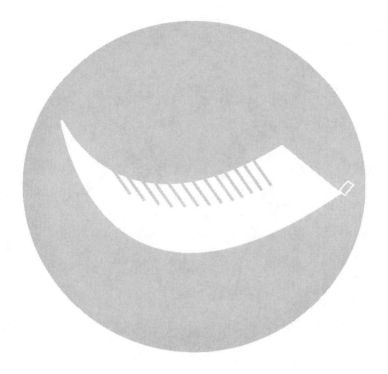

LILITH
(<u>Lill</u>-ith)
Sumer

SEXUALITY

Free women from repression. Guard and guide our spirit of wisdom, our sexual energy, and our womanly essence.

The first version of creation in Genesis says, "God created Man in his own image, ... male and female he created them." The woman in this simultaneous event was Lilith. When Adam suggested intercourse, Lilith insisted on equality in their relationship and refused to lie beneath him. When he insisted, she ran away. From that day forward, she has been portrayed as a demon and as representing the unbridled sexuality of the female. This view was first presented in Hebrew literature and later became a part of world mythology. Sexual temptation was credited to the bewitching Lilith. She was considered so dangerous that in a first-century writing, men were admonished that "it is forbidden for a man to sleep alone in a house, lest Lilith get hold of him."* Fear of sexuality was personified in Lilith.

Lilith is depicted with talon feet, suggesting an earlier relationship with the Bird Goddess, who helped women in childbirth and watched over infants. These associations were reversed in Hebrew writing to make her a dreaded figure. Birthing women feared that she would steal the baby, mothers that she would kill their children. Amulets with the names of three angels, Senoy, Sansenoy, and Semangelof, were used for protection.

Lilith is sometimes linked with two other early goddesses: Inanna and Ishtar. Another name for them was Divine Lady Owl. This may be the initial association of the owl and Lilith. In Hebrew literature, she is called the screech owl. The owl, also known as the bird of wisdom, is often shown guarding Lilith, along with the royal lion. Both were early goddess symbols of power and authority. Originally Lilith was Lil, a Sumerian Queen of Heaven whose name meant air or storm.

This much-maligned mythological figure is reemerging today to be reexamined on her own terms. She embodies a conviction of sexual equality, a willingness to be assertive, and a feeling of self-worth. These are inspiring qualities for women today as we strive to reach our full potential.

*Patai, Raphael. *The Hebrew Goddess.*

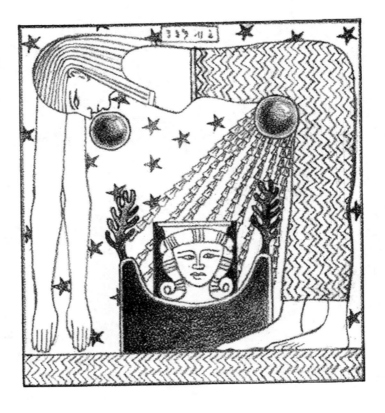

NUT
(Noot)

Egypt

PROTECTION

May the warmth of your overreaching embrace
strengthen the earth and awaken me to my
place in your starry firmament. Your
body, the heavens, wraps around
me and protects me.

Nut arched her body, the heavens, over that of her husband/brother, Geb, the earth. Her fingers and toes touched the corners of the planet and marked the eastern and western corners of the horizon. Her belly sparkled with stars and her hair fell to the ground like nourishing rain. Each night, it was said, she swallowed the sun. It traveled through her body and each morning she birthed it once again: a new day was born.

Nut as the Sky and Geb as the Earth existed in a constant embrace until the Great Sun God, Ra, ordered Shu, the Atlas of Egyptian mythology, to separate them. Shu had been created by

Ra and was the father of Nut and Geb. He had to hold Nut up in the air, such was her desire for Geb. But each night, Shu tired and Nut descended to the Earth to resume her embrace with Geb. The sun once again began its journey to rebirth, and the stars on her belly shone in the night. The pink at dawn was thought to be colored by the blood she shed giving birth to the sun.

Nut is often portrayed as the Heavenly Cow. When Ra grew tired of being birthed on the obstreperous and turbulent earth, he asked Nut to take him to heaven. She assumed the form of a cow and lifted him on her back higher and higher into the heavens. Her legs began to weary of her burden, and the gods Horus, Seth, Thoth, and Sopdu came to her aid, one supporting each leg. Thus they became the four pillars of the earth. Nut was also the caretaker of the dead, and her image was painted on coffin lids so that the soul of the dead might lie within her starry embrace.

Nut speaks to us today of the oneness of all creation. The earth, the sky, life, and death are all part of life. The image of her spangled body watching over all that was, all that is, and all that ever will be is as comforting today as it was to the ancient Egyptians.

SLEEPING GODDESS
of MALTA
(<u>Mall</u>-tah)

Malta

GATEWAY DREAMS

Guide my dreams that I may remember them
and hear their message. Open these
gateways to the Goddess that I
may be aware of your
eternal presence.

Malta is a small and barren island in the Mediterranean off the coast of Sicily. Goddess figures and temple sites dating from about 3500 to 2500 B.C.E. have been found there. The temples were built in the shape of the Goddess, so that entering the temple was like entering her body. There the worshiper was in harmony with the earth forces she represented.

These temples were enormous. Giant stones formed rounded chambers, representing female breasts and hips. Megalithic figures were also found, although both temples and statues are now partially destroyed. These statues are similar to those found as far away as Ireland to the west and Turkey to the east. Some of the temple rooms were painted red. Bronze Age figurines found in France have traces of red paint on them. The room thought to be a birthing room at Çatal Hüyük in Turkey is painted red. These similarities suggest a universal spirituality at that time.

The strangest of the Malta temples, called the Hypogeum, is thought to have been used for divination and healing. The temple has three levels and descends thirty feet to bedrock and water. In it are many egg-shaped chambers, some painted with red. A chamber called the oracle room features a hole in the wall. A voice speaking into this hole can be heard throughout the whole temple. Similar chambers where oracular or priestly pronouncements could be made have been found in Egypt and in Northwest Indian long houses.

The chamber on Malta contained a tiny figure now called the Sleeping Goddess. Her shape is that of the colossal statues found on the island. She has a small head and feet, huge hips and legs, bare breasts, and wears a fringed skirt. Lying on her side, she appears to be sleeping or dreaming and was probably a divination priestess. Visitors went to the temples to be healed, to have dreams interpreted, or to be guided into altered states of consciousness for initiation. The atmosphere in the Hypogeum is intense and strange even today.

The temples and statues found on Malta show us the powerful and mysterious energy that still pours forth from these ancient sites. We are reminded that dreams and meditative states of consciousness are to be honored and trusted.

SNAKE GODDESS of CRETE

(Kreet)

Crete

ENERGY

Goddess of the snake, your trance inspires me to
practice detachment. Your serpent energy
enables me to find solutions to my needs
in the bounty of your gifts.

The joyful free society of Minoan Crete (3000–1500 B.C.E.) produced many superb works of art. The Snake Goddess is foremost among them. She stands with arms outstretched, holding a snake in each hand. Her wide-eyed gaze suggests a trance. Her breasts are bare, a symbol of the care and nourishment provided by the Goddess. Her skirt has seven tiers, a Bronze Age spiritual number symbolic of wholeness. On her head, a guardian lion offers protection, reminiscent of the lions that guard the Birthing Mother of Çatal Hüyük. The net design on her skirt indicates her role as the "weaver of life."

The snake, included in all goddess cultures, symbolizes energy and the regeneration of life. The snake is synonymous with the life force. Ancient societies attributed great powers to this creature because of its periodic rejuvenation and amazing vitality. This symbol is also associated with water. The serpent emerges from water where life began and is the vehicle of the energy that has its source in water. Much snake symbology has been discovered on Neolithic artifacts. It was considered primordial and mysterious.

As she stands erect, deep in trance, the Goddess seeks to connect the life force of the universe to the people she blesses. She weaves this heavenly energy with our earthly needs to strengthen and support us. This goddess then is the guardian of spontaneous life energy. She is creator, nourisher, and caretaker.

GODDESS of WILLENDORF
(Will-an-dorf)
Austria

CARETAKER

*Goddess of the ancients, whose spirit is reemerging in
our time, bless the earth and bring harmony to
all people. As a symbol of life, nourishment,
and abundance, inspire me to honor
and care for the earth.*

Though no legends or stories are
known about her, the Goddess of Willendorf is an earth mother
who offers nourishment and abundance.

Though she looks massive, the figure is only four and a
third inches high, fitting nicely into the palm of the hand. She
was probably used as a personal household goddess. Her body
is heavy with pregnancy; her small arms, one wearing a bracelet,
rest on her huge breasts. Hefty thighs support this image of
bounteous fertility. Her featureless face suggests an image of
everywoman, rather than a specific personality. Her hair is ar-
ranged in seven rows of curls, or circles. Seven, which is the

number of moving planets and represents wholeness, is known to have been a sacred number in the Bronze Age (c. 3500 B.C.E.). This same symbolism may well have had significance when she was made twenty thousand years ago.

When she was found near Vienna, Austria, there were still traces of red ocher on her. Red, the color of life-giving, life-sustaining blood, has been found on many Paleolithic and Neolithic figures.

Her form suggests abundance, and her downcast head and folded arms project an appealing sweetness. As one of the earliest goddess figures ever found, she reaches out from ages past to connect with us today.

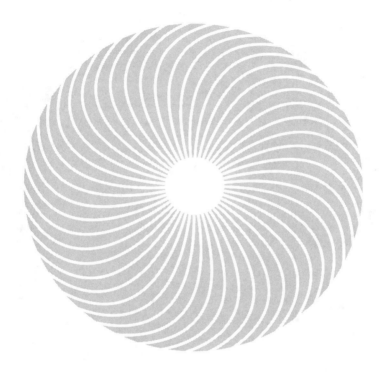

SOURCES & SUGGESTED READING

Aburdene, Patricia and Naisbitt, John. *Megatrends for Women*. New York: Villard Books, 1992.

Austen, Hallie Iglehart. *The Heart of the Goddess*. Berkeley: Wingbow Press, 1990.

Baring, Anne and Cashford, Jules. *The Myth of the Goddess*. London: Arkana, Penguin Books, 1991.

Bell, Robert E. *Women of Classical Mythology*. New York: New Oxford University Press, 1991.

Caldecott, Moyra. *Women in Celtic Myth*. Rochester, Vermont: Destiny Books, 1992.

Duerden, Dennis. *African Art, an Introduction*. London: Hamlyn, 1974.

Eberhard, Wolfram. *A Dictionary of Chinese Symbols*. London: Routledge & Kegan Paul, 1986.

Edwards, Carolyn McVickar. *The Storyteller's Goddess*. San Francisco: Harper & Row, 1991.

Eisler, Riane. *The Chalice and the Blade*. Cambridge, Mass.: Harper & Row, 1987.

Gadon, Elinor W. *The Once and Future Goddess*. New York: Harper & Row, 1989.

George, Demetra. *Mysteries of the Dark Moon: The Healing Power of the Dark Goddess*. San Francisco: Harper & Row, 1992.

Gimbutas, Marija. *The Language of the Goddess*. San Francisco: Harper & Row, 1989.

Grimal, Pierre, editor. *Larousse World Mythology*. London: Hamlyn, 1965.

Hamlyn, Paul. *Egyptian Mythology*. London: Drury House, 1965.

Holy Bible, Revised Standard Version. Toronto: Thomas Nelson & Sons, 1952.

Inal, Hasan, translator. *A Guide to Çatal Hüyük.* Konya, Turkey: Konya Museum, 1983.

Johnson, Buffie. *Lady of the Beasts.* San Francisco: Harper & Row, 1988.

Jones, Kathy. *The Ancient British Goddess.* Glastonbury, England: Ariadne Publications, 1991.

MacCana, Proinsias. Celtic *Mythology.* London: Hamlyn, 1975.

Michaildou, Anna. *Knossos.* Athens: Ekdotike Athenon, S.A., 1982.

Monaghan, Patricia. *The Book of Goddesses & Heroines.* St. Paul, Minnesota: Llewellyn Publications, 1990.

Mookerjee, Ajit. *Kali: The Feminine Force.* Rochester, Vermont: Destiny Books, 1988.

Mookerjee, Ajit. *Tantra Asana: A Way to Self-Realization.* New York: George Wittenborn, 1971.

Nicholson, Irene. *Mexican and Central American Mythology.* London: Hamlyn, 1967.

Parrinder, Geoffrey. *African Mythology.* London: Hamlyn, 1967.

Patai, Raphael. *The Hebrew Goddess.* Detroit: Wayne University Press, 1990.

Pinsent, John. *Greek Mythology.* London: Hamlyn, 1969.

Stone, Merlin. *Ancient Mirrors of Womanhood.* Boston: Beacon Press, 1991.

Stone, Merlin. *When God Was a Woman.* New York: Dial Press, 1976.

Temizsoy, I. *The Anatolian Civilizations Museum.* Ankara: No date.

Walker, Barbara G. *The Crone.* New York: Harper & Row, 1985.

Walker, Barbara G. *The Women's Encyclopedia of Myths and Secrets.* San Francisco: Harper & Row, 1983.

Wolkstein, Diane and Kramer, Samuel Noah. *Inanna, Queen of Heaven and Earth.* New York: Harper & Row, 1983.

ABOUT THE AUTHOR

Dee Poth is a corporate art consultant. She has conducted art tours in the United States, Canada, and England, served as editor and writer for a community newspaper magazine, and has been a museum docent. She has traveled extensively to visit many of the world's archeological and sacred sites including Turkey, Egypt, Greece, Morocco, China, Japan, Italy, France, Great Britain, and Mexico. She sees the re-emergence of the goddess as part of the women's spirituality movement.

About the Design and Illustrations

The illustrations of the goddesses are by Rene McCullough, an artist and illustrator. She has taught at the Portland Art Museum School.

Design Studio Selby conceived the design of the book, package, and meditation cards based on the inherent beauty and harmony of the Golden Mean. As a principle, the Golden Mean expresses the idea of returning to the source or uniting again with divinity.

The illustrations are based on actual artifacts and objects found in museums around the world, selected by the Author. The goddess symbols were created to depict ancient designs associated with each goddess and her story.

TIMELINE of Goddesses in THE GODDESS SPEAKS

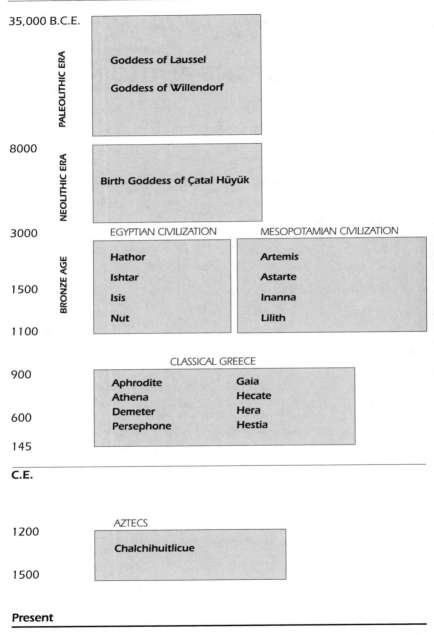

35,000 B.C.E.

PALEOLITHIC ERA

Goddess of Laussel

Goddess of Willendorf

8000

NEOLITHIC ERA

Birth Goddess of Çatal Hüyük

3000

EGYPTIAN CIVILIZATION

MESOPOTAMIAN CIVILIZATION

BRONZE AGE

Hathor   **Artemis**

Ishtar   **Astarte**

1500

Isis   **Inanna**

Nut   **Lilith**

1100

CLASSICAL GREECE

900

Aphrodite   **Gaia**
Athena   **Hecate**
Demeter   **Hera**

600

Persephone   **Hestia**

145

C.E.

AZTECS

1200

Chalchihuitlicue

1500

Present

B.C.E. means Before Current Era   *C.E. means Current Era*

35,000 B.C.E.

The Goddess is a global manifestation. Her images have been found all over the world including very early figures from Siberia and Russia (c. 25,000 B.C.E.) and Neolithic evidence from Lebanon, Afghanistan, Thailand, and China. This timeline represents only the goddesses who tell their stories in THE GODDESS SPEAKS.

PALEOLITHIC ERA

NEOLITHIC ERA

8000

3000

BRONZE AGE

1500

1100

900

600

145

C.E.

1200

1500

Present

AGEAN CIVILIZATION

Snake Goddess of Crete

Sleeping Goddess of Malta

INDIA

Kali

AFRICA

Ala

CELTIC BRITAIN

Bridgit

CHINA

Kuan Yin

SIBYL PUBLICATIONS

Sibyl Publications is a small press of nonfiction books to empower women. Books are positive, calling forth women's strength and wisdom. We are dedicated to women's voices being heard.

Two New Books From Sibyl

MYTHMAKING: Heal Your Past, Claim Your Future
Patricia Montgomery, Ph.D.

Capture the power of myth by writing your life story in myth form. *MYTHMAKING* reveals the importance of telling your story and demonstrates with step-by-step instructions. Read thirty inspiring myths written by women in midlife as they claim their voice.   ISBN 0-9638327-3-5 $14.95

THE GODDESS SPEAKS: Myths & Meditations
Dee Poth

Evoke the wisdom of 25 ancient goddesses through this inspirational card set and book of stories about the goddesses. Colorful illustrations based on goddess images in museums around the world. 25 cards and 120-page book packaged together for daily use.   ISBN 0-9638327-2-7 $29.95

Please send the following books:

_____
_____
_____
_____

To order books:

Phone orders: 1-800-240-8566 and have your VISA card ready.

FAX orders: (503) 235-8577

Mail orders: Sibyl Publications • 123 N.E. Third Avenue, #502
Portland, OR 97232-2972

Shipping: Add $2 for the first book and $1 for each
additional book.

Please send me announcements of future books by Sibyl Publications.

Name _____
Address _____
City / State / Zip _____

Payment: ☐ Check   ☐ VISA
Card Number: _____
Name on card: _____ Expiration date: _____
Signature: _____

Call toll free and order now

Table of Contents

The Injester

The Injester

Preface

❀ At my home in Velletri we have a huge fridge that defies the rules of consumer society. It's not one of those big Philcos, a spectacular polar white pot-bellied refrigerator. Instead, ours is made out of wood & takes up an entire wall in the kitchen.

Through its four windows you can peek into its insides and rejoice at the site of cold cuts, cheeses, veal, sides of beef, hanging majestically from shiny hooks.

This fridge is our family chapel.

Every now and then, in the morning, my wife catches me kneeling before this idol, this totem of the human adventure. I'm down there rapt in contemplation, waiting to receive an inspiration for lunch ...

This image, certainly paradoxical, gives you an idea of how ascetic my attachment to the prosaic pleasures of the table is, and thus my attachment to life. In fact, when all is said and done, I shall be regarded as a martyr of the hearth. Although, generally speaking, rather than my own flesh, I lay down, with infinite care, little milky veal chops over burning coals.

Cooking is in my blood. And there, I think, one will undoubtedly find red & white cells but also, in my case, a substantial amount of tomato sauce.

I'm addicted to the stovetop. I suffer from acute *spaghettitis*. For me, the kitchen is the most arousing part of the home.

No one understands better than I do Quasimodo's hermeticism: for a pale olive, I could *really* lose my mind.[1]

I know the back doors and the best cooks of the most renowned restaurants in Europe.

Acting? Sometimes that seems more like a hobby. Eating, on the other hand, I do that full-time.

And I really feel alive before a pan. The sound of frying oil is music to my ears. I wish I could use the scent of a good ragù as an aftershave. A plate of tangled fettuccine or the oblong shape of a roast are, to me, vital sculptures, worthy of Henry Moore.

After making dinner, my greatest satisfaction is getting the approval of my friends and fellow diners. Now that I think about it, from cooking, I get something I used to get on stage and that now, with cinema, I'm missing: a direct contact with an audience.

As I indulge in this love of food I suffer neither middlemen nor rules: I'm the creator of the scene and its performer, the deity that transforms the inert words of a recipe into a flavorful & colorful reality, harmonizing and measuring the ingredients, sensing, even emotionally, when things are perfectly cooked, participating viscerally in the frying of potatoes, suffering with garlic in boiling oil, rejoicing in *soffritto*, basking in every sauce,

1. It is a common misconception that Salvatore Quasimodo (poet, 1901–1968), noble prize laureate, was the author of the line "For a pale olive, one can lose their mind." Actually, the line belongs to Renzo Laurano, the pen name of Luigi Asquasciati (1905–1986), writer, journalist, and bon vivant. The line was then used in a comedy by Giovanni Mosca (1908–1983), who might be the source of misattribution.

losing myself in the smells and aromas, loving the tiny leaf of basil that was just picked, sacrificed on a mound of steaming maccheroni in tomato sauce.

My cooking is artistic. I suffer for it like few others do. And that's why the scenography that accompanies it is so important to me, the atmosphere that surrounds it, that entire flow of pleasant sensations that come from memory or the environment, & which influence heavily the dish before you, enriching it with ancient and new meanings.

Just as every object whispered distant & half buried memories to Proust, food reminds me of times lost and found again. And a boiled chicken, for instance, brings me back to grandma, to Sundays in Cremona, to mustard; and fresh raspberries conjure up those ancient & rare vacations in the mountains with my parents.

Greed, gluttony: silly words, dictated by current morals, punitive and masochistic. Everyone is free to make their own choices, even to die stuffed with foie gras or consumed by intercourse. Let's bring to light these two great, healthy, and materialistic passions, too long confined to the ghettos of sinful behavior. Let's exhume the epicurean ideals that preached joy, life, and that made great the Roman world & the Renaissance; let us wholeheartedly reconnect with the uninterrupted and secular flow of drool, sperm, and shit; let's return, especially when it comes to food, to that place that's becoming evermore elusive, beseeched by armies of preservatives, frozen foods, and tin cans.

Once upon a time, there was a grandma, a mother, a field, a vegetable patch.

Let's recreate them. It's up to us.

Now that the spiel is over, a few necessary warnings. This volume is made of three parts.

The first, which I entitled "auto-gastro-biography," includes a series of memories that deal with different times in my life, from the furthest away to the most recent. Starting from autobiographical premises, I wanted to write a few *tranches de vie* in which, as it often happens in everyday life, food is present in one way or another. To a gastronome like me, talking about myself through food was the best way, perhaps the only way, to build a narrative.

The second part is comprised of the easiest of my recipes; I love simple cooking, the kind that doesn't take too much time, even though I'm a stickler for details & a perfectionist even when it comes to making spaghetti with butter, or frying an egg. I warn you that you might already know some of these recipes — also because I divulged many of them, every week, through the microphones of *Gran Varietà* [2] — but I'm certain you'll discover

2. Gran Varietà was a radio program broadcasted by RAI (The Italian Public Broadcasting Company) between 1966 and 1979, every Sunday morning between 9:35 and 11 AM. It included comic sketches and songs and was one of the most popular programs of the '60s and '70s.

something more, or maybe less, or just different, that will help perfect, if I say so myself, their execution & therefore the final products.

The third and final part of the book is devoted to *La Grande Bouffe (The Big Feast)* & the recipes for the dishes shown in the film. A dazzling finale of fireworks that won't fail to satisfy your imagination & most of all your palate.

All that's left is for me to wish you a happy reading and *Buon appetito* with

Ugo Tognazzi

Autogastrobiography
(Visceral Confessions)

1930
Auntie Broth

I had only been alive three days when my uncle Milan FC tied a little red and black bow around my manhood. I've always wondered what would have happened had I been born a girl instead of a boy.

My uncle Milan FC wasn't even my real uncle, but just one of my dad's business friends whom he chose to be the godfather at my baptism. I called him uncle the way all children do when forced by their parents, who try to show greater familiarity to the strangers that habitually frequent their households.

As for real aunts and uncles I already had about twenty of them: half on my mom's side and half on my dad's, plus this fake uncle who, to me, was the most uncle of them all since he took me to see soccer games and would send me postcards signed by the players.

The real aunts and uncles were divided into the following categories: the doll aunties, uncle coal, uncle cashier (on mom's side); rich uncle, plastic uncle, uncle inventor, auntie broth, uncle fabrics, pretty aunt, poor uncle and other less remarkable ones (on my dad's side). All these nicknames were made up by uncle Milan FC.

He was so Milan FC that:

A) He lived in San Siro, naturally.[3]

3. San Siro is the neighborhood where the Milan FC Stadium is located.

B) His apartment was entirely decorated in red & black.

C) Even his slippers had red & black stripes.

Every wall was literally covered with fancy pictures of him shaking hands with soccer players. Whole teams with five forwards standing, three midfielders kneeling, right and left backs sitting and the goalie laying down, ball pressed against the ground.

There was a picture of the fabulous team Uruguay, "*Campione del mundo.*"[4] Piola's acrobatic bicycle kick. Meazza's iconic header. Bartolini with his white head-band; and the Milan FC teams from 1910, 1911, 1912, 1913, 1914 (intermission for World War I), 1919, 1920, 1921, 1922, 1923, 1924, 1925 (with the Fascist salute), up to 1930 or thereabouts.

On Sundays, if Milan FC won, he would get drunk; if they lost, he went to bed without dinner at 8 PM. He managed to convince my dad to leave our building when he found out that Viani, the midfielder of the historic rival Ambrosiana-Inter, had moved in. The very same Viani who, by the way, would later become the wizard-coach of Milan FC, the best talent scout of the post-war years.

My dad, who didn't care about soccer at all, but didn't want to ruin his business relationship with my uncle, moved the family to Porta Magenta, a little closer to

4. The Spanish "mundo" is here substituted for the Italian "mondo" and is meant as an homage to the great South American soccer team.

San Siro, and thus I was free from catching the *Interista* infection.[5]

I never asked why this uncle so fond of nicknames called my dad *Ceolin*, and me *cavaliere* and my manhood, permanently marked by the red *&* black bow, *menagramo*.[6] What I do know is that before taking me to games he would cut a hole in my pant pocket and I was supposed to pass through it a little wooden devil painted in red *&* black. I would hold it there, with my hand in my pocket, pressed against my *menagramo*. Only when Milan FC scored a goal could I take it out and wave it around as a sign of jubilation.

One Sunday Milan FC lost 5 to 0. Uncle went to bed without dinner and died of a heart attack. In his spiritual will and testament he left me his passion for Milan FC along with the other aunts and uncles. Most of them have since gone to join him. Rich uncle, since "lucky in wealth, poor in health." Uncle inventor ended up the same way. His greatest achievement was that of figuring out how to open envelopes without tearing the letters inside. He sewed a cotton thread along the edge of the envelope, leaving a piece of it hanging out (more or less

---

5. An Interista is a fan of AC Milan's rival team, Inter.
6. *Ceolin* is a rather uncommon last name; *Cavaliere* means "knight"; *Menagramo*, on the other hand, is a little more complicated: a sullen, gloomy person who the community believes brings bad luck, a jinx. This unusual nickname might be connected to an apotropaic superstitious ritual predicated on the paradox of calling the young man's manhood a jinx when in fact it brings the team good luck.

the way cigarette packs work, with that piece of cellophane sticking off the corner). But then he quit inventing *&* joined the Edison company. Poor uncle was run over by a car, in the name of the progress that seeks to end poverty and does it by eliminating the poor.

Uncle plastic, however, is still alive, as he was always destined to last longer than the others; and auntie broth is also alive and kicking, or one could say she is alive *&* cooking.

Her nickname was given to her at a family gathering. Brothers-in-law and sisters-in-law on my dad's side would get together every year for a Christmas lunch. In case of emergencies, these family gatherings would take place on non-holidays.

One year, my father got really sick and, during one such emergency gathering, a complex plan for aid and council was devised by everyone, from rich uncle to poor uncle. Among the various resolutions, there was one of an exquisitely economic-domestic nature; and that was: to convince my mother that she could make an entire meal out of a single bone. Auntie broth was charged with the task of explaining how: "Go get a beef bone, but a good one, eh, you got to choose the right one, one with all the tendons and bits of meats still stuck to it. With the bone, you can make a nice broth, especially if you add a good onion, herbs, *&* some carrots, this way you'll have some vegetables already cooked for later too. Take the tendons off the bone and season them, those are really tasty. With the bits of meat you have left, you can make

a few nice meatballs. That way, with one bone you'll be all set for three days. You and your children!" From that moment on she was known as Auntie Broth.

Maybe this is why those Sunday afternoons at the stadium — with the little wooden devil pressed against my *menagramo*, & uncle Milan FC who would take it out of my pocket to wave it around after every goal — were first and foremost my escape from those meatballs.

Meatball Recipe

First off, let's clarify that making meatballs, for me, means using any type of leftover meat: boiled, broiled, roasted, chicken, beef, whatever. To this meat, I then add a sandwich roll soaked in milk. People tell stories of that one time I made meatballs using a boiled potato in addition to the roll soaked in milk: a resounding success. To the leftover meat, well minced, add leftover prosciutto or salami, or even a piece of leftover sausage, blanched. And a leftover clove of garlic, minced with plenty of parsley (leftover). If by chance you don't have all this leftover stuff, it's okay, some of it you can also go out and buy. But it's really not the same, for a meatball made out of leftovers is much tastier.

If you don't have leftover parsley, remember you can also use basil.

Don't forget a bit of nutmeg, not too much. And a whole egg (two eggs, if you're making more than 20

meatballs). And how about two spoonfuls of Parmigiano? Or even pecorino if you prefer. Salt & pepper to taste, naturally.

All of this must be meticulously mixed by hand, and turned into little balls the size of a walnut, which you will then roll in flour and squeeze at the two ends. The tiny earths thus created will be dipped in an egg wash, salt and pepper. Roll the meatballs over breadcrumbs and fry them. Remember, half oil, half butter. I almost didn't let you in on this secret but I'm selfless, in the kitchen as in life.

I forgot: lemon zest. If it's not included in the mixture, the meatball won't give off the same aroma.

Public Service Announcement

If among your leftovers you happen to have some porchetta, don't hesitate to throw it in the mix. I have a fond memory of a great porchetta laden meatball eating session: a friend of mine had 36 of them.

1932
No, Not Gorgonzola...

My grandma from Cremona cried because my father didn't eat Gorgonzola.

That was my maternal grandmother, that is to say my mother's mother. She addressed my father with the formal "Lei" because he was from Milan, he worked in insurance, and she was intimidated by him. That rejection of Gorgonzola is, at its heart, an offense to the countryside by a man who's from the big city.

It was 1932. My father used to say that Cremona brought him bad luck. He drove a FIAT 509 Spider, not very suited to a family of four; that's why I rode laying down against the rear plastic window. When he would see a car with Cremona plates he would touch his balls and drive with one hand.[7]

However, Cremona is where he met my mother. I wonder: could that be the reason?

I believe he met her when on leave, since he did his military service in Cremona. He must have got her pregnant up against a wall between 8 and 9 PM just before getting back to the barracks in time for curfew. And he must have married her two months later. Otherwise why would my mother insist on the absurd lie that I was born prematurely at 7 months?

7. Touching one's testicles is a widespread practice based on the superstition that such contact will ward off evil and bad luck. A practice still carried on in Italy today when an ambulance or funeral procession crosses one's path.

My mother was a saint; so much so that she's no longer with us. She was a proper lady. So much so that she's no longer with us. She fell in love with my father because he was from Milan and was named Gildo. And also because he didn't like Gorgonzola. After they married she got pregnant again, this time in accordance with all the rules, and 9 months later my sister was born.

Thus the family was complete. At that point my father no longer wanted to sell oil in San Vito, near Casalbuttano, in the Cremona province. He was from Milan after all. That's why he went into insurance, which is a Milanese trade, and moved the family first to Bergamo, then to Bassano del Grappo, Thiene, Padova, Vicenza, and finally Verona. He got it in his head that farmers needed insurance against hail and thus gained the reputation of a jinx, and that's why he would quickly run out of clients & we would have to move.

When my father wasn't at home he was out working. We didn't see much of him. When he came back, he was always quiet. We thought he was quiet because he was from Milan, but instead he was quiet because he hadn't gotten any new business.

Whenever he did get business he would change furniture, city, and clothes. When he took us to Milan the first time he bought us all new outfits. My mother was so happy and so transformed that one day she didn't recognize herself & walked into a mirror at Cobianchi's (1930, Piazza del Duomo).

On March 23rd of one of those years it was my birthday: to celebrate the occasion my father took us all to

Cremona. I was dressed as a *Balilla*, my sister as a *Piccola Italiana*, and my father wore his Fascist uniform.[8] I don't remember what my mother wore.

And my Cremona grandmother cried because my dad didn't want to eat Gorgonzola.

Potato Gnocchi with Gorgonzola

Gnocchi should be made at home, with ½ cup of flour and 2 ¼ pounds of potatoes. You all know how to make them but if you really don't have the time I give you permission to buy them from the store.

Ingredients

1 pound of gnocchi
½ cup of Gorgonzola
½ cup of butter
½ glass of heavy cream
A handful of pistachios
A drop of brandy
Salt & pepper, *of course*

8. Under Fascism *Balilla* was the paramilitary organization that trained young boys between the ages of 8–14; the *Piccola Italiana* for girls between the ages of 8–13. Both organizations required members to wear uniforms to enhance the Fascist identity of the Italian youth. Regarding the father, the text speaks of *orbace*, which was a rough woolen cloth often died in black, used to make Fascist uniforms for adults.

Shell the pistachios after soaking them in some luke-warm water so as to soften them slightly. Pound them in a mortar or chop them with a knife. Cut the Gorgonzola in small pieces along with the butter and melt them in a bain-marie, stirring with a wooden spoon. When everything has melted add the heavy cream *&* keep stirring for another five minutes. Before taking it off the stove, salt lightly, add the drop of brandy *&* the chopped pistachios.

Pour this sauce over the warm gnocchi *&* add freshly cracked pepper.

So good you're going to faint. Take my word for it.

1935
Grandpa Mustache

There's a Cremona I know pretty well, made up of small streets, paved with river rocks, with a thin strip of cobblestone down the middle. A Cremona that doesn't exist anymore.

A long time ago my Grandpa Mustache would push his wooden cart up and down that strip of cobblestone; on it were two big metal cans filled with milk, one on each side, so as to keep balance, for the cart had only two wheels and there was always the chance it could tip over, or even lift Grandpa Mustache up in the air with him still holding onto the two front poles.

At the center of each wheel of this green wooden cart, there was a peg I would often stand on to take a trip around our neighborhood in Cremona, as Grandpa Mustache yelled toward windows and into the wind: "Iiiilk!," which meant "milk!"

Among my childhood memories this remains one of the most fun. At that time cars were mythological beasts and the trolley was a luxury for a lucky few. Getting around on the peg of one wheel of that cart, painted green like the trolley, was much better than walking on foot. Especially since, every now and then, Grandpa Mustache would let me sound the brass trumpet. In short, I was a cart-mounted trumpeter.

We would stop at every building entrance, at every front door. Grandpa Mustache's cry would echo through

the halls, up the staircases: "Iiiilk!" I would add that final touch with a long blow of the trumpet. Then all the women would come down with their little pots & my grandpa, using a ladle, would pour the milk into a measuring cup and then into the pots.

It was a thick kind of milk, slightly yellow, that tasted more like milk than any other milk I've had in my life.

The day before it was sold, the milk would sit in a cool room that opened onto the courtyard of Grandpa Mustache's house. It was a typical Cremona house, one of those that are about to disappear for good: that is to say, one of those country houses that once stood on the outskirts of the city, but that are not part of the old city center.

At night, in that cool room, I would help Grandpa Mustache keep flies off the milk. That was fun too. He would give me some money for every 50 flies I snagged.

Then there was a milk that Grandpa Mustache would churn into butter, but only for his own use. That one attracted a lot more flies, partly because the cream was thicker and therefore more appetizing; and partly because that milk was stored in those large copper plates that made great air fields for the flies to land on, compared to the smaller openings of the metal cans.

Grandpa Mustache always seemed happy to sell milk door-to-door. He got satisfaction out of pausing at every entrance. It was as if he lived with all the people in the neighborhood, he knew their business, fears, desires, sorrows, joys. He always had a kind word for everyone,

& everyone would always have a word for him. He knew
who was sick, who had just given birth, who was cheating on their wife, who had just left, and who had just returned. It was as if, everyday, he read a few pages from
that thick novel: life.

Unfortunately, at one point, for reasons of public hy-
giene, Grandpa Mustache had to give up his cart. They
made him sell his milk in a shop.

Far from being a step up, this was a source of great
pain for him. It was as if they had locked him up in prison.
In my memory, when he had his cart, his mustache curled
upwards; contrarily, as he was standing sadly behind
the counter of his milk shop, the ends of his mustache
drooped downward.

He wasn't happy that his clients came to find him; he
felt like a convalescent at the hospital being visited by a
number of relatives. And, on top of everything else, he
couldn't stomach the fact that the milk had to be bot-
tled, boxed, ready to be delivered. Not being able to use
his measuring cup frustrated him. He felt like a sculptor
that could no longer use his chisel. He didn't last long.

Then one day he decided to sell the milk shop and
open a coal shop. Perhaps, in his naive way of looking at
things, he wanted a radical change, including the color of
the goods he sold. From white to black. I think he chose
to sell that specific product as an antithesis to milk because he felt coal, at the vey least, would never be sold
in a can. And what's more, you can't see flies landing on
coal. He hoped he could go back to using the measuring

cup, selling the coal from his cart door-to-door... Boxes, progress, technology be damned.

Instead he died, poor grandpa with his drooping mustache. And it was because of a box. A box filled with explosives. A bomb that got into his bedroom & killed him in his sleep.

Technology always had it out for him, poor grandpa with no more mustache.

Recipe For A Dessert Made With Milk, That Is: Crème Brûlée

Ingredients

12 eggs
Vanilla Extract
One liter of milk & a bit of cream
Sugar

This was grandpa's favorite dessert when his mustache still curled upwards.

In fact, this dessert would make anyone's mustache curl.

In a bowl, place 12 yolks & add 12 spoonfuls of sugar; whisk lively, as if making a zabaione, add 2 teaspoons of vanilla extract, the cream and milk.

After mixing well, pour everything in an oval shaped oven dish, lightly greased with butter. Let it rest for half

an hour, then remove the light foam that forms on the top. Place in the oven, in a bain-marie, and cook it for 40 mins at 400 degrees.

When firm, remove it from the oven & cut off the slightly burnt crust. If this step proves too difficult, let it be, that's how I do it.

In a small pot, melt 8 tablespoons of sugar into a caramel. Pour it on top, and put it in the fridge until it's time to serve.

1936
Seven Servings of Salary

All grandmas make the same soup. "But nobody makes it as good as my grandma!" everyone says. An orange color soup, with little eyes. That is, that bit of fat that comes to the surface in the form of small circles: little eyes that look like tiny dancers moving around, performing an intricate gastronomic choreography. If the soup has rice in it, a few grains often end up in the middle of these circles, while the green of the parsley floats around them.

A soup that was quite fatty, but not too fatty. Poured in white bowls set on a long table without a tablecloth in a dark kitchen. Many bowls. My grandma had six daughters, a son, a husband, and a young shop apprentice. My grandma's daughters made Lenci dolls on that kitchen table, before the soup showed up every evening.

I know how to perfectly paint the head of a Lenci doll: the shade above the eyes, the heart-shaped mouth, the red dots on the nose. Back then I was a little ashamed of it. Now nobody lets me paint them anymore.

The shop apprentice always sat in the same place at that table. He was a special kind of apprentice: 50 years old, or maybe even older. Shop apprentices, if they didn't move on, stayed apprentices their entire lives. And they died apprentices, especially if they worked in a shop that sold firewood and coal.

The apprentice in the firewood and coal shop my grandfather ran was ageless as far as our clients were concerned. The black dust that covered his face completely hid his wrinkles. It was hard to determine the color of his eyes because he always looked down. When you carry baskets full of coal on your back, you must watch where you put your feet. His body was shaped like an S.

Hunched over, eyes to the ground, this human S showed up every night at grandma's house to eat this soup. Which was his entire salary. Plus his tips, naturally. Who knows if it meant "good evening," that mumble he would utter as he crossed the kitchen threshold, or perhaps a disguised curse. It certainly wasn't addressed at my grandmother who was dishing out his salary, but maybe to himself, aware of being forced to remain an apprentice the rest of his life. Nobody answered that hello-curse-mumble. Grandma was busy with the soup, her daughters talking about dolls, her son was never there, grandpa had already eaten, and I was observing intently. He sat at the table and kept the same posture he did while standing, an S, only just a bit shorter. His black face, held a foot from the table, with the orange soup in front of him. His eyes constitutionally focused on the bowl, his hand holding the spoon, and a regular slurping rhythm as he ate. A monotonous sucking sound, always the same. A supping he used to cool down the boiling liquid, and to enjoy that steam that lingered on his face, moistening it.

Then, suddenly, silence. My grandmother knew this was a sign the first bowl of soup was gone. She would

swap out the empty bowl, careful not to bump his chin, and replace it with another filled with the orange soup with the little eyes.

He would "slurp" 8, 10, 12 bowls. Always following the same rhythm. His shiny face had orange-black beads of sweat dripping down into the bowl. The soup turned darker *&* darker, his face lighter *&* lighter. Soup, sweat, coal, all disappeared inside his chest. Then he would get up. And then, when I looked at him, I could finally see his face, two blue eyes, a defeated gaze, along with all his 50 years of age. Too many for an apprentice.

Another mumble-curse-goodbye, and he'd leave with a clean face, freshly washed by the soup.

Grandma's Soup

Ingredients

½ cup of pancetta
A sprig of parsley
Two cloves of garlic
Half a twig of rosemary
All chopped finely with a mezzaluna
Rice
Oil
Provolone or Parmigiano

I know many will resort to a food processor, if they have it. But there is a difference between a food processor & a mezzaluna. The appliance will give you a mangled pulp, while chopping patiently using a mezzaluna you'll get a different kind of pesto. The difference will be clear at the end of the cooking process.

Add tomato paste to the herb mixture.

In my grandma's day, tomato paste was almost black in color because of how concentrated it was. Nowadays it has a much kinder appearance and is much less violent, so it will be hard to get that same powerful but pasty flavor the soup had back then. Anyways, let's say you have to add to the mixture as much double-concentrated paste so the soffritto takes on a deep dark red color (which will turn orange once water is added). I remember that grandma added to the mixture and the paste two or three cubed potatoes and two liters of water. Wait until the potatoes are cooked through. Grandma, using a fork, would smash the potatoes, holding them inside a ladle. You smash them too. It's only right that one should follow these procedures according to the old ways, so the soup will also taste like it did back then. That's the only way the soup will have that flavor that's now all but gone.

Once it was cooked, grandma would add indifferently rice or pasta. I have the vague suspicion that she might have added a bit of olive oil too. Or else the little eyes wouldn't appear. To finish the soup grandma would add some grated provolone, which was the poor man's

cheese. I would recommend trying provolone today too. The tang of provolone will add to the soup an even more intense flavor. For those who don't like provolone, Parmigiano.

I'm not saying you should make this soup every night, but every now and then have fun wasting time in the kitchen. Maybe it's the only wasted time you'll never regret.

1939
Tongues & Raspberries From Long Ago

I used to put in my pocket a *michetta* fresh from the oven. My 18 year old crotch would keep it warm and fragrant until later when, at the office, the first pangs of hunger would begin.

That bread, warm from oven *&* body, was excellent. As exciting as the cigarette I used to smoke in the bathroom. I used to buy two of them on the way out of the house, *&* I would put them in my other pocket. I would get on my bike, ride down Via Milano, under the railway bridge, take a stretch of dirt road and arrive at work: the salami factory. The only factory in a city, Cremona, entirely devoted to agriculture. Death squeals welcomed me at the entrance. Still on my bike, I would cross the large courtyard that separated the slaughterhouse from the accounting department, without stamping my time-card, since I worked in the office and not on the factory floor. And I would sit at my desk every morning with punctual tardiness.

There were about a dozen desks, laid out in two rows, all facing the wall. Through a large glass, the office manager would look over our shoulders, bent at work.

There was no smoking, maybe to avoid contaminating the stench of butchered swine that filled the air. I used to go to the bathroom at 9 *&* 11, to smoke those two cigarettes; I would linger a few extra minutes in the

locker-room to sniff Nicetta's dress, the only woman in the salami factory. Nicetta was allowed to start work a few minutes late so she could use the locker room to change into her black work coat.

She worked two desks behind mine. I fell in love with her when I asked her to borrow an eraser. Not that I needed it, but as I reached over for it I was able to brush my face against her hair.

Her dress in the locker room was like a sprig of bergamot on a mound of manure. I would smell that bergamot every morning and, as a consequence, keep asking Nicetta for that eraser. One day the office manager asked me to try and make less mistakes, or to go to the stockroom and get my own erasers. But I kept asking her; and every time Nicetta turned red, which gave me hope.

I was told that one of those Sundays she was going to Milan. I asked about her arrival time and I showed up at the station. I had left Cremona 7 hours before on my bike. When she saw me on the platform she turned red and didn't say anything. She walked passed me with a shy greeting. I had gone to Milan by bike just to see her turn red.

Every morning the salami factory slaughtered about 500 pigs. A grim concert of animals and knives that lasted 3 hours. The afternoons were silent. That's because, in the afternoon, the pigs were turned into sausages, salami, prosciutti, while us clerks transformed all that processed flesh into numbers.

Everybody knows that no part of the pig goes to waste, not even the tail. The factory sold everything except the tongues, which was offered as gifts to both workers and clerks, as is also the custom in bullfighting. That meant I received a monthly salary and a weekly tongue. My mother would boil it, roast it, braise it, stew it with sweet and sour sauce. The tongue came already corned and weighed about 2 pounds. Unfortunately there were only three of us in the household. That meant we ate tongue almost everyday, for years.

When it rained the clerks wore galoshes. They went into the locker room, took off their raincoats, hung them on the rack and, underneath, neatly laid out, they would store their galoshes: in a row like that they looked like a small army of giant, shiny cockroaches.

Once, after smoking my cigarette and sniffing Nicetta's dress, I shuffled all those galoshes around. The other clerks immediately knew it was me, since I was the only one who didn't wear them. They quickly reported me to the office manager who started to eye me even more attentively through the big glass, thus uncovering the trick of the pencil under my chin. It was a trick born of necessity: around 2 in the afternoon I would be overwhelmed by the need for a nap, and so I had devised a way of catching a few winks without leaving my desk and, more importantly, without getting caught by the manager. I would stick a large eraser on the pencil's tip, and I would then place the other end on the desk and my chin against the eraser. With a pen in my right hand and my elbow

squarely placed on a large binder, I would find the perfect balance between chin-eraser-pencil. With my left index finger I would press the tab button on my calculator after initiating a multiplication. With my finger pressed on that button I could generate an endless amount of numbers. The repetitive sound, on top of everything else, helped lull me to sleep. In that position, with my back to the manger, I would get a bit of shut-eye.

One day I woke up feeling as though I was about to suffocate: I was drowning in the calculator's paper tape. I was fined, but also rewarded, for they took away my weekly corned tongue for a while.

One morning there was a competition among us clerks to see who could make the best raspberry in honor of the office manager, who was obviously away for the day. Every raspberry, per regulation, had to be timed & a specially appointed panel was charged with judging the best in relation to its length. The raspberries were performed according to seniority, from oldest to youngest. The manager unexpectedly returned as I was making mine.

He fired me.

So I left the salami factory on that gloomy September day as the raspberries still echoed in my head while, in the background, the 270th pig squealed as they butchered it.

Through a window, Nicetta watched me, smiling, as I picked up my last corned tongue.

Stewed Beef Tongue

If using fresh beef tongue, remember to first sprinkle it generously with salt, leaving it to brine for at least 48 hours. If using corned tongue, you can get started right away; boil it for an hour in a pot filled with water until the first layer of skin peels off easily.

After peeling it, poke holes in it with a paring knife and stuff it with lardons of prosciutto fat.

Separately, prepare the base for the stew: ¼ pound of pancetta, ground, ⅓ cup of butter, two diced onions. Sauté. Add the tongue, peeled and lightly floured, and brown it, pouring in, every now and then, some red wine, never more than 1 cup. Add 4 cups of broth (or 4 cups of water and two bouillons), a few bay leaves, some cloves, marjoram and a fragrant bundle of carrots, celery, and parsley. Add salt & pepper and cook the whole thing on low for at least 2 hours.

After that, remove the tongue and pass everything else through a food mill to get a uniform sauce. Add 2 tablespoons of butter. If the sauce is too watery, add a pinch of flour.

Let the sauce simmer for another 5 minutes, then pour it over the tongue.

Public Service Announcement

If after eating this dish for lunch, and maybe even dinner, you still have leftovers, remember that stewed beef tongue, finely cubed, is an excellent stuffing in chickens & veal roasts in aspic.

Sweet And Sour Veal Tongue

Place the tongue in boiling water. When perfectly blanched, the skin should easily come off. After peeling it, put it back in the boiling water, adding just the right amount of salt. At the same time, start preparing the sauce. Dissolve in 2 cups of dry white wine, ½ tablespoon of flour, a handful of pine nuts, ¼ cup of sultanas, a few crushed amaretto cookies, a tablespoon of sugar, and some lemon zest. Let everything simmer for 6 minutes.

Slice the boiled tongue, arrange it on a frying pan, and pour the sweet and sour sauce over it. Cook for another 5 minutes then serve.

Yet another *Public Service Announcement*

If you prefer sour to sweet, replace 1 of the 2 cups of white wine with ½ cup of vinegar *&* a tablespoon of sugar.

1941
In The Navy, Nobody Cares
If You Can't Swim

It was a miracle I didn't drown in the Po River that day.
From the boat, a friend of mine, terrified and a worse
swimmer than me, tossed me an oar. I grabbed it just as
my mouth, at this point filled with slimy water, let out
a last gargling "Help!"

Had I joined the Fascist Youth, I would have had
to wear those leg bindings as part of the uniform. But I
couldn't stand them. That's why I decided to become a
sailor. The pre-military class for the Navy offered, instead
of those bindings, wide, bell-bottom trousers. It also im-
plied an early draft, a detail I was not aware of. The start
of the war caught me off guard, unprepared, especially
when it came to swimming.

My mother cried a lot at the Cremona station and I,
through the train window, tried to grab onto her as if
she were that oar from that boat on the Po River.

At the La Spezia Navy Command Center they were
looking for a fast typist. They announced it over the
loudspeakers in the courtyard of the barracks where I
had been assigned. The Command Center was not on a
battleship but in a building and I had seen a typewriter
before, although from a distance, and so I was very *fast*
to run out, before anyone else, & reach the commander
who was in search of a typist.

"You're not a fast typist!" the commander exclaimed after dictating the first sentence of a letter. "I may not be the best typist,"[9] I replied, "but I don't know how to swim, and the ocean scares the crap out of me."

That's how I became the secretary to the secretary of the Special Secretary headed by Commander De Lalla. I worked directly under a chief (that's what we called sergeants in the Navy) who had a strong Bolognese accent and, from the very first day, started calling me *testicolo* (knucklehead), a gracious and censored version of the noun *coglione* (dickhead), a term widely used among the lower ranks of the armed forces.

From morning to night I would type long letters to mothers, wives, widows, relatives, or friends of sailors, commissioned & non-commissioned officers. In those letters, the commander always professed himself to be *truly* regretful that he could not do anything to accommodate their relatives' requests regarding reassignment from the corvette, a transfer to another destination, the state of their advancement in rank, an early shore leave, or a long leave of convalescence.

For the officers' wives, letters ended with warm wishes; for the rank and file, with best regards.

9. Here the Italian makes a train pun that cannot be rendered in English. Tognazzi describes his typing skills as a "scartamento ridotto," that is "narrow gauge." The commander was looking for a fast typist, *veloce* in Italian, which also refers to a type of train. Not only are his typing skills not *veloce*, like a train, but also they run along/on a narrow track.

It didn't take me too long to figure out why the Bolognese chief called me *testicolo*: because the commander called him *testicolo* too. Every morning my chief came out of the commanders' office with his head hanging low, the file marked "signature" under his short arm (both of them were short, but the one holding that file got shorter everyday), and a grimace of anger & shame on that big red face of his. He came into our office and the bang of the door he violently slammed behind him drowned out a horrific and liberating profanity. He would slouch in the armchair behind his desk & would slowly scan the horrible mutilations that the red pencil had inflicted on each letter. Passages mercilessly underlined, cutting remarks, or even, worst of all, a giant red X covering the entire page. He would lift his eyes from the desk, look at me, and mumble a "*testicolo*," unclear if it was addressed to me, the commander, or himself. Then he would bury his big head between his shoulders in a pointless attempt to restitch, restore, rectify, redo those damn letters. Sometimes he would spend the whole night working on them. Then he would ask me to type them up, even three or four times, hoping that an aesthetically pleasing composition might hide the repeated mistakes of grammar & syntax, which I would often fix from the vantage point of my middle-school education. The whole process left him increasingly confused & disheartened, especially since he never made it past the 5th grade.

In the office there were three other sailors assigned to "advancements," & one to "sinkings." His job consisted in crossing out in red the outline of a ship. He would open a huge sheet of paper where the entire Italian fleet was shown to scale; he checked on a dispatch the name and date a ship went down and, with a precise red mark, crossed it out. Some days, he worked a lot. But his main preoccupation was making precise red marks. Had he spent any time thinking about it, his red marks would have probably come out crooked.

One day the chief got it in his head that one of us had crabs and ordered us to shave those hairy parts where these shy little creatures prefer to hide. A week later, the only one who was savagely scratching himself was the chief. One hand on his crotch and the other on his noggin for hours, staring down at the notes for those damned letters he needed to write for the commander. I felt sorry for him. One afternoon, while he was out, I took care of that unofficial correspondence myself. When he got back he found a dozen letters all typed up and ready for the commander's "signature." He was extremely perplexed as he headed to get them signed, especially since the letters looked absolutely correct. The suspicion of having overlooked some mistake and the uneasiness of having to rely completely on me, made him hesitate. Then, like one who steps before a firing squad, with the file under his short arm, double chin pressed against the stiff collar of his uniform, he entered the commander's office.

His cheeks were bright red and his smile unnaturally wide, which testified, as he was coming out, to the fact that for the first time, that morning the commander had not inflicted red wounds on the white paper of those letters. I became my chief's immunity. From that day on, my daily leave started at noon (for the other sailors, it remained anchored to 6 PM).

Under-chief Del Re was the only one smiling when he read a dispatch from the deployment office: a list of 400 names destined to ship out for northern Africa, and my name was among them. Instead, my chief turned pale as he saw himself orphaned of his literary expert. He disappeared in a flash from the office with the dispatch in his hand & didn't come back till late afternoon. Huffing and puffing he slammed the door behind him, stared at me like a Navy father, and threw a sheet of paper at me:

"Look at what I did for you, *testicolo!*"

On the dispatch, my name no longer appeared among the 400 destined for Africa. It had been crossed out. With the commander's red pencil.

A month later, Bomba, the sailor assigned to sinkings, drew a red line through that ship that was supposed to take me to Africa. 380 went missing. Given the unfortunate episode on the Po River, I'm pretty sure the chance I was going to be among the 20 survivors was pretty slim.

For a while I loved my Bolognese chief. Then, unfortunately, a new recruit was assigned to our office: Lucio Ardenzi, at the time a very well known singer on EIAR, famous for his rendering of *Ombretta sdegnosa del*

mississipì.[10] He managed to put together a variety show for the armed forces; he had an entire theater at his disposal and he enlisted me as his M.C. He was booed while I was applauded. My personal success in the following shows was interrupted only by two air raids. Sailor Tognazzi was about to become an artist. My Bolognese chief started to hate me, calling me "artistic *testicolo*." Commander De Lalla moved up the "signing" by one hour to make it easier for me to get to rehearsals. The command gave me an I.D. card that I could use to return to the barracks whenever I wanted. But I would never go back, for I had met Bianchina.

Bianchina's family owned a laundry for sailors *&* she sang *Ho un sassolino nella scarpa, ahi!* (I have a pebble in my shoe, ouch!) in the armed forces show. I fell in love with her. She was sixteen, had a Spanish face, the whitest teeth, and mesmerizing breasts. When she said yes I became the most elegant sailor in La Spezia. I would exit the gate of the barracks, cross the street, take the three steps down, and enter Bianchina's laundry, holding a package under each arm: one with dirty laundry and the other with steaks. Bianchina, who hid behind the shop door waiting for me, would grab me by the arm,

10. EIAR stands for Ente Italiano per le Audizioni Radiofoniche, the Italian Institute for Radio Broadcasting, which was the public service broadcasting for Fascist Italy. *Ombretta sdegnosa del mississipì* (Scornful Ombretta from Mississippi) is an aria from Giochino Rossini's opera *La pietra del paragone*. In 1941, the director Mario Soldati included it in his film *Piccolo mondo antico*, an adaptation of Antonio Fogazzaro's 1895 novel of the same name, making it a popular success.

lead me to the back, &, over a pile of military laundry, she would offer up her mouth to kiss, her breasts to touch, and a uniform, washed and pressed, to wear. In exchange, I would give her the intense warmth of my 20 years, my Po Valley sensuality, my laundry to wash, and a few steaks. I had gained some admirers in the barrack's kitchen. I was an artist. I was dating the most beautiful girl in La Spezia.

At one point there was talk of transferring me to Rome to perform in hospitals. By now, my Bolognese chief really hated my guts. If he could have, he would have personally shipped me out to Africa. As for my transfer to Rome, he opposed it with everything he had. And thus our hatred became mutual. He sent me to the brig for 7 days. So I organized a show for my fellow inmates.

The flying fortresses put an end to the hostilities with a carpet-bombing campaign that blew up the general command along with commander De Lalla. We received orders to evacuate. The Bolognese chief was sent to Viareggio, where he didn't have to write any more letters for his commander. He no longer needed me. I was in Rome until the armistice of September 8th.

Military Cannolicchi

I call "military cannolicchi" that pasta shaped like short grooved tubes invariably used in mess halls for minestrone.

The recipe is quite simple; the important thing is having a glass handy because that is the unit of measurement.

Here are the ingredients for the usual 6 people

1 pound of cannolicchi, ditalini, or ditali
½ glass of tomato sauce
1 glass of graded Parmigiano
1 glass of black olives from Gaeta
1 glass of chopped ham
½ glass of mayo
½ glass of heavy cream
Salt if needed

I know you're thinking I'm a little crazy for that glass of ham, but if you take a thick slice and chop it in little pieces until you fill a glass you'll see how "practical" this system is. Let's move on. While waiting for the pasta water to boil, place in a large bowl the ½ glass of mayo, ½ glass of heavy cream, ½ glass of tomato sauce (when I say mayo and tomato sauce, obviously, I'm not talking about the ones that come in tubes and cans; but how can I expect you to prepare your own tomato sauce & a nice mayo from scratch, right then and there, if I promised you that this a rather simple dish to make? So let's give in to tubes & cans and move on). Add, to the bowl, the black olives, pitted and chopped, and finally the glass of ham.

Mix everything until you get a sauce that resembles the color of salmon. If it's a little too dark, add a bit more heavy cream; if it's too light, add some more tomato sauce. What about the glass of Parmigiano? Add it now & mix everything again.

Now that the cannolicchi are ready: drain them, sauce them, & eat them immediately, while still warm.

1942
There's Watermelon And Then There's Watermelon

When they asked me where I lived I would always say: the "Poli house." Technically that was the name of that white, rather drab building: three gates, four floors, one big courtyard.

However, everyone else called it the "railman's house" since it was entirely populated by stokers, machinists, brakemen, and conductors of the National Railway. And that bothered me a little, since my father worked in insurance.

At the "Poli house," a very pretty lady had recently arrived, the wife of a soldier that had been captured. At least that's what Giupe had told me, the son of a local train conductor, when I had gone home on my first short leave (I was still a sailor-typist at the general command in La Spezia). I hadn't gotten the chance to see this new pretty lady, but I knew she lived in apartment 16. I was four numbers up.

From my balcony on the first floor I could see the usual youngsters playing on the Torrione: a modest sized embankment reinforced by ancient, worn out bricks & riddled with holes that had been made during the various attempts to climb it. On top grew a fig tree, and from its branches you could see into my apartment. I never managed to see my house from that tree. A couple of bad falls, an undetermined number of slaps from my mother,

and the jeers of the children had all forced me to give up a long time before.

My second short leave happened to be in August, three days in total, including travel. It was really hot & I was out on the balcony, still dressed in my sailor's uniform — the white one — so everybody could see me. I was looking down the dirt road bleached by the midday sun, and at the Torrione, deserted at that hour, without a sliver of shade in sight.

The father's of Giupe, Pinino, Beppe, & Gianni, instead, casted black shadows, every now and then, as they quickly crossed the area separating the Torrione from the front of the building, heading to apartments 17, 18, and 19 of the "Poli house." The station was just a few hundred yards away, you didn't even need a bike. They were coming on foot, still wearing their railway clothes, the cap with a visor that looked like it had been polished with coal, covered in locomotive soot, carrying that little square suitcase of black cloth that protected, like a safe, the leftover black bread that everyone was forced to eat in 1942.

In Cremona, and throughout the entire Po Valley, the heat lingers all summer. It seems like it will never leave. That day we were having one of those classic heat waves when the only thing that's cool is darkness. The kind of darkness, to be clear, that one can only find in

old osterie." Doors and windows shut, protected by heavy curtains, keeping the sun out and the darkness in; a coolness tinged with the smell of wine barrels.

"Is your mother home?" The voice came from the street, and, leaning from my balcony, I saw her as she walked along the side of our building, negotiating that violent heat. It was the tenant of number 16. A very pretty lady, Giupe had said. She wasn't ugly that's for sure, but to me she seemed a little round. Her face, her body, everything.

"Come up & I'll introduce you to my son!" my mother answered, peeking her head out.

She came up, very slowly.

"Nice to meet you."

"This has to be the hottest day ever!"

"How long is your leave?"

"I'm so thirsty!"

"The more you drink, the thirstier you get!"

"What we need is a watermelon..."

"Why don't you go get one, Ugo?"

"Sure thing! Where's the bike, mom?"

"If you want, you can ride on the crossbar..."

The bike tires made a heavy furrow in the dirt road. The woman, round as she was, made it difficult to keep balance and carry her weight. But I still really felt like eating watermelon.

11. In the landscape of Italian dining establishments, an *osteria* is perhaps the most humble: traditionally they only served wine and guests would bring their own victuals to consume. Nowadays, most *osterie* have kitchens and serve traditional, simple, local fair.

"Ciao, Chicken!" I shouted at the boy standing in front of his mother's shop on Via Milano where they sold poultry and eggs. Obviously, I wanted them to see me carrying that woman on my bike.

Cremona watermelons are as round as soccer balls. They're a dark green. If they sound like a drum when you tap them with a finger, that means they're good, and, on the inside, they are as red as the worker's flag. When you open it with a knife it will "crackle." I thought the same was true of the round woman I was carrying on my bike.

Her mouth was red, and her teeth, pearly white, revealed a smile that was already a promise.

Had I given her a tap in that certain place I know, she would have sounded like a drum. She certainly seemed like she could crackle.

I was peddling with my dirty thoughts, sweating, panting, & brushing all my desires against her body-watermelon.

We didn't say a word until we got to the shack out in the country. The same on the way back; you could only hear my groaning from exertion against her neck shimmering with sweat & smelling like a bar of soap. A watermelon on the handlebars for mother, a watermelon on the crossbar for me. A round thing for each of us, but to quench two different thirsts.

One last curve between the Torrione and our building, and we rushed through the door of apartment 20 at the "Poli house." We left the bike on the ground with one wheel still spinning.

I had just enough time to put the watermelon (the garden variety) on the kitchen table. "That was fast!" my mother exclaimed. Then a stroke of luck: not a single match in the whole house to light the last cigarette. "I have some matches at my place," the woman said.

And so we rushed downstairs to apartment 16 of the "Poli house" for a big helping of watermelon; it had been too long.

It was already dark when, sneaking like a cat along the wall between number 16 and 20, I couldn't help but feel that my leave was off to a great start.

The Torrione with its fig tree was a black stain on the dark night. I climbed the stairs two at a time, holding my shoes in hand so as not to break that wartime silence.

Our door was ajar. My mother was sitting at the kitchen table in the dark, crying. The watermelon, still untouched, in front of her.

Fruit Salad With Watermelon

The only healthy way to eat watermelon would be to slice it up and stick your face in it, eating & quenching your thirst. They say this way is also good for your skin.

Fruit salad is the classic recipe for watermelon. Let's revisit it.

Cut into small pieces any leftover fruit you have in the house. There's always a misshapen apple, a bruised orange, a neglected pear that has been overlooked by everyone for the past two weeks.

To the miscellaneous chopped fruits, add two big slices of watermelon, seedless and cubed. It goes without saying that pieces of walnuts and pineapple are optional but, in reality, are almost mandatory. Plus a shot of maraschino, or maybe two, will greatly improve the aroma of this fruit salad.

If you really want to add an artistic touch to the recipe, spray a bit of whipped cream on top of each bowl using that special contraption. But be careful not to leave it sitting around: your son, like mine, will use it as a gun.

Ingredients

2 pounds of mixed fruit
1 or 2 slices of watermelon
1 glass of white wine
3 chopped walnuts
The juice of 2 lemons
1 or 2 shots of maraschino
2 tablespoons of sugar
Whipped cream

1943
The Viscount of Castelfrombron

Nothing seemed out of the ordinary that afternoon of September the 8th. Even though I was in the barracks. Somebody should have at least told us something. Yet nothing. Another afternoon like all the rest. From the main office, I had picked up a "post theater" pass since I had two free tickets for a variety show. I told officer Santoro to come with me and then we left, both wearing a *ricottina* (that's what we called the little sailor's cap in the summer when we covered it with a thin white cloth that made it look like ricotta cheese).

The show was at Teatro Valle. A charity event organized by a newspaper to gather on stage singers, actors, and dancers. Closing the show was the Quartetto Cetra. Yes, the famous one, except there was still no woman in the group. I remember them well: Giacobetti, Chiusano, Savona, De Angelis.

The gallery looked like a cheese stall at the local market with all those *ricottine* sitting on the balustrade: little white stains perfectly aligned that not even the darkness of the theater could erase. Then the spotlight shined a purple-yellow-blue-red circle on the performers: Dea Garbaccio, a radio nightingale; Harry Feist, a famous solo dancer of small-time theater; the singing trio Aurora; Princess Branciforte, known then as Ondina Maris; Lucio Ardenzi, who kept the same name, but at the time was a singer and not a theater impresario.

I remember the scant interest of the audience, the distracted applause, in spite of the prestigious lineup on the marquee. An atmosphere that seemed almost fore-boding.

The show was reaching its end when the MC an-nounced: "The Quartetto Cetra!" They came on stage, all four of them, with canes & top hats, and belted out their biggest hit at that time (and later too).

The Viscount of Castelfombron
kin to the great Bouillon

They accompanied the song by waving their canes, bowing, tipping their hats, swirling in perfect sync. You could tell they were professionals.

Challenged Count Labov
with a slap of his glove

Every now and then they would dance to the rhythm, moving sideways without stepping too far away from the microphones' limited range.

That night at the embassy bar
they saw each other from afar:
two perfect bows and a grin
and the seconds are sent in!

Suddenly the audience came to life. From my seat in the gallery I saw, toward the back of the theater, out of

the darkness, a lighter shadow moving forward: it was a man who, like a ghost, ran down the aisle between the two sections of seats.

Meanwhile, the Quartetto Cetra sang:

Down the trail they go
Faces grim, top hats in tow

The ghost reached the first row, leaned down toward the seat on the left, and whispered something to the gentleman sitting there. The man got up and then it was his turn to whisper something to a man sitting on the other side of the aisle. Raising his arms, this man yelled at the top of his lungs: "Armistice!"

The entire audience turned around, many jumped to their feet, the whispers turned to shouting. We sailors threw our *ricottine* from the gallery to the floor. On stage, the Quartetto Cetra kept singing *&* dancing:

Paces counted, weapons drawn
the two rivals fought till dawn!

The shouting turned to ruckus, the ruckus to clamor, then to riot!

At that point, one of the Cetras stopped, opened his arms toward the theater and, in a pleading tone, said: "Please show some respect! We can't go on like this!"

He quickly rejoined the other three, put his top hat back on, and all together, visibly annoyed, took it from the top:

The Viscount of Castelfombron
kin to the great Bouillon

Challenged Count Labov
with a slap of his glove ...[12]

Rigatoni Quartetto
(Four Cheese Rigatoni)

Ingredients (serves 6)

1 pound of rigatoni
⅓ cup of grated Parmigiano
⅓ cup of grated Gruyere
⅓ cup of gouda, cubed
½ cup of mozzarella, cubed
4 cups of milk
7 tablespoons of butter
2 tablespoons of flour
A pinch of nutmeg
A handful of breadcrumbs

First prepare the béchamel placing half the butter in a pot. Once melted, put in the two tablespoons of flour & slowly add the milk, simmering it on low. Finish the béchamel with a pinch of nutmeg &, naturally, salt & pepper.

12. In order to preserve the musical quality of the original song we at times altered its meaning.

In the meantime, cook the rigatoni and, after draining them, mix in the remaining butter.

Grease an oven pan, pour in the rigatoni in layers: over each one, evenly distribute the various cheeses.

Over the last layer of rigatoni pour the béchamel and sprinkle the top with the breadcrumbs. Bake it until a golden crust appears. Serve hot.

1944
Cremona *Amarcord* [13]

They called him Bill. He was completely off his rocker but smart as they come. He ran the 400-meter hurdle; was a "littore," of what I don't know; & had a tic in one eye.[14] One Sunday morning he was seen hanging from the balcony of his 3rd floor apartment. While holding onto the railing he yelled at his terrorized mother, who was watching the scene from the sidewalk below: "If you don't give me two liras, I'll let go!"

The "two liras" clearly date this episode.

A few years later, around the end of '43, Bill & I were chatting in front of the galleria in Cremona. The "galleria" was built by the regime. The architect who designed it was also responsible for all the other "works" that now prevent Cremona from being one of Italy's most beautiful provincial towns.

At the time, people used to say that one of the four columns holding up the galleria was crooked. Those with a sense of humor observed, but only under their breath, that the column was the least crooked thing of those

---

13. In Bolognese dialect *amarcord* means "I remember." The expression was used by the director Federico Fellini for his 1973 film, which won an Oscar for best foreign picture.

14. The title of "littore" was bestowed upon young Fascists who had excelled at the yearly national competition, called "littoriali," in a variety of fields such as art, culture, science, and sport.

decades; others would say the column might be crooked but the architect was surely a square.

But let's get back to Bill and I in front of the galleria.

With his tic in one eye, it looked like Bill winked at everything I said. His hands deep in his pockets, his back against the column, every now and then Bill would push his shoulders against it. Was he trying to set it straight without anyone noticing? He still believed we would win the war. I didn't care at all. I only wanted to act, & I told Bill that before the armistice I had written a script for a show, but now I had to change a few things. Bill was annoyed and asked me if I thought things had really changed that much; I said no, that I was talking about a script, and so Bill told me that when you believe in something, you have to believe it in all the way, and I didn't understand if he was talking about the script or politics.

Bill stopped being a believer two years later, on a trip to Genoa-Bari, aboard a truck labeled "theater props," locked inside a trunk labeled "personal effects."

After 28 years I can confess to it: that was my trunk. Bill told me I saved his life, and I thought that if saving a life was that easy, it's impossible not to do so. But am I writing a story or a public apology?

Bill pushed against the column again and told me that if I was going to stage that show within the next month, I could do it at the Teatro Ponchielli, the opera house. I told him I already had a "group of financiers," actors and singers of the "Primule" company, a conductor and a costume designer.

The "group of financiers" was composed of a young funeral home owner; a daddy's boy, or better yet, an uncle's boy, since it was his uncle who gave him the money; as well as an administrator of the local farmer's cooperative. The actors of the "Primule," recruited from the various amateur drama groups throughout the city, could perform, sing, and play instruments. The conductor owned a factory that made crank organs & the costume designer was my mom.

"What do you want?" Bill asked a boy in short pants who for the last few minutes had been standing between the two of us listening to our conversation.

"Nothing," the boy said. "I want to be part of the show."

"Doing what?"

"The prompter even," said the boy in short pants, standing there until I gave him some sort of assurance. "My name is Gino," he concluded.

I ran into Gino again, now wearing long pants, two years later, in Milan, in front of the Teatro Mediolanum. "What are you doing here?" I asked him. "Nothing. I want to be part of the show." "Doing what?" "The prompter even." By then I had already become a "professional" actor and I was preparing for my national debut. Rehearsals had started a few days earlier. The day of the dress rehearsal, Gino surprised me by upholstering my entire dressing room in green silk damask with a crystal chandelier in the center. It looked like Eleonora Duse's dressing room.

The evening of the debut (such a disaster that it would warrant a chapter on its own), during the intermission between the first and second acts, Gino's parents came backstage. Amid their distracted compliments, I noticed they kept looking at the damask of my dressing room and at the chandelier. I thought they were pleased & marveled by all that splendor. I was wrong. The silk damask and chandelier were part of a room in their apartment that had been locked during the war because a grenade had come through the window damaging the floor. Gino had taken the damask off the walls and the chandelier from the ceiling and used them to decorate my dressing room. But I swear I knew nothing about the china and silver!

The understandable aversion to the theater Gino's parents developed that evening naturally turned into full blown hatred when Gino decided to join the "company's" tour outside Milan. On a trolley headed for the station Gino's father tried one last time, unsuccessfully, to convince him to abandon the idea of joining the corrupt world of the theater. Gino took advantage of an unscheduled stop to get off the trolley & run like a madman toward the station.

His father ran after him, and, in order to stop him, started to yell: "Thief!" Immediately two bystanders jumped on Gino and started to rough him up. His father caught up to them and, out of breath, started defending his son. "Don't hurt him, he's my son!" Naturally, the two bystanders, upset at his deceit, started to rough him up

instead. And Gino seized the opportunity to resume his run toward the station.

Gino, in short pants, was still standing there between Bill and me, stubborn, unwavering, relentless. "Let me at least be the prompter," he insisted.

"Get the hell out of here."

Bill pulled me to one side and told me that the show was going to be "for the military and the Fatherland." A month later, pasted to the columns of the galleria, the posters read:

UGO TOGNAZZI
presents
A CLOUD ON HOLIDAY
by
UGO TOGNAZZI
a satirical revue in two acts
performed by
UGO TOGNAZZI
directed by
UGO TOGNAZZI
song lyrics by
UGO TOGNAZZI
costumes by
ALBA TOGNAZZI
Prompter:
Gino

The curtains, the wings, and the costumes were all black, purple, and white, made out of that velvet used to line coffins. It had been procured by the funeral home owner, our financier. Teatro Ponchielli sold out. Opening night Bill sat in the box closest to the stage with Roberto Farinacci.[15] Gino, now installed in the prompter booth, wore a tuxedo. For the show's finale, we all sang together:

Primule
we are Primule
we sing you this song...
up in the sky,
among the clouds,
these melodies belong...
We're happy to entertain
and thankful we remain...
If you deny us an applause,
disappointment it will cause...
Primule
we are Primule,
whence happiness draws!

15. A prominent member of the Fascist party, Farinacci was a general, journalist, and politician. He led the Fascist takeover of Cremona in 1922, before Mussolini's march on Rome. Farinacci was the prototype of the more provincial, more intransigent wing of the Fascist regime.

I was almost shipped off to Germany because as I sang the satirical song *Lassa pur lè*, which in Cremona dialect means "shut up," it looked like I was pointing at Farinacci's box. I swore I didn't do it on purpose. After all, the proceeds from the show were all meant for "the military *&* the Fatherland."

We ended up 64,000 liras in the hole. Adjusting for the value of the currency, I calculate that I managed to take away 4 rifles from the Fascists of the Repubblica Sociale Italiana.

This theater memory, although distant, brings to mind a version of "amatriciana" I make and sometimes call "Patriot bucatini." The name comes from the final decoration of the dish which resembles a certain kind of effect often used in the revue shows of the time: to guarantee an applause at the end, they would parade around a starlet wrapped in the Italian flag, wearing a Bersagliere helmet.[16]

Perhaps, as you bring this dish to your table, you could play in the background a brisk military march and force your guests to applaud.

16. The *Bersaglieri* are a special division of light infantry in the Italian army. In military parades throughout the peninsula, they can be seen marching at a quick pace, playing a brass instrument, and sporting a helmet adorned with black capercaillie feathers.

Patriot Bucatini

Ingredients (for 6 people)

⅓ pound of smoked pancetta
2 ounces of prosciutto
1 large onion
6–7 tablespoons of oil
6 tablespoons of butter
1 glass of dry white wine
1 pound of peeled tomatoes
1 large bunch of parsley
½ a red chili pepper
1 clove of garlic
1 cup of Parmigiano
½ cup of aged pecorino
1 pound of bucatini

Pour half the oil & 2 tablespoons of the butter in a pan. When the butter & oil begin to simmer, add the clove of garlic (smashed) then remove it as soon as it begins to brown. In the meantime, cube the pancetta (cubed, in a manner of speaking, mine look like tiny sticks), & slice the prosciutto in long strips.

To the pan, first add the pancetta then the prosciutto, cooking them until almost crisp.

I forgot the red chili.

In a different pan add the remaining oil & another 2 tablespoons of butter; add the onion, sliced (not

chopped). When the onion has turned golden add the glass of dry white wine. When most of the wine has evaporated, add the peeled tomatoes.

Mix slowly with a wooden spoon. It's best if the tomatoes keep some of their shape. Cook for 10–12 minutes. At this point, pour in the contents of the other pan. Cook for another 5–6 minutes. If you have nerves of steel and don't get easily overwhelmed, you can prepare this sauce while the bucatini are cooking. Drain them when al dente. Pour them into a sizable serving bowl and add the remaining 2 tablespoons of butter. Mix well, then add the sauce, reserving a ladle full.

In the meantime, mince finely the parsley & grate the Parmigiano and aged pecorino, mixing the two together. To the pasta in the serving bowl, where you have already mixed in the butter & sauce, add half the cheese and mix again.

Now you're left with minced parsley, half the grated cheese, and the ladle of sauce. If you think about the colors, you'll quickly see where I'm going with this.

Sprinkle the parsley on the outer part of the steaming serving bowl; then, closer to the center, draw another ring with the cheese, as wide as the first one; in the middle, pour the ladle of flaming red sauce. What do you get? A patriotic cockade covering a bowl of tasty bucatini.

Serve with a military march in the background: I recommend the Bersagliere theme.

1951
Somebody's On Corso Sempione

"You live right next door to the university," my father would say emphatically to cheer me up. "Next door, my foot! We're all the way out in Lambrate!" I would reply without looking at him. Instead, I would just stare out the window at a train rolling down the track with its beautiful white smoke that looked like cotton balls. "You have to make do for now," my father added. "If you get a job in television you can buy yourself a nicer apartment on Corso Sempione."[17]

My three room, two bathroom apartment (but the bathroom windows opened onto a private stairwell) overlooked, like skyboxes at the stadium, a small soccer field flanked by the railway embankment.

I would often see a long train stopped right over the field. I wondered why trains stopped there, just as they left the Lambrate station. Maybe, I thought, the engineers wanted to catch a bit of the game. In fact, one time I remember seeing a ship sitting in the middle of the sea from the bleachers of a stadium built next to the harbor. In Italy, everything stops for soccer.

17. Corso Sempione is a boulevard in Milan that dates back to the time of Napoleon and was modeled after the Champs-Elysées. Tognazzi's father boasts that his son lives in "città degli studi," a neighborhood in Milan where the Politecnico and the state university are located as well as the RAI television studios. The reality is that he lives in Lambrate, a district in Milan known for its railway yards and the Lambretta scooter factory.

Anyway, my apartment was closer to Lambrate than the university. Only my dad, an unrepentant bourgeois, insisted the opposite was true. As far as I was concerned, that was my first real *home* after a decade spent in "Artist Hotels" scattered across Italy.

One time, in Naples, right after the war, I was lucky enough to find lodging in a seedy hotel in Via Forcella. The door to the room they gave me had a sign that read: "Chambre particulière."

I wondered what was so "particulière" about it beside the filth, or the wall paper half torn from the wall that looked like a morbid flag at half-mast covered in spiders and roaches. The flag of my small debacles.

In Rome, in a pensione where Walter Chiari was also a guest, I spent a Christmas alone with a plate of white rice & Lauretta Masiero.[18]

During a stay in Palermo, the police broke into my hotel room. In the bed next to mine slept a sixteen year old girl, Neapolitan, a dancer in my company "Bataclan." Her mother had entrusted her to me with a thousand recommendations. They took us to the station in a black carriage drawn by a white horse. In front of our carriage there were 4 others carrying as many couples — actors,

18. Walter Chiari was a very well known and loved actor and TV personality of the '60s & '70s. Lauretta Masiero was an actress who gained fame when still young as a starlet in revue theater. She eventually crossed over to television and became a national star.

actresses, dancers — caught, like us, in promiscuous situations in the rooms of that hotel. What happened was that a few Palermo barons had reported our room arrangements to the police, hurt by the girls' refusals to spend the night with them. The women were subjected to a medical examination; & the men weren't released until they signed an official declaration of their intention to make honest women of their concubines by marrying them. An actor caught with two girls in his room had to promise to marry them both.

Every time I went to Torino with the Revue Company, I'd turn into a "voyeur" because I always stayed in a hotel room with windows that faced inward, onto the courtyard (those with an outside view cost more). From them I was able to see and count, through the openings in the shutters of the room across from mine, a dozen couplings every night.

Now my windows finally looked onto a wholesome and athletic soccer field and I could enjoy the view of a railway embankment. I only needed some furniture & an angel at the hearth.

For too long I had been making love in cars, or in those sad pensioni; and this itinerant love did not suit the very beautiful English girl I had met in London and who I subsequently convinced to follow me to Italy, charmed by her pointy nose and overwhelmed by her long legs.

And, what's more, by then she was also pregnant.

And so she fit perfectly inside my first apartment in public housing.

A green telephone, left over from a theater set, placed on an empty Cinzano crate, in the hallway; a Vespa I'd use to cross the stage; on the walls, instead of paintings, my smiling face above the title "Paradise for All": the poster for a revue show with Alba Regina (a starlet from South America, daughter of Italians and mother of two Argentines) and with Lia Cortese, from Ferrara, who sang naked on top of an enormous white swan: "I feel I'm yours when you tell me you're mine"; mattresses on the floor, with two Chinese rugs.

The first advertisements I did from the stage paid for the kitchen. The first TV ad contract afforded me a stereo turntable and a beautiful 24" screen with a bottom so round it took up half the living room. Still no couch.

Pat swirled around me as if dancing and lifted her long legs as she crossed the room. She would say *coccaina* instead of *cucchiaino* for spoon, and called everything "marvelous." She thought the two Chinese rugs were "marvelous" when we turned them into tapestries for the baby's room the same day she helped me slide a bed frame underneath the two mattresses. "Marvelous" she called the crystal chandelier, the only mistake while on a beautiful trip to Brianza. Even the bar cabinet she called "marvelous." "Marvelous" was the idea of eating like two parrots perched on top of stools around that bar cabinet, for we had an acute lack of dining tables, nor was there much dining to be had. I was "marvelous" when, sporting an apron with the Union Jack, I was busy with the first infrared beam of my life, ready to create my first great

culinary achievement: an enormous roasted chicken. Enormous because it wasn't a roaster but an old hen best suited for broth. A "marvelous" hen though.

With the addition of a crib and a stuffed animal, the bedroom's walk in closet, with its huge wardrobes painted in baby blue, was transformed into a nursery. Completely green, instead, were the carpet, the bedspread, and the dresser: to match the telephone. Naturally, all of this was also "marvelous."

Pat's legs were becoming increasingly bigger, monumental; her classic ballet pirouettes were getting heavier by the day; and her comment about the first roast I burnt was "*porca miseria*," that is, "damn it." "Fuck," which is not a classy word, was uttered when she caused the first short circuit while attempting to bring the music into the bathroom.

I could tell her British "mood" as soon as I walked in the door. And let me tell you it usually wasn't British "humor."[19] If Beethoven or Bach were playing there was going to be trouble. Glen Miller, instead, was a good sign.

My father moved to Piazza Donegani: another apartment in Lambrate, not the beautiful one he had hoped for in Corso Sempione. Even though television had welcomed me with open arms & a contract for 10 episodes.

Later my father sent me a long letter in which he asked for my blessing to remarry. I gave it to him; & in

19. The Italian plays on the false friends "umore" (mood) and "humor."

the meantime Pat had gotten fat all over, not just her legs but also her hands, so much that taking off her wedding ring at night was no longer an option. One day she tried to make mashed potatoes. Her recipe consisted of 2 boiled potatoes smashed under her butt.

When I was away for stretches at a time, her favorite meal was bread dipped in an unopened can of sardines. I never understood if she had misplaced the can opener, wanted to save money, or she was just crazy. "Marvelous" was becoming increasingly less frequent. One day she climbed all the way onto the roof to fix the TV antenna. She was wearing blue coveralls, like a mechanic, which made her look even more huge. I watched her from the balcony, frightened, with my Union Jack apron flapping in the wind.

One day, looking out the window, I saw they were digging up the field with an excavator: I thought they were replacing the turf. The next day, the arm of a crane came crashing into our apartment window. Luckily, the only thing broken was the glass.

My son was born the very same day they completed the project, planting a red-white-green flag on the roof of a huge building owned by Edison. Ricky was never going to see the train, nor the soccer games.

We moved out. Now I live in Rome, my father in Varese, and my son in England.

And Pat is on Corso Sempione.

Authentic English Bollito

It's a very simple recipe. After all, it's only boiled meat. But it's an authentic British bollito. I've eaten tons of it in England, at Pat's house. I'm giving you the recipe so you can have, here in Italy, one the most beloved dishes of British cuisine.

Ingredients

2 pounds of corned brisket
½ pound of salt pork
2 bay leaves
4 peppercorns
½ boiling chicken
4 large carrots, scraped
5 large potatoes, peeled
2 medium turnips, peeled
2 large onions
1 medium sized head of cabbage, quartered
Horseradish sauce

Pat down the brisket with a dry cloth. Tie it with twine & place it in a big pot. Add enough cold water to cover the meat and bring it to a boil. Drain the water and rinse the meat. Repeat this step once more. Then cover the meat with boiling water and add the salt pork, bay leaves, and the peppercorns. Cover and boil for 3 or 4 hours, until tender. After the first hour, add the chicken to the pot.

Let it cool, and remove the excess fat from the broth. Add the carrots, onions, potatoes, and turnips and boil for an additional 20 minutes. Finally, add the quartered cabbage and continue to boil until all the vegetables are cooked.

Serve the bollito on a very hot plate, garnished with the boiled vegetables. Accompany it with horseradish. Bring out some *salsa verde*[20] as well, for those with an aversion to novelty.

20. In this context, salsa verde is the traditional accompaniment to boiled meats in northern Italy. It's made of anchovies, parsley, egg yolks, breadcrumbs, garlic, capers, vinegar, oil, salt, & pepper.

1962
A Swedish Girl By The Flask

How nice it is to have a pied-à-terre. You feel different. More important. "You know," you'd say to friends, "in my pied-à-terre in Milan ..." Speaking about a pied-à-terre in Milan implies that you might own others, scattered up and down the Italian peninsula.

The one in Milan, actually, was my only pied-à-terre. The first one of my life. And I couldn't believe how quickly I got someone to move in with me. That someone was Ingrid. I don't remember where or when I met her; nor do I remember if she was wearing her chiffon dress that, generally speaking, is the only thing lovers seem to remember in old songs.[21] Made of chiffon or not, it didn't really matter, since Ingrid mostly preferred to wear only her birthday suit. And that's really how I remember her: naked, walking around the house, with her 2 big tits pointed forward, like 2 wonderful directional arrows. Ingrid. Swedish from head to toe.

"You actors," she would say, "always cheat! I have to keep an eye on you 24/7." I must say the surveillance she kept me under was a bit peculiar. She kept me in bed. On a short leash, in a manner of speaking. Every now and then she would take a short walk, from the bed to the shower, a pattern that clarifies even further the kind of surveillance she exercised. Under the sheets of that

21. Here Tognazzi refers to an old song popularized by Achille Togliani and Claudio Villa, *La signora di trent'anni fa*.

Milanese bed there was more activity than in Piazza San Babila.

Ingrid. An unstoppable center. Always going for the basket. Always revved up. Maybe a little too revved up.

Those who know me know that I'm certainly not afraid of *these* kinds of situations. On the contrary. But Ingrid, as time went on, surprised me, if nothing else for the regularity and consistency of her performance. At first I thought it was due to the mythical "northern heat." Later, I began to suspect she might have been using some kind of illegal substance. Also because, in spite of my national reputation in these matters, I thought I might have had to resort to the same solution if things kept going as they were, even if just to keep up with her and thus preserve the good name of the Italian male.

One day I decided to follow her, *afterwards*, when she left the bed telling me, as usual: "Excuse me, I'm going to get something to drink..."

Ingrid. I caught her drinking a third rate Chianti straight from the flask. That was her aphrodisiac. Wine. After getting her fix, she would slip back in bed and just go crazy.

Wine. Not very sophisticated. But I didn't care. After all, sophistication had nothing to do with the show we put on under the sheets.

And so, the next night, I put the flask of red wine on the nightstand. When Ingrid saw it, she looked at me with lustful eyes, grabbed my hair, brought her lips close to mine and whispered: "Pig!"

That was my downfall. Put yourself in my pajamas. A crazy Swedish girl that turns sour Chianti into a brothel drink. She guzzled it down and demanded I do the same. One, two flasks a night. At dawn the bedroom smelled like a tavern. The more flasks we emptied the more uninhibited Ingrid became.

After the 3rd "performance," by then completely drunk, she would be overcome by fits of depression mixed with jealousy: she would slap me, scratch me, bite my ears. All of which, on top of everything else, wasn't very Scandinavian of her.

The conclusion to this adventure came suddenly, on a night in August. Ingrid, at the peak of an orgasm, smashed a flask on my forehead.

Bleeding, as she was biting my ass, I called the police. They took her to the station, her and a flask of her drug. Out in the hallway I saw her grab the Carabinieri sergeant. "Pig!" she was screaming. "You're a pig too!"

She left me a souvenir. A small red mark, on the top right side of my left buttocks.

If you look at it, it seems like a wine-colored birthmark.

Mulled Wine

Everyone knows how to make this, but I wanted to provide my own version as a tribute to Ingrid. Who, like a good Scandinavian, had no need to "alter" her wine. She would drink it "au natural."

77

If Bayer had invented cold medicine made of mulled wine, perhaps it would have been even more successful than aspirin. For the flu, a cough, and all those ailments, mulled wine is always the best, for it combines business and pleasure: it heals while getting you drunk.

So boil as much wine as you want along with a certain amount of various drugs (the legal ones, naturally): cloves, cinnamon, blood orange. Sweeten with a generous spoonful of sugar or, preferably, honey. Drink hot.

1964
An American Carbonara

20 years from now, when I look back on my acting carrier, maybe I'll have one regret: not giving it up to become the greatest chef in America, perhaps, the world.

It's a fairly straightforward story, but I'm sure you'll find it entertaining. In any case, I'll have fun retelling it.

The appointment was in New York City, in a suite on the 48th floor of the Hilton Hotel for the official press conference for the release of the film *The Wedding March*. It was going to be a party for 350 people; the idea for the main event came from the Italian producer, who suggested I cook pasta for everyone. The main actor of the movie was going to cook the main course of the evening.

The Americans were excited by the idea, while I almost fainted. It's not that I don't like cooking pasta. I wouldn't mind doing it from morning to night. But I had never cooked for 350 people before.

Like a general preparing for battle, I immediately wanted to scope out the terrain, that is the suite. It consisted of five large rooms, each furnished in a different style. Naturally, I paid little attention to the furniture, as my focus was the kitchen. I found it in the very back, and it wasn't small at all. There was a fridge as big as a wardrobe, and a stove with six burners.

I checked each burner, examined the pots, & quickly checked on the crowd busy with its martinis.

I ventured a quick estimate: they could only eat pasta in turns, in groups of 30. We would be there until 8 AM the next morning. That wasn't dinner, that was murder.

I asked about the hotel's kitchen. They brought me down there in the elevator.

To their surprise I timed how long the elevator took to get from the 48th floor to the ground: 56 seconds exactly.

The New York Hilton's kitchen lived up to the reputation of this great hotel chain. I immediately examined the pots: they weren't pots, they were pools. I told them to fill them with water, and I poured in 4 or 5 pounds of salt before jumping back in the elevator. On the way up, it took an extra second to arrive.

I returned to the guests in order to study them for a bit. Most of them were American. Hopelessly American. I had to decide what kind of spaghetti to make. I made a quick mental survey of all kinds of pasta options to figure out which would be best suited to those Yankee palates. I immediately eliminated spaghetti with basil & tomato because they could have mistaken it for a pizza. I didn't have time for a ragù, which after all wouldn't have been a novelty for them. I scraped the amatriciana out of concern for the taste of American canned tomatoes. By exclusion I finally arrived at carbonara.

Carbonara might have just done the trick. That's because it is the sauce that most resembles the American taste. It is made of sautéed bacon and scrambled eggs. Where can you find anything more genuinely American

than that? Naturally, I wasn't going to stop there. I would add some heavy cream, which Americans put on everything, and, finally, a bit of alcohol, which, given all those martinis they had been drinking, would have fit right in.

What is pasta, in the end, if not processed grains? And isn't American toast the same thing? We Italians see pasta as a mysterious & magical product, a miraculous food that God almighty sent down to earth to make up for the many deficiencies of our country. But in the end, if you really think about it, it's nothing but bread done a different way. And please don't tell me that pasta was invented by the Chinese, because even though it's true that they gave us the first spaghetti, they have been coasting ever since, & all you get from them is a boiled, whitish little spaghetti as a side. On the other hand, we Italians, thanks to Neapolitan street smarts, cunning, & imagination, have developed a dizzying array of pasta forms, like fireworks: orecchioni, fusilli, penne, farfalle, lumaconi, ziti, mezzi ziti, zitoni, bucatini, rigati, rigatoni, cannolicchi, and so on!

But let's get back to New York. There I was, about to cook a typical Italian dish that seemed tailor made for America.

When the producer saw my smile, he realized I had made up my mind.

Now began my battle against the clock. It was truly a chrono-carbonara, because the central problem of the whole operation was: don't let the pasta overcook. Get it from the kitchen to the 48th floor, sauce it, & serve it al dente.

That's why I had timed exactly how long the elevator took to get up to our floor. I also had to factor in the 10 seconds it would take to transfer it from the service elevator (the kitchen was 4 floors below in the basement).

In the meantime, the cooks had diced 10 pounds of bacon. 250 eggs and 100 additional yolks had been whisked and were nervously waiting to join the sautéed bacon. The whole thing would then be poured over 60 pounds of spaghetti, on top of which 10 pounds of grated Parmigiano would be dusted, while 4 pounds of cream and 10 shots of cognac would top it all off.

I knew, from experience, that the type of spaghetti chosen for that evening had a cook time of 11 minutes.

When, after my signal, 60 pounds of spaghetti, divided into 6 portions of 10 pounds each, were thrown into 6 pots of boiling water, the clock read, I still remember, precisely 9:31 PM.

At 9:40, very nervously, I gave the command: "Drain pasta!"

The 60 pounds of spaghetti were being drained as a phone call confirmed that, in the meanwhile, the condiments (that is, sautéed bacon, eggs, cream, Parmigiano, and cognac) had safely reached the 48th floor.

At 9:40 and 12 seconds we left the kitchen riding the elevator to the ground floor.

At 9:40 and 31 seconds we entered the elevator headed up to the 48th floor. That ride lasted forever.

At 9:41 and 25 seconds we entered the suite where 6 stainless steel food warmers awaited us, steaming.

In 10 seconds the pasta was transferred into those 6 containers. In 20 seconds it was sauced by an army of very nervous cooks under my unflinching and by now crazed supervision.

At 9:42 on the dot I gave the signal to charge. And while the 350 guests rushed in, I flopped onto a rather uncomfortable Louis XV.

The pasta olympics were over. Perhaps a world record had been broken. But was it worth it? How did that industrially prepared carbonara taste?

I started hearing some of the guests say, while eating: "Terrific!" My English is not that good but I knew that "terrific" is close to "*terrificante*" (terrifying). I felt like a piece of sautéed bacon. I was sweating. I didn't know that "terrific" can also mean "fantastic." Luckily, later on, I started to also hear "Fantastic!," "Fabulous!," "Marvelous!," Wonderful!," "Divine!," "Shocking!" etc.

All you could hear was people chewing. In 10 minutes they polished off 60 pounds of pasta.

At this point, the producer came looking for me and found me hidden behind a velvet curtain. Then he introduced me: "Here's the author of tonight's dish!"

He barely finished the sentence when somebody was already patting my back. They started hugging me amidst squeals, laughter, and cheers. I got about 100 kisses greased with bacon. They kept at it for at least another 10 minutes. In the meantime, however, the producer tried to clarify the situation: "He's not a professional cook!" he explained, nervously. "He's an actor, the film's protagonist!"

"Really?" the guests asked politely. But you could tell they didn't care either way. All they wanted to talk about was that "terrific" carbonara and they would try to pronounce the name, mangling it: "Care-bone-era ..." And after a little while the whole room echoed "care-bone-era ..."

My "care-bone-era" became infamous in a matter of days, and I began a tour that took me to Oklahoma, Dallas, & New Orleans; not so much to promote the movie as to cook my triumphant dish in the homes of the richest Americans.

One evening, as I was giving an equally successful performance in the villa of the owner of a big supermarket chain, she quickly asked me: "Mr. Tognazzi, why don't you come to America? ... You could make a name for yourself in America!" "Everybody would know who you are! ..." And I said: "I would love that ... If only!" I already pictured myself in Hollywood, doing movies with Shirley MacLaine. And she said: "So come, and I'll open a chain of fabulous restaurants for you. We'll make a ton of money. It'll be a huge success! You'll be known as the greatest chef in the world!"

Movies are hard. Carbonara is easy!

My Care-bone-era
(Spaghetti Carbonara)

Ingredients (for 6 people)

1 pound of thin spaghetti
1 cup of heavy cream
6 eggs (minus 3 whites)
⅓ pound of bacon
¼ pound of prosciutto, lean & fat
3 ½ tablespoons of butter
¼ pound of grated Parmigiano
4 ½ tablespoons of pecorino
Chili flakes
Cognac (or brandy)

Beat the 6 yolks & the 3 whites in a bowl. Add the cheeses, the heavy cream, salt & pepper, and mix well.

Sauté the bacon, and after a little while, add the prosciutto (both bacon & prosciutto cubed).

Drain the pasta when al dente, mix in the butter, then add the egg sauce, and finally the sautéed meats. The final touch is the cognac, half a shot.

If it's too runny, put it back on the stove for 10 seconds.

1970
800,000 A Head: That's Cheap!

"I'm going to tell you something but act like you don't know: in a few minutes, we're going on strike!" That's what the hairdresser whispered into my ear, as she handed me some eyeliner.

We were in hair & make-up at the TV studios in Turin.

"Who's going on strike?" I asked without turning, looking at her in the mirror.

"We are. Hair and make-up. I'm sorry you came all the way from Rome for nothing." She gave me a laid-back smile, with the air of someone who had been very pretty before gaining weight. I looked at her in the mirror then I looked at myself. I saw her as a thinner woman; and I saw myself as a thinner, younger man, staring into a mirror similar to this one, but in Milan, ten years earlier, when I did the sketch show "Un, due, tre," with Vianello.

There he was again, sitting in the chair next to mine, we were rehearsing our lines as the hairdresser handed me some foundation. Raimondo, instead, got a black pencil; he was going to use it to add a few more hairs to his bald forehead.

"Let's skip this line in rehearsal, that way we'll surprise them when we're live," I said to Vianello.

The hairdresser gave a complicit smile.

"One of these days they're going to kick us out!"

Which is exactly what happened when we made fun of Gronchi, then President of the Republic.

"If there's a strike, why bother even getting ready?" I said, with the Rimmel brush in my hand.

"But officially you don't know anything about it!" said the hairdresser.

"Too bad, my face is looking good today," I added.

"I bet you would have looked great on screen," she answered.

"You know what?! I'll keep it on. I'm going out tonight and there's going to be a lot of beautiful women, they might even find me handsome!"

"Good, keep it on! You can't really tell anyway!"

A loudspeaker rumbled:

"Attention, all personal in hair and make-up: please make your way immediately to studio A for an urgent announcement."

"Here we go!" said the hairdresser as she ran off. At the door she turned and, as if apologizing, added: "You know, we're going on strike because you're here. If we don't strike when someone important is here, we don't get anything. You see?" And she ran off.

I was proud to be so important as to determine when a strike should take place, but I was really sorry to miss that evening's show, and I'll tell you why.

For the first time, I was going to perform in front of millions of viewers while preparing a dish, two actually, for the upcoming Christmas holidays.

I went up to studio A. Everything was ready for the show; but as I walked in all the cameramen walked out, in solidarity with the hair and make-up strike. Things were

a bit chaotic in the room. The cameras looked like rider-less martian horses. A group of cackling children came down the bleachers & were herded toward a carpeted corral. Umberto Orsini, the program's MC, shrugged his shoulders and told me: "All this because they don't want to hire another make-up artist!"

In the back of the room three kitchens had been set up: stoves, fridges, pots, dishes, & various ingredients. Maestro Giovanni D'Anzi was staring sadly at his Gorgon-zola pâté. But the one who was completely lost was chef Bergere, one of the most famous Italian cooks. In his pot there was a half boiled goose, and he was moving for-ward with his béchamel: "So what should I do now," he asked, "should I scrap the eel?" "No, let's wait a bit..." Orsini answered. "If the strike is called off, we'll go ahead with the show and we'll need the dishes to be ready. Go ahead, cut up the eel and put it in the oven, in the meantime I'll check what's going on with management."

I, foundation on my face, stared at the fond on the bottom of the pots. The onions were sautéing. The to-mato sauce was thickening. Should I turn it down, turn it off? I wouldn't want to be seen as a scab. Orsini returned. "Not going to happen. The station doesn't want to give in. They're not hiring another make-up artist and they're cancelling the episode."

"What about lunch?" I said.

"We'll eat it. The table is set. Everyone is welcome to stay. It's the network's treat."

About 10 of us stayed behind.

I threw in the pasta. I put the finishing touches on the risotto. Maestro D'Anzi stopped shaping his pâté, took off his apron, & asked when was the next train for Milan.

Bergere had just opened a 5,000-lira bottle of wine. "I'd stay if I were you," he said.

We sat at the table. I had never been in such a large dining room. The boom mics, the dark cameras, the bright lights all looked like modern sculptures, futuristic decorations of a space-age kitchenette.

Corgnati, the director, had brought from his cellar a bottle of Nebbiolo that managed to even surprise the wine expert Veronelli.[22]

A round of applause welcomed the second bite of my salmon spaghetti. The risotto, instead, turned out a little too al dente, I thought, but Corgnati told me that Torinesi preferred it that way (at the table he was the only one from Turin). The sauced goose was excellent, the eel very good. The singer Mino Reitano walked into the studio dressed as Othello. He waved with his arm stretched out as if he had just finished a song, sat down and, as he was eating, started to cry.

"Is he always like this?" I asked.

"He's not really crying," they told me. "That's how he laughs!"

"The episode we were supposed to shoot today, how much did it cost?" I asked.

22. Luigi Veronelli (1926–2004) was a well-known Italian gastronome & wine critic.

"Somewhere between 7–10 million," answered some-one who must have been a well-informed executive.

"That means the network has just spent all these mil-lions to buy lunch for 10 people?"

"That's right!"

A pause.

"Well, pass me 300,000 worth of eel, eh!" I concluded.

Cognac Risotto

Ingredients

1 pound of rice
1 cup of heavy cream
½ cup of prosciutto
½ glass of white wine
1 stick of butter
1 onion
1 quart of broth
1 shot of cognac

Sauté the onion in butter. How? Slowly, naturally. Add the prosciutto, finely chopped, and sauté a bit longer. Then add the ½ glass of white wine and let it evaporate. Pour in the rice & mix well. Add the broth (if you have it, use meat broth, otherwise use a bouillon) & mix slowly, trying to keep some liquid in the pan (*all'onda*, making waves, as the Milanese say), for about 15–20 minutes.

When the rice is almost ready, that is al dente, pour in the cream. Turn off the flame & keep stirring as you warm up the shot of cognac in a small pan; when ready, light it on fire and pour it over the risotto. Use Fundador: it is very aromatic, and doesn't cost that much.

With the risotto aflame, turn off the lights: you'll save on electricity & your dish will make a strong impression.

Fair warning: often, as happens to me, the cognac won't ignite. In restaurants, when they show those beautiful flames, they're cheating: in addition to cognac, they use grain alcohol.

What do you want me to say, who's stopping you from doing the same!

1972
Burrata In Olgiata

"How many pounds did you gain while making *La Grande Bouffe*?" That's the question everybody has been asking me for the past two years.

It's the question Baroness X (I won't name names because I have family: a wife & who knows how many children) asked the other night as she welcomed me into her villa in Olgiata.

Olgiata: the most exclusive residential neighborhood in Rome, a place where an actor like me (not exactly a complete unknown), is considered a pleb who clowns around on screen, someone who can add a bit of "color" to a dinner party.

Moving on: the other night in Olgiata, at 10:45 sharp, as per the invitation printed on toilet paper (always refined these nobles: they call it British humor).

I arrived at the gates of Eden by car: a checkpoint blocked the driveway, with two guards dressed liked paratroopers. A barrier dividing the plebs from the blue bloods. I explained who I was for 15 minutes (ID, passport, signature on a mysterious pad, worse than getting into the RAI building).

And finally I got in.

Promenades, driveways, intersections, signs that intimidated me: "Golf Course," "North Pool," "Stables," "East Pool." A pool for every cardinal point.

And the villa? It was hidden in the middle of a forest of century-old trees: naturally, there were also traps, bottomless pits, quicksand, strangling vines, all to keep the taxman out. No bill collector has ever managed to deliver an injunction of payment. In fact, these were the kind of people that opened many accounts and hardly settled any of them.

It was full of Roman Mama's boys. Very different from the ones you find in Milan. They say, "Daddy just went to Porto Santo Stefano," knowing full well their fortunes will soon be squandered. They remember how daddy made "his money" with the ministry, planting telegraph poles along the railway line between Rome and Reggio Calabria.

The Milanese ones, at least on the surface, try to hide the family's woes: "Daddy's in Paris on business" (but they probably known their old man is also in Porto Santo Stefano).

The first course arrived. They all watched me. "Let's see if he'll burp like he did in the movie," they thought. "What a pig."

I disappointed them: despite my hunger pains, I only ate two grains of rice and a little prosciutto.

I finally found a friend in a 30 something little person from Puglia. Brunette; chubby, cartoonish face; flapper dress. She said she hadn't been to the movies since 1967. She's just my type: she's not expecting me to burp like in *La Grande Bouffe*. A few words reveal she & I have known each other forever when it comes to the kitchen.

She's an unconventional Pugliese: she's not defensive of tomatoes sauces, olive oil, colorful southern recipes. (My best friend was from Naples: we had a falling out over the difference between using oil and butter when frying an egg; like any reasonable man from Cremona, I was on the side of butter. A year ago, the lawyers were called in.) After chatting for 15 minutes, the little person and I established a sort of erotic-culinary relationship.

Half an hour later we reached an orgasm: we invented a new recipe, "spaghetti with burrata."

This is the crucial moment of our spirited dialogue.

She said: "Get a 4 pound burrata from Puglia: cut off the top and hollow it out..."

I said: "Yes! We'll use the cheese and butter from the inside to dress a pot of spaghetti, salted and cooked al dente!"

She said: "Let's add basil and parsley to the spaghetti, what do you think?"

I said: "That sounds great! Then a cup of ham cut in ribbons!"

She said: "Yum, wonderful! Come on, let's mix everything in the pot! But slowly, slowly... In the meanwhile, let's talk about us, me and you..."

I said: "Let's pour everything back into the belly of the burrata and dust it with Parmigiano!"

She said: "You're killing me! Let's put the top back on it and put everything in the oven in heat... whoops, I meant to say on high."

I said: "Let's keep it on medium, until the skin of the burrata turns golden brown, the color of your skin!"

She said: "Now it's ready, quickly, let's bring it to the table!"

At that point, I made my move.

The Baroness caught us naked in the yellow parlor.

That was the end of Olgiata for me. When it comes to Puglia, instead, that was just the beginning of a long exchange: and not limited to gastronomy.

Recipes

(For any clarifications,
call 1-800-UGO-TOGNAZZI)

Black Truffle Crostini

As a member of the "Order of the Fuscella" (the fuscella is that special hoe used to dig up truffles when the dog starts scratching in the right spot); as an honorary fellow of the "Truffle Brotherhood"; as well as a close friend of the Urbani brothers, who are the most renowned truffle hunters in Italy, and the monarchs of Scheggino in Umbria, I feel compelled to share a few truffle recipes with you. I'll start with these delicious crostini, for which you'll need the following ingredients:

- Black truffles (canned if out of season) or truffle paste
- Anchovy fillets (one fillet for each truffle, or two for each spoonful of truffle paste)
- Extra virgin olive oil (the bright green kind, if possible)
- Garlic, two cloves
- A tiny pinch of salt
- Soft white bread (or an Italian loaf with crust removed)

Coat a pan with olive oil, add the two garlic cloves and sauté them, after smashing them with the palm of your hand. Let them golden, pressing them with a fork to get all the juices out, then remove them and throw them away.

Take the pan off the stove and let it cool for a few minutes. In the meantime, slice, or better yet, grate the truffles. Mince the anchovy fillets and add them to the pan, which by now has cooled, mixing everything with a fork. Then put the pan back on the stove on low heat. Add the grated truffles, or the truffle paste (or both of them, since you could use half and half), leave it on the stove for a few minutes without letting it fry and add just a tiny pinch of salt.

Meanwhile, brush the slices of bread with olive oil. Brown them in the oven and then spread the mixture on them. Serve the crostini to your guests before sitting at the table, while still warm, on a tray.

Pork Liver Crostini

I don't belong to the "Brotherhood of the Pig," mainly because I don't think one exists just yet. However, its inception cannot be far off. The only thing that remains to be decided is whom to elect as its president.

In spite of all that, I have been preparing pork crostini for a long time, and with resounding success, especially when my guests are other "injesters."

Let's see what you'll need:

1 onion (finely chopped)
Pork liver (twice the weight of the onion)
Capers (enough to fill half the onion)
Butter (same weight as the onion)
A splash of brandy (nothing to do with the onion)
Salt & pepper

The unit of measurement, as you've read, is the onion. When buying the pork liver, consider that if you use an onion as big as an orange, you'll need ¾ pound of liver. This amount will make one crostino each for about 20 people. At this point, if you're still with me, let's get started on making these darned pig liver crostini.

Melt the butter in a pan & sauté the finely chopped onion on low without browning it, adding every now and then a tiny splash of brandy. In the meantime, pass the pork liver through a grinder, add it to the onion and let it cook for about 10 minutes on low, stirring often. Now

add the chopped capers, cook another 5 minutes, salt and, if too dry, add a bit more butter, splashing it, at the end, with a few more drops of brandy. Spread the mixture on the crostini (which you have already toasted in a pan with a bit of butter) and serve.

Bresaola Dressed "My Way"

When bresaola is really good, from Valtellina, perfectly aged, it should be eaten as is, thinly sliced, without any condiments: its overwhelming aroma and sharp taste cannot, and should not be altered. But since my father, for years now, hasn't been going up to Valtellina, from Varese, where he lives, & then driving all the way down to Rome to deliver two expertly-chosen bresaole, I am forced to dress whatever bresaola I can find here, either too young or too dry, too hard or too soft. The kind you find all too easily in a grocery store.

Yet, if properly dressed, I can outmaneuver even the industrial bresaola, trick the guests, and thus brilliantly produce an appetizer.

On a serving tray, place thin slices of bresaola, slightly overlapping them as to form a continuous bright red surface. In a bowl, mix ½ a glass of olive oil, the juice of 1 lemon, a tablespoon of mustard, a pinch of salt, a generous pinch of freshly ground pepper, and mix everything vigorously with a fork. Knowing how to mix vigorously is an art mastered by few. Mince a handful of parsley and theatrically sprinkle it over the bresaola; then, following your instincts, pour the contents of the bowl to make abstract decorations on this very concrete appetizer.

I forgot to mention that the parsley should also be vigorously minced.

Egg Cups With Chicken Liver

1 clay ramekin per person. 2 eggs per person, 2 table-spoons of heavy cream per person, 1 tablespoon of Par-migiano, 3 or 4 chicken livers along with the hearts, a handful of dried mushrooms, a little bit of butter, sage, and brandy.

In a small pot melt the butter, add the sage & the dried mushrooms, which you have previously soaked in warm water and then chopped. Cook a few minutes then add the chicken livers, chopped. Sauté for a few minutes & add a shot of brandy. Remove the sage.

Get the ramekins. In each, place the two eggs, which you have previously whisked a little with a fork. Add the heavy cream then mix in a pinch of salt and a spoonful of cheese for each ramekin.

Equitably divide the chicken livers, mushroom, and the sauce among the ramekins. Put them in a preheated oven and let them cook until small bubbles appear and the egg comes together.

Serve with oven mitts unless you want to burn your fingers.

Canapé: A Sheet Of Prosciutto With A Pillow Of Stracchino

The title is longer than the actual recipe.

Soak a few slices of white bread in milk. Spread the stracchino on top and cover them with the prosciutto. Place them in the oven and cook until the prosciutto fat becomes translucent. Serve piping hot, as a first course.

Truffle Brioche

I don't want to take credit for other peoples' creations. This is something I ate one evening at Maxim's in Paris.

It's very easy.

From your local bakery, buy some unsweetened short crust pastry. Then procure, either legally or illegally, a couple of white truffles. If you don't have the money to invest in white truffles, you can settle for Périgord black truffles, whose stock on the "Delikatessen Market" is undervalued, also because they're our truffles from Norcia that, once exported, are then sold as Périgord.

Thoroughly wash the precious truffles, then soak them in port wine for about 1 hour. Then shape the short crust pastry into little ovals and top with 1 or 2 truffles, 2 butter curls, salt & pepper.

Put in the oven. Medium temperature: 350 degrees max. When the pastry becomes golden, all that's left is to serve it to your guests, but don't forget to insure them against theft.

If your dinner companions are distracted and don't appreciate the intrinsic value of the pastry, steer the conversation toward the truffles and politely point out how the going rate for good truffles this year is 120,000 lira per kilo, wholesale.

Pork Ribs, Mao Style

Serves 2. If they bring their appetite, you'll need 12 ribs, separating them into individual pieces. You'll need soy sauce, which is now readily available everywhere. Then garlic, a glass of white wine, vegetable oil, a pinch of nutmeg, cinnamon and, should you find it in your kitchen, in one of those little containers that are now ubiquitous, some ginger. That's not all: you'll also need some raw cane sugar, the brown one.

Now let's move on to the execution. In a large bowl, place: 3 or 4 tablespoons of soy sauce, two garlic cloves that you have already smashed in a mortar or minced finely, half a glass of white wine, a tablespoon of vegetable oil, a pinch of cinnamon, nutmeg, ginger, a little chili pepper, and 3 tablespoons of raw cane sugar (or 3 tablespoons of regular sugar), salt, and mix, mix, mix. The result is a sauce for covering the pork ribs. Let them marinate for 2, 3, even 4 hours. The longer they marinate, the more they absorb the flavors of the sauces.

On a tray, place the ribs next to one another, and put them in a preheated oven until they brown completely on one side. Take them out, turn them over, and brown the other side. Serve on a platter without the sauce and eat them.

As an appetizer.

That's the best part, you can eat these as an appetizer.

Lentil Soup With Chestnuts

Soak 1 pound of lentils overnight. The next morning buy a dozen roasted chestnuts from the closest vendor. Chop them with a mezzaluna, after having removed the skins, of course.

In the meantime, put the lentils on the stove, boiling them with salt, pepper, a teaspoon of vinegar, & a sprig of sage.

While the lentils are cooking, prepare a soffritto with oil and cubed pancetta. When the pancetta has turned translucent, add the chopped chestnuts, stirring slowly with a wooden spoon. Then, after adding a tablespoon of tomato purée, stir quickly and toss in a sprig of marjoram as well.

When the lentils are done, add them to the soffritto, along with a little broth if the soup is too thick.

Toast some bread to make crostini, place them at the bottom of the bowls, and ladle the soup on top.

Orecchiette With Bastard Sauce

If you can't find orecchiette, use fusilli, fischioni, or con-chigliette; any type of concave pasta that can hold the sauce I'm about to describe.

Use peeled tomatoes, a little onion, garlic, basil, a bit of olive oil, a bit of butter, salt & pepper. Place all the ingredients together in a pot and cook for twenty minutes. Pass it through a food mill until smooth. Cook the orecchiette al dente and drain them. To the sauce add 8 tablespoons of mascarpone. Cover the pasta with the resulting sauce. Then grate a whole small smoked ricotta (you can get it from a specialty cheese shop) but first remove the skin. A sight to behold, when you bring it to the table: a serving bowl of pasta topped with a little mound of grated ricotta. Mix only after the guests have taken it all in.

End of the Season Risotto

4 cups of rice, a good vegetable broth, 10 tablespoons of butter, 1 onion, 1 celery stalk, 1 carrot, 1 bunch of parsley, 2 well-ripened tomatoes, some white wine, 2 zucchini, 1 eggplant (not too big), a small bunch of basil and Parmigiano. These are the stars of this end of the season risotto that serves 6. And now let's bring them to the stage.

The curtain opens on 7 tablespoons of butter sautéing: the onion, celery, carrot, parsley (all finely chopped). They're still sautéing when enter: zucchini, eggplant, and basil (also chopped). The audience erupts in applause. It's time for the white wine, which splashes on stage every now & then. And here come the tomatoes (also chopped) making their triumphant entrance into the pot. When everything is properly sautéed, a trumpet blast introduces the rice. A general mixing follows. Every now and then, a ladle pours vegetable broth as the risotto absorbs it for 15 to 18 minutes. The flame is turned off while the rice is still al dente. As the rice rests in the pot, the remaining butter descends delicately; from on high, falls a silent snow of Parmigiano. The curtain drops on this gastronomic atmosphere à la Chekov.

Applause. Requests for an encore.

Primavera Soup

3 artichokes, 2 pounds of fava beans (the fresh ones in their pods), 4 potatoes, ½ pound of green peas (also fresh), 2 onions, and ½ pound of peeled tomatoes, stop. If you don't like canned tomatoes, buy fresh ones & peel them in boiling water, stop. Also 2 bouillons & a pinch of oregano, period.

These are, telegraphically, the main ingredients. The next step is very easy: clean all the vegetables & chop them into small pieces. Start with the artichokes.

Remove the leaves and quarter the cores. You already know how to keep them from browning: quickly put them in some water with lemon juice.

Shuck the fava beans and remove the skin from every bean (I know, a laborious task). Peel the 4 potatoes and chop them. Shuck the peas (sorry to be so pedantic but those who follow the recipe to the letter might throw in the peas still in their pod!), roughly chop the onions, the peeled tomatoes, and put everything in a large pot. Add water, but not too much; you want the soup to be somewhat thick. As it cooks, add the 2 bouillons. Let it simmer & don't worry if the potatoes cook faster than the artichokes. Remove from the stove only when you're sure the artichokes are fully cooked. A second before you turn off the stove, add a hefty pinch of oregano, so as to cover the top of the soup. Stir, taste, adjust the salt,

pour in a large serving bowl. Bring it to the table along with some cheese. Slice the cheese on some rustic bread and put them on the bottom of the individual bowls. Ladle the soup over them.

You'll say: that's it? Try making it first then taste it without preconceptions. I'm sure you'll notice how different it tastes from your average soup.

Remember, good cooking is all about nuances.

Lombard Risotto

I call it Lombard to distinguish it from the traditional Milanese risotto. My small tweaks make it a risotto suited for the entire Lombardy region (and it wouldn't be out of place in Lucania either, trust me).

For 6 people you'll need: 4 cups of risotto rice, about 7 tablespoons of butter, beef bone marrow, a glass of white wine, the usual onion, 2 quarts of a good meat broth, 2 packets of saffron, a handful of dried mushrooms (which you have soaked in warm water), 2 lengths of Luganega sausage (about 6 inches each), & naturally some good Parmigiano.

You'll need a rather large pot, with high sides, in which you'll put the butter, bone marrow, and minced onion; sauté everything on low, so as not to brown it, & slowly add a glass of white wine, bit by bit, as needed. Then add the dried mushrooms, after having soaked & chopped them. Stir everything & pour in the rice. Keep stirring so the rice becomes coated with the soffritto. When it starts to stick to the bottom of the pot, add the warm broth, a ladle at a time, to keep the rice moist *all'onda* (making waves).

Three quarters of the way through, add the saffron packets, which you have stirred in some warm water. When cooked, add a bit more butter, just after turning off the stove, along with some grated Parmigiano. In the

meantime, you have sautéed the sausage (cut in pieces), with a bit of white wine or, even better, a shot of cognac or brandy.

Pour the risotto in an oval serving dish (a round one works too), & top it with the sausage cooked in cognac.

As I'm writing this it's 6 PM. I have just enough time to make it myself for dinner. Please excuse me.

Tagliolini à la Bella Anna

I dedicate this recipe to signora Anna, who I hope still remembers those crazy evenings together, when, among other things, we created and ate these delicious macrobiotic tagliolini, discovered by chance in her kitchen cupboard.

Buy some brown buckwheat tagliolini, which are dietetic, macrobiotic, & slimming. If you can't find them, you can also use egg tagliolini, which aren't even close to being dietetic, not at all macrobiotic, & are very fattening.

Ingredients (for 6 people)

1 pound of tagliolini
½ pound of pancetta
½ stick of butter
Garlic, sage
1 ½ cups of fontina cheese
A few handfuls of grated Parmigiano

Cut the fontina into long thin strips, cube the pancetta, and crush the garlic clove. Put the butter, pancetta, sage, and garlic in a pan. Sauté slowly. Remove the sage, and then the pan from the stove. In the meantime, boil the tagliolini. Drain them and put them in a serving bowl. First, mix in the fontina, which should melt; then add the pancetta and mix again. Sprinkle in the Parmigiano and serve.

I can never forget how they taste. Maybe because I ate them with beautiful Anna.

If the woman you're eating them with is called Marisa, that's okay too.

Spaghetti, Tramp Style

A variation and elaboration of a dish that's commonly called *puttanesca* ("whore style").

Ingredients for 6 people

1 pound of spaghetti
4 tablespoons of olive oil
2 cloves of garlic
1 chili pepper
1 can of peeled tomatoes
1 can of tuna
4 or 5 anchovy fillets
1 ½ cups of store bought mushrooms
A handful of capers
A fistful of Italian black olives
Oregano & a little salt

Preliminary operations: crumble the tuna. Clean and slice the mushrooms. Chop the capers. Pit and chop the olives. Are you with me? Let's move on. Big iron skillet: oil, garlic, chili pepper. Remove the garlic and chili pepper once they're sautéed. Throw in the tuna. After a little while, add the anchovies, and stir; then add the tomatoes, cook and let evaporate for about 5 minutes. Add the mushrooms, simmer for another 5 minutes, add the capers & the olives, mix and, when ready, sprinkle with oregano.

Furious Penne

This is a variant of penne *all'arrabbiata* ("angry style").

Ingredients: 1 pound of penne, 1 pound of fresh peeled tomatoes, & a glass of vodka. If you manage to get your hands on a specific kind of vodka, a Polish vodka infused with chili pepper (formidable, terrific, very strong, very spicy, lethal), you can do without the fresh chili pepper.

Cook the penne. At the same time, pour some oil in a pan, add 2 cloves of garlic, which you'll remove when they turn slightly brown. After removing the garlic, take the pan off the stove and add the fresh peeled tomatoes with bay leaves. Immediately add the glass of vodka. This is the procedure if you have the infused vodka. If you're using fresh chili pepper, you need to add it earlier.

Let's review quickly: oil and garlic in the pan; remove the garlic, add the chili pepper; remove the chili pepper; take the pan off the stove; add the tomatoes and bay leaves; add the Vodka, put back on the stove. Cook a bit longer, drain the penne, mix with the sauce, and eat.

This dish is not recommended for individuals with ulcers & colitis. For them, I recommend a more peaceful version: "penne of tranquility." With butter only.

Spaghetti, Scheggino Style

Scheggino is a magnificent town in Umbria, to which I dedicate this spaghetti with black truffles. If you can't find it fresh, buy two cans: 1 of truffle paste & the other of whole truffles, preserved.

Take the usual pound of spaghetti, toss it into boiling water & let's get started, this is a very quick dish. As the spaghetti cooks, grab a pan & add 6 ½ ounces of extra virgin olive oil, ideally the slightly green one. Add 2 cloves of garlic and remove them once golden brown. Remove the pan from the stove and wait for the oil to cool. Add 4 chopped anchovies, stirring gently. Then immediately add the truffle paste, and continue to stir off the stove. Now it's time for the whole truffles, which you will mince or slice, depending upon your preference. Now cook on very low for about 3 minutes, then remove and add fresh parsley, chopped. This last step must happen as the pasta is being drained, so the parsley doesn't wilt too much. Mix and thank your lucky stars that allow you to taste such a great and easy-to-make dish. It's not cheap though, since truffles don't exactly grown on trees.

Andalusian Gazpacho

Everybody knows regular gazpacho. Mine, on the other hand, is Andalusian.

You'll need: a large serving bowl, a blender, and 3 or 4 small plates. Also, two pounds of fresh ripe tomatoes, ideally San Marzano, nice and red; a large cucumber; 2 onions; 3 cloves of garlic; 4 tablespoons of olive oil; a few toasted almonds; salt *&* pepper; a pinch of sugar; paprika or tabasco; a tablespoon of vinegar and a glass of white wine.

On the small plates mentioned above you'll place: a handful of mint or parsley; bread cut into cubes; cucumber slices.

Let's get stared.

In a blender, put the tomatoes (peeled, naturally) *&* the onions. Blend, blend, blend, blend. Did you blend? Good. Add the garlic cloves, which you have previously crushed; add the almonds, which you have previously minced; add the sugar, salt, pepper, paprika, the glass of wine, and the handful of mint or parsley (I'm giving parsley as an option for those who don't like the taste or smell of mint). Every now and then add a touch of oil, which will make the blending easier. After working these ingredients in the blender, the Andalusian gazpacho is pretty much ready. Pour it in a serving bowl,

where you have placed ice cubes, since this soup must be served cold.

And let's see: when you serve it, what will you add to each portion of gazpacho?

The toasted bread cubes and the slices of cucumber. If you like, you can also add thin slices of onion, & chopped bell pepper.

A version of gazpacho for those with a weak stomach: take some milk, blend it well without adding anything and drink it lukewarm.

Onion Soup

This is a French onion soup with an Italian twist. Pardon my chauvinism, but I'm sure this little tweak will make it more palatable to our countryman sick with nationalism.

The ingredients are: 2 pounds of onions, 1 stick of butter, the usual bouillon, since nobody ever makes it from scratch; Parmigiano (this is the Italian tweak, something the French definitely don't have) & some Gruyere. Be careful. If you go to the deli and ask for a ¼ pound of Gruyere, he'll give you ¼ pound of Emmental, which is not the same thing. I must insist: give me Gruyere or give me death. How can you tell the difference? Emmental has large holes. On top of everything else, it's a scam: you get more air than cheese. Gruyere, on the other hand, has very small holes.

Let's move on: you'll also need toasted stale bread, and that's something that even those of us who aren't industrialists have around the house.

Cut the onions into very, very, very thin slices. Sauté them in the butter, delicately. The process must be slow, very slow, which means that you'll have to be patient. When you see the onions are about to turn brown, add a bit of broth or, even better, a bit of white wine. When done, pour the golden onions into the broth and cook for another 30 minutes, until it turns creamy. In the meantime, grate the Parmigiano, & cut the Gruyere into thin

slices. Once the onion broth is cooked, pour it into small terra-cotta bowls. Have you got any of those? If not, you can use one large terra-cotta bowl. At the bottom, place the stale bread, sliced & toasted. Ladle in the broth. At the same time, melt ½ stick of butter in a small pot, and let it simmer until it takes on a hazelnut color. While the butter simmers, sprinkle the bowls with many handfuls of Parmigiano, and add the slices of Gruyere. Add the hazelnut colored butter. When everything's done, add a few drops of port wine. Put the bowls in the oven & let the cheese form a brown crust.

Salmon Linguine

In the '60s I used to go to Norway often — for "personal" reasons. The layover at the Copenhagen airport, an unavoidable part of flying from Rome to Oslo and back, allowed me to restock my kitchen with an amount of smoked salmon that was absolutely disproportionate to my needs; even more so considering I don't even like smoked salmon all that much, but my guests do like it a lot, especially when I don't have it in the house.

So it was out of this salmon excess that one day I came up with this linguine.

Today you can easily find salmon in vacuum sealed bags: it doesn't taste like anything, and more often than not, it's not salmon but some other kind of fish died pink.

I recommend you buy the real thing or alternatively you can wait for the day after an important lunch, when you have a lot of left over appetizers, such as smoked salmon, caviar, or foie gras.

But I really don't feel like peering into your wallet as I'm about to unveil the secrets of this recipe.

For 6 people

1 pound of linguine or lingue di passero
½ pound of smoked salmon
⅓ pound of prosciutto (lean & fatty)
6 or 7 peeled tomatoes
A cup of heavy cream

½ glass of white wine
(And a shot of brandy)
1 stick of butter
1 onion
Very little salt, maybe none at all

Mince the onion, put it in pan with butter, let it sauté slowly, without browning, adding every now & then the white wine. Let the wine evaporate, julienne the prosciutto, that is cut it into thin strips, then add it to the pan.

You should julienne the salmon too, but for the time being, leave it aside. After cooking the prosciutto for 2 minutes, introduce the peeled tomatoes. Cook for another five minutes on high heat. Remember: if the tomatoes add too much water to the sauce wait for it to evaporate. At this point add the heavy cream, enough to turn the red of the tomatoes into a pink similar to the color of the salmon. Only at this point, not a moment earlier, you should add the smoked salmon, stirring and leaving the flame on for no longer than 1 minute. The salmon is supposed to warm up, not cook. Splash with a shot of brandy. Mix the remaining heavy cream into the cooked and drained linguine. Finally, add the salmon sauce.

The serving dish should be oval in shape, extremely hot, and the guests a little "sophisticated."

Fettuccine, Circeo Style

Dino Risi inspired this recipe. The director of *The Monsters* and *Il Sorpasso* called me *&* said: "I'm coming over to say hello and then I'm off to Circeo. I'm with my kids Claudio and Marco and with Carlo Vanzina."[23]

When friends say, "I'm coming over" it really means "I'm eating at your place." And so now I'm hustling to prepare something "different."

Here's the gastronomic play-by-play:

Natalina from Frosinone, the seasonal cook at my house in Tor Vajanica, had already prepared, without my knowing, some luxurious fettuccine. A phone call from my fishmonger: "I've got some fresh clams, kick-ass shrimp, and live prawns." "Send over a bit of everything," I tell him. And here I am, figuring out the Fettuccine, Circeo Style.

I take the shrimp and blanch them a bit, then peel them but keep the tails on. In an iron skillet, I put a little oil, a garlic clove, a bit of white wine, half a chili pepper, and toss in the clams. I put it on the stove and wait for them to open. I peel the prawns while still raw, I chop off the tails and put them to the side. I mince a bunch of parsley while Natalina removes the clams from their shells and sets aside a cup of their precious juice. In the

---

23. Carlo Vanzina (1951–2018) was an Italian film director, producer, and screenwriter, famous for a string of very successful comedies. He apprenticed with the legends Mario Monicelli *&* Alberto Sordi.

meantime, I boil some water for the fettuccine *&* open a can of peeled tomatoes, draining off the juice. I grab the pan, pour in some oil, throw in 2 garlic cloves, smashed, a bit more chili pepper and let it all sauté. I remove the browned garlic, throw in some of the clam juice, and, as it evaporates, I cook the prawns for a few minutes. I add the shrimp *&*, after little while, the clams themselves. I add a few of the peeled tomatoes with a fork. I introduce a bit more of the clam juice and let it simmer for 5 minutes: just the time it takes for the fettuccine to cook. I drain them while still very al dente so that they will finish cooking in this exciting seafood sauce. I place everything on a hot serving dish *&* Dino Risi, his sons Claudio and Marco, Carlo Vanzina, my wife and I eat 3 pounds of it. End of the gastronomic play-by-play.

Mutton Sausage Risotto

It's not easy to find Mutton sausage up north, but Milan, for instance, with all its "authentic" Pugliese and Abruzzese restaurants, has made this tasty food item available at your average butcher shop.

However, if you can't find mutton sausage, you can use regular sausage, even though the dish won't turn out quite the same.

Provisions for 6 people

2 quarts of broth
1 pound of risotto rice
1 onion
1 stick of butter
½ glass of dry white wine
1 large sweet red-yellow bell pepper
½ pound of mutton sausage
2 shots of rum
1 packet of saffron
Parmigiano
Salt & pepper

Prepare the onion and bell pepper by finely mincing the first and placing the latter in a warm oven until the skin turns black. Remove the skin with your fingers (watch out: it's hot) and cut the bell pepper into long strips. In a skillet, put ⅔ of the butter and the onion for

the usual soffritto, adding a bit of white wine & the bell pepper strips. Let it cook a few minutes more, throw in the rice and give it a lively stir as you pour in the remaining white wine. Let it fry a bit & then cover the rice with a few ladles of broth. Using a wooden spoon, make sure it doesn't stick to the bottom. Half way through the cooking time, add the packet of saffron dissolved in a cup of broth. At this point, about 8 minutes before the rice is done, do the following: place the sausage, still whole, in a small pot & throw in the 2 shots of rum. Cook until the fat is rendered and the rum has evaporated. 2 minutes before taking the risotto off the stove, add the remaining butter and two big handfuls of grated Parmigiano. Cut the sausage into pieces and add them to the risotto along with the liquid of the small pot in which it cooked. Dust with pepper and serve.

This risotto is certainly "different" from any other you might have had.

Spaghetti Aglio, Olio, & Peperoncino (Garlic, Oil, and Chili Pepper) with the Addition of Anchovy & Parsley

It's a long title because I wanted to highlight the novelty in the "plot" of this recipe. The anchovy provides the "saltiness" often missing from spaghetti aglio-olio; the parsley lightens them up. If you agree, follow me in this preparation.

Spaghetti in boiling water. Drain when very al dente.

In a pan, the oil, garlic (thinly sliced), & the chili pepper (coarsely chopped). High heat, to be reduced once the garlic takes on some color. Remove from the stove, add the anchovy, and mix using a fork.

In the meantime, chop the parsley. Now bring everything together but make sure you carry out the two operations (cooking the pasta & making the sauce) at the same time, so the oil stays very hot.

Drain the pasta, put a little of the boiling water at the bottom of the serving tray (a tray is better than a bowl because the sauce would end up at the bottom of the bowl, thus an unfair advantage to the last guest to be served, that is to say the host and that's not very nice!).

Remove the water from the tray that is by now nice and warm and use it to mix the sauce with the spaghetti. Finally, cover with the minced parsley.

Champagne Risotto

When, after an evening of partying, you have half a bottle of leftover champagne, make some risotto with it the next day.

For 6 people you'll need

1 pound of rice
1 onion
1 ¼ stick of butter
Parmigiano
Chicken stock (or a bouillon)
Salt & pepper

Grab a shallow pot, and melt the 1 stick of butter along with the diced onion and let it simmer slowly, without browning. Pour in ¼ of the champagne, stir, and let it evaporate a little. Throw in the pound of rice, stir again, let it fry a bit, and very slowly add in the other ¼ of champagne. Keep stirring and when the rice dries out, start ladling in the chicken stock, until you've just covered the rice entirely. Stir every now & then, and let it simmer for about 15 minutes. When the rice is just right, turn off the flame and add the rest of the butter and a good amount of Parmigiano. Cover the pan for 1 minute. Serve hot.

Fettunta (A.K.A. The Oily Slice)

This dish maximizes wellness and minimizes expense. It's kale soup.

Cook the kale leaves in 2 quarts of water. When they're just about done add 2 bouillons for flavor, and a little salt if needed. Rub a garlic clove over a few pieces of stale bread and toast them in the oven. Coat them with some olive oil. Grab enough bowls for all the diners & place a slice of toasted bread at the bottom of each. Pour in 2 ladles of the kale soup.

It's the tastiest meal in the world.

Spaghetti With Caviar

Do you want to surprise your husband? Make this for lunch tomorrow. It'll be a big surprise, especially when you tell him how much caviar costs! But it will also be proof of how much your husband loves you: if, when eating this spaghetti, he looks happy and not worried, that means he truly loves you.

The recipe is simple, although it requires a bit of financial strain: first, you need to prepare a roast beef, which naturally you'll eat as a second course. For your spaghetti, you'll need the sauce from the roast beef, which you'll use to dress the pasta as soon as it's cooked & drained. Then sprinkle the caviar on top and mix.

Expensive cooking is the easiest kind. Or is it the other way around? I can't remember.

Tuna Linguine, or Lasagnette

Ingredients

1 pound of linguine or lingue di passero or trenette
1 onion
½ stick of butter
olive oil
½ glass of dry white wine
A pinch of chili pepper
1 pound of peeled tomatoes (drain some of the juice)
½ pound of tuna
4 anchovy fillets

Put the water on to boil and let's begin.

Thinly slice the onion and sauté it in a shallow pot along with the butter and a bit of oil. After a little while add the white wine, which will evaporate, and the chili pepper. Then add the peeled tomatoes. In a different pot, cook the tuna (using a drop of oil) along with the 4 anchovy fillets (chopped). After cooking for 10 minutes, add the tuna to the sauce, mix, and keep cooking for a few extra minutes.

That's it.

Don't forget to put the linguine in the water when it boils.

Wet Nurse Bean Soup

This is not a soup meant to help wet nurses lactate. It's just that I learned it from a wet nurse. She was from Friuli. It's a special version of a famous dish they call "iota."

Ingredients for 6 people

¾ pound of borlotti beans
1 ½ tablespoons of white flour
2 bay leaves
Garlic
Oil
¼ pound of smoked pancetta (cubed)
A jar of sauerkraut (that's right, you can buy it already made in a jar)
A generous tablespoon of yellow flour
Aalt & pepper

Avoid cheese. If Carnacina sees you add cheese, he'll disown you.[24] But since everybody's entitled to their own taste, perhaps you could put the cheese bowl on the table.

Grab a good pot, terracotta if you have it, and fill it with cold water. Add the beans & the bay leaves, and let it boil until cooked. In the meantime, in a different pan, sauté

24. Luigi Carnacina (1888–1981) was a famous Italian author & gastronome.

a garlic clove with some oil. When the garlic browns, add the white flour and toast it. When it turns light brown, pour it into the pot with the beans. In another pot, sauté the cubed pancetta in a few drops of olive oil; add the sauerkraut and let it simmer for 10 minutes, until they take on as much flavor as possible. Add a bit of salt and pepper and, every now & then, add a ladle of the bean's water. Finish with the tablespoon of yellow flour. Mix this delightful mess well. Let it cook for another 5 or 6 minutes and then pour everything into the bean pot, which you'll put back on the stove for another 15 minutes.

Some friendly advice: prepare the soup ahead of time, about an hour before serving it. It's excellent when lukewarm.

Spaghetti With Fresh Tomato

This is the famous dish where spaghetti is dressed with fresh, uncooked San Marzano tomatoes, oil, and basil. It's very simple. All you need to do is mix the piping hot spaghetti with these ingredients. I came up with a personalized version that I'll share with you.

While cooking 1 pound of spaghetti, grab some rosemary, sage, bay leaves, oregano, chili peppers, garlic, & mince finely. Chop the San Marzano tomatoes. A few minutes before draining the spaghetti, pour 6 ½ ounces of olive oil into a small pot and heat until it begins to smoke. As soon as the spaghetti are ready, drain and place them in a hot serving bowl. Cover them with the minced herbs, then add the chopped tomatoes and, finally, the hot oil. To maximize flavor, cover the serving bowl for 20 seconds. Remove the lid. Mix quickly and serve.

Rigatoni With Sausage And Cream

A clash of violence and tenderness: the sausage attacks, the cream surrenders.

That being said, *for 6 people*

1 pound of rigatoni
1 big onion
1 stick of butter
Milk
4 sausages
The usual glass of heavy cream
Parmigiano
A pepper mill at the end because the pepper needs
    to be fresh *&* aromatic

Execution: on one side put the usual pot to cook the rigatoni. On the other place a large pan in which you sauté the minced onion in ⅔ of the butter. To avoid excessive browning, add, to the onion, a bit of milk, every now and then. When the onion has almost completely melted, add the sausages, skinned and chopped with a mezzaluna. If needed, add a bit more milk. Cook for 10 minutes.

Drain the rigatoni, stir in the remaining butter, add the sausage sauce, the heavy cream, and the Parmigiano. Mix quickly and bring it to the table just as quickly. On the contrary, very slowly, almost lovingly, take your pepper mill and crack a bit of fresh pepper over your own bowl.

Because not everyone likes pepper.

Green Gnocchi

You'll need a blender for this one. If you don't have a blender, you're screwed.

Two hefty handfuls of basil, a bundle of parsley, ½ stick of butter, 1 cup of heavy cream, & a tiny little piece of garlic. It goes without saying that you'll have made the gnocchi from scratch beforehand.

Boil them while you blend the ingredients mentioned above. If you blend long enough you'll get a sort of unified mix. Add the glass of heavy cream and blend again until smooth. Salt & pepper and the sauce is done!

Drain the gnocchi, dress them with another ½ stick of butter, and add the sauce.

If you don't like it, you're a lost cause.

Caribbean Risotto

Pretend you have on hand some shrimp, baby squid, and clams fresh from the Caribbean. Instead of going down to the fish market, buy all this stuff from the freezer section, which besides being a whole lot cheaper, is also the safest bet hygienically.

For 6 people

1 pound of risotto rice
¾ pound of shrimp (peeled)
a dozen baby squids (cleaned & chopped)
½ pound of clams
1 ½ sticks of butter
2 tablespoons of tomato purée
Lemon zest

Now there's one problem: you'll need a pot of fish broth. Ideally you'd use a scorpion fish but I doubt you'll find it frozen. So let's do this: if you can't make some broth out of fresh fish, make any broth, even vegetable. As you can see, I'm easy.

Now for the preparation. In a large pot sauté the onion, sliced thin, using ½ stick of butter, then add the tomato purée. Add the baby squid and keep stirring until they soften. Now it's time for the clams. As for the shrimp,

instead, keep them aside and I'll tell you why in a minute. Now pour in the rice, stir well, and add, every now and then, a bit of broth, letting the risotto simmer for 15-18 minutes, depending on whether you like it al dente or well cooked. 10 minutes before taking it off the stove, put a bit of butter in a small pan, and add 1 clove of garlic and the shrimp. 3 minutes later, remove the garlic and throw in a shot of cognac. Cook a little longer and 3 minutes before you take the risotto off the stove, add it to the pot. Keep your eye on the clock: 2 minutes before you take it off the stove is when you'll add the lemon zest. Stir well and at go time, that is to say once cooked, add the remaining butter. Serve hot.

Go ahead, admit it: you never thought to add lemon zest before.

Pasta With Bell Pepper (2 Versions)

Ingredients

6 bell peppers
1 pound of spaghetti
2 cloves of garlic
Olive oil
Chili pepper (optional)
Chopped parsley

For the second version, add

¾ pound of mezzi ziti or penne (substitute for the
    spaghetti)
1 jar of Italian black olives
A handful of capers
4 tablespoons of breadcrumbs

Version #1

Put the bell peppers in a hot oven. When the skin is burnt, peel them (let your children do it, so you don't burn your fingers). Cut the bell peppers in strips. In a pan, pour some oil & add the two cloves of garlic, smashed. Let it sauté (if you want, now's the time to add the chili pepper). Add the bell peppers & cook for 5 more minutes.

Drain the pasta and dress it, adding a handful of parsley only at the very end.

Version #2

Prepare the same sauce as version #1 but add the capers, pitted Italian black olives, and minced parsley. In a different pan pour in some oil and when hot, add the breadcrumbs, letting them fry for a few minutes.

Spread the bell pepper sauce across the bottom of an oven dish. On top of that, the penne cooked al dente and two tablespoons of the breadcrumbs. The bell peppers again, penne, & breadcrumbs. Basically, layer them until you run out of ingredients.

Put it in the oven until the last layer of breadcrumbs has formed a golden crust.

Green Lasagna, Valtellina Style

Ingredients

1 pound of green lasagna (wide as a finger)
a good-sized savoy cabbage
1 onion
1 stick of butter
1 garlic clove
A sprig of sage
2 ½ ounces of fontina
A pinch of pepper

In a large pot boil both the roughly chopped cabbage and lasagna sheets. When cooked, drain them.

In the meantime, cut the fontina into thin slices. In a pan, sauté the onion, garlic, and sage in butter.

In a warm tray, place a layer of lasagna and cabbage, then the fontina slices, pepper, and half the soffritto. Make a second layer the same way. Bring it to the table and stir just a minute before serving.

Smoke and Champagne Risotto

Ingredients

1 pound of rice
1 stick of butter
1 onion
2 quarts of broth (yes, bouillon is okay)
2 small balls of smoked provolone (hence the smoke)
Parmigiano
Pepper
2 glasses of champagne

Prepare a soffritto using ⅔ of the butter and the onion, finely chopped. Little by little, add the two glasses of champagne, to prevent the onion from browning as it slowly cooks. Add the rice & stir. Pour in the remaining champagne and, finally, enough broth to completely cover the rice. Let it cook for 10 minutes, then add the 2 small balls of smoked provolone after peeling and cubing them. You'll see, they'll melt into the rice making it creamy.

Finish cooking, & 2 minutes before taking it off the stove add pepper and the remaining butter.

Praised be Capogna, the Milanese chef who taught me this most delicate recipe.

Rancho Grande Eggs

If you happen to find a can of tortillas in your local *Delikatessen*, you could try this vaguely Mexican dish.

Ingredients (for 1 person)

2 eggs
2 tortillas
1 large bell pepper, yellow or green
2 peeled tomatoes & 1 tablespoon of tomato paste
1 spicy chili pepper
¼ onion
A little oil
A little butter

Finely chop the bell pepper, tomatoes, and onion & throw them in the pan with the oil, together with the tomato paste and chili pepper. Salt and let it cook on low for about 20 minutes. Keep warm. Fry the 2 eggs in some butter until the whites set. Put the tortillas on a plate, put the eggs over them, and cover with the sauce. And that's it.

Austerity Frittata [25]

Ingredients (absolutely not imported)

4 potatoes
1 medium sized onion
¼ pound of smoked pancetta
1 cup of milk
A little butter
As much oil as needed
6 eggs, obviously
Salt & pepper

In a pan with some butter fry the potatoes, which you've thinly sliced beforehand. To help with the frying, every now and then add a little milk. The onion, finely minced, goes in another pan and is sautéed in butter. Cut the pancetta into thin slices and fry it a third pan.

In a mixing bowl, beat the eggs and stir in the potatoes, onion, and pancetta. Using a fork, mash and mix everything with the eggs. Salt, pepper, and the frittata mixture is ready. The most difficult part is frying it. Do you know how to flip a frittata? You should see me when I flip mine. I'm magnificent. Remember to always use a lid, never a plate, when flipping a frittata.

Always eat them hot.

Or completely cold.

25. Tognazzi is referring to a very specific time in history: the 1973 oil crisis. In order to cope with skyrocketing energy costs, the Italian government issued a number of drastic measures that limited the public's ability to travel & consume certain goods.

Oregano Meatballs

In times of austerity it's fashionable to substitute ground beef for beef-beef, which is very expensive. I want to follow suit, suggesting a small *&* economical kind of meatballs.

You'll need ¾ ground beef, 1½ ounces of prosciutto, a dinner roll without the crust (any kind you can get your hands on), which you'll soak in milk to better mix it with the beef. Add an egg or 2. This is an easy one; I believe all housewives have prepared it at some point in their lives. Later I'll tell you how to prepare a sauce that will make these taste even better.

In a pan melt 5 tablespoons of butter *&*, one by one, add the meatballs, lightly floured, frying them on each side. When cooked, remove them from the pan and let them rest on a paper towel, keeping them warm.

Now to the sauce, which will first require 1 small, easy step: with a fork, try to remove the butter solids from the bottom of the pan where you fried the meatballs. Then add 2 more tablespoons of butter. To brighten up this sauce, add a shot of dry marsala wine, let it evaporate, then add a pinch or 2 of oregano, depending on your taste. The sauce is ready. Put the meatballs back in the pan with the sauce and cook thoroughly. Naturally, if the sauce starts to dry, add a few tablespoons of hot water, perhaps mixed with a little bouillon. That's about it.

Mom's Spinach

I'd like to tell you how my poor mother made her spinach. Yes, it's done the same way you do yours, but ...

First off, my mom cooked it slowly in butter, very slowly, on very low heat, and she added a pinch of nutmeg along with the usual salt and pepper. Toward the end she would add ½ glass of milk, also very slowly, a bit at a time. When the milk completely evaporated she added a bit more. Then she'd throw in a handful of grated Parmigiano. In short, she used all the ingredients that go well with spinach.

What do you want me to say, mothers are always the best cooks.

Spinach Salad

Since you now have a bunch of spinach, rather than cooking all of it, set a little aside. Wash it thoroughly, because we'll use it for a nice salad that is well known to some, but perhaps a novelty to others.

½ pound of smoked pancetta, cubed. A handful of walnuts. 1 ½ ounces of Gruyere, cubed, 2 slices of white bread, or even regular bread. Then, some oil (which is optional, I'll explain why), some vinegar, salt & pepper.

The dressing is prepared as follows: in a pan, sauté the cubed pancetta until crispy. Do the same with the bread slices, which you've previously cubed. Mix everything with the walnuts and Gruyere, and toss it into the spinach, adding oil, vinegar, salt & pepper. Alternatively, you can substitute the oil with the fat leftover from cooking the pancetta.

This recipe wasn't my mother's. It was my aunt's.

Green Cauliflower Gratin

Here are the ingredients for this delicious gratin: 1 cauliflower, green if possible, or a romanesco; a béchamel made with ½ quart of milk; 4 tablespoons of Parmigiano; 1 thick slice of ham; a bit of butter; and some bread crumbs.

The preparation is so simple that I'm tempted not to explain it at all. Certainly it's not a thrilling dish, there's no twist at the end.

Boil the cauliflower or romanesco. Then run it though a food mill and put it aside in a bowl. In the meantime, make the béchamel, which you'll add to the cauliflower purée, along with 4 tablespoons of Parmigiano. Cube the ham and stir into the mixture, which you'll then pour into a greased oven dish. Put several curls of butter on top, the remaining tablespoon of Parmigiano, and the breadcrumbs. Cook in the oven for about 10 minutes, until it forms a golden brown crust. Serve warm. Not piping hot.

Artichoke Salad

Ingredients

Parmigiano
Black truffles (if you can't find them fresh,
    you already know: in a jar)
Olive oil
Lemon
Salt, pepper
And, naturally, artichokes

Remove the outer leaves & cut the hearts into thin slices. Place them in a salad bowl, add the Parmigiano (also thinly sliced). Now slice the black truffles and mix everything, adding oil, lemon, salt & pepper.

That's it.

What else can you ask of an artichoke salad?

Rice Salad, My Way

For 4 people, you'll need

¾ pounds of rice
a can of tuna
2 hotdogs
A handful of capers
3 cucumbers
Some basil
3 tomatoes
1 bell pepper
3 hard boiled eggs

The preparation is obvious, but I'll tell you anyways. Cook the rice, drain it, and let it cool a bit. Mince the tuna, capers, and basil. Chop everything else in small pieces. Dress the rice with oil, lemon, mustard, & then add all the other ingredients. If you have a small piece of left over Emmental, cube it & add it along with salt & pepper, naturally.

Seta Eggplants in Velvety Parmigiano

You're not far off if you think this dish involves eggplants. Not the skinny ones but the fat round ones, of the seta variety, light purple in color. The oven dish is very important, it's the protagonist of this recipe. Best if it's round. Then you'll need: grated Parmigiano, oregano, butter, olive oil, salt & pepper. I think it's fairly simple. You could figure it out on your own.

Slice the eggplants into disks about ¼ inch thick. Pour the olive oil into the oven dish, then neatly arrange the eggplant slices across the bottom. On top of the eggplant, place a good amount of butter curls, enough to almost completely cover them. On the butter, sprinkle the oregano, this too very generously. Then the grated Parmigiano. Place in the oven & check often: when it becomes golden, soft, moist, take it out & eat immediately, while still warm.

This dish has received 3 stars at the yearly national competition of gastro-austerity.

Baby Birds In Polenta

Do I really need to tell you how to make polenta? Make it hard or soft according to your geo-political preferences. As for the baby birds: make sure they're very small. Poor things, how awful.

For 4 people, you'll need 12 or 16.

Sprinkle a lardon of pancetta with salt, pepper, and sage. Stuff the baby birds with it. Use a toothpick to keep them in place, passing it through the belly of the baby bird. When finished, place these poor little birds in a terracotta pot, covering them with just enough water.

I'm almost moved to tears when I think about this dish. But what can I do? That's life.

Cook the poor little birds until the water has completely evaporated. Then add ½ stick of butter and let them sauté.

When the poor little birds are nicely browned, 1 minute before taking them off the stove, add ½ quart of heavy cream. Stir well & let it thicken slightly. The poor little birds will be wrapped in the comfort of this abundant white sauce when they meet the yellow polenta.

After asking the Lord for forgiveness and having thanked Him for our daily bread, you may now scarf down the poor baby birds.

Holy Shank

What's a holy shank? It's the shank of a cow. Let me explain: when you order ossobuco, they take the shank *&* cut it up into a bunch of pieces. Here, instead, you're going to buy the whole thing.

The preparation is simple: put it in an oval Dutch oven with some oil and butter, as much as needed. Brown it well, turning it from time to time and adding a bit of white wine every so often. Let the wine evaporate and when the shank is well browned, add 2 onions, chopped in large pieces. Then add 2 bouillons *&* 4 cups of water. Keep cooking for a few hours, on low, so the onions melt, the water reduces *&* everything turns into a nice sauce that you'll run through a food mill to make it smooth and dense. Bring it to the table, slice the shank *&* pour the sauce over it while still hot. That's it.

After talking about this recipe on the radio, a gentleman wrote me asking to borrow my chainsaw to cut the bone. He was convinced, poor thing, that each portion was to be cut across the shank. Lengthwise, my dear sir, lengthwise. When you get to the bone throw it to your dog; you'll make him happy.

My Stroganoff Filet Mignon

For 4 people, you'll need 4 filets; unless you have 4 very hungry people, in which case you'll need 8. You'll also need some pulverized dried mushroom (keep it on hand, it's very useful, it can be a good substitute when you don't have access to fresh mushrooms), a shot of cognac, 4 teaspoons of mustard, a splash of Worcestershire sauce, and the usual cup of heavy cream.

Take the filets, put them in a pan, and brown them in butter. Keep them warm. In the same pan, add the cognac and let it burn off. When done, add a bit of pulverized mushrooms, the 4 teaspoons of mustard, the splash of Worcestershire, the cup of heavy cream & stir gently for a few minutes over medium heat. The sauce is ready. Arrange the warm filets on a serving platter, cover them with the sauce, and serve immediately.

If you're having friends over for dinner, try to cook the filets at the table, on a portable stove. It makes it more festive. And sure to impress.

Maria's Duck

Who's Maria? She's the angel of the hearth at my place. Since my wife isn't allowed in the kitchen, I'm only the only one who can go in and poke around. The other day Maria told me: "Let me prepare the duck the way I like it," and I let her do it. However, on the sly I kept an eye on her and now I can give you the recipe. Actually, I'm going to suggest a whole meal based on duck.

Ingredients: A whole duck, olive oil, butter, onion, garlic, carrots, celery. Simple, right?

For the sauce: hang onto the duck's liver & heart, 4 small tomatoes, black truffles (optional), dried mushrooms.

Let's begin: cut the duck into pieces and, while still raw, place it in a pan with some olive oil, half a stick of butter, onion, carrots, celery (coarsely chopped), and garlic (finely minced). Let it cook on very low heat. Check on it every now & then. I give you permission, if needed, to add a few ladles of warm water and a piece of bouillon for flavor, in addition to salt, naturally.

When the duck is done, make some time for the sauce. Into another pan, transfer the duck's drippings, add a piece of butter, a bit of white wine, and once it has evaporated, add the liver and heart (better if you have 2 of each), finely chopped. Let it cook a little bit, then add

the 4 tomatoes, which you'll smash in the pan right away. Let it cook for another 7 minutes, and just before taking the pan off the stove add the black truffle, grated. You can substitute it with mushrooms; remember to soak them beforehand, then chop them, & add them before the tomatoes.

The duck sauce can be used to dress a pot of tagliatelle. Naturally, the duck itself will follow.

Wintertime Guinea Hen

Guinea hen is very good in December. And in January too. Guinea hen is *always* very good. If you make it in May, call it "Springtime Guinea Hen."

The ingredients are: a guinea hen (obviously), 4 slices of pancetta, butter, olive oil, a shot of brandy, ½ cup of marsala, and some milk.

Quarter the guinea hen. In a wide pan, melt the butter in the oil, lay down the 4 slices of pancetta, and let them cook a little. Add the 4 pieces of the guinea hen, keeping some distance between them in the pan. Brown them well, tops, bottoms, breasts and thighs, then add the shot of brandy. Let it evaporate, & then pour in the ½ cup of marsala. After 2 minutes, cover with a lid but every now and then take a peek to check how things are progressing. Add the milk a little at a time until fully cooked.
Serve with polenta.

Pork Tonné

Don't get scared: it's just like veal tonné but I use pork instead.

Ingredients: about 1 pound of pork loin, ⅓ pound of tuna, 4 anchovy fillets in olive oil, a tube of mayo (I know you don't feel like making it from scratch), a handful of capers, ½ lemon, a bottle of dry white wine. And keep a blender handy.

Tie the loin as if making a roast, then boil it. Tuck 2 bay leaves between the twine and the meat, and pierce it with 2 cloves. Pour the white wine in an adequate container that is big enough to hold the loin. To the wine add enough water to cover the meat completely. Put it on the stove and add, as per usual, 1 onion, 1 carrot, and some salt. Let it cook about 40 minutes. Remove the meat & chill it in the fridge. But hang onto the broth.

Now we'll turn to the blender, in which you'll put: the tuna, the 4 anchovy fillets, a bit of broth, and the juice of ½ lemon. Blend until you get the right consistency. Add the mayo and blend a little longer.

Add the capers (but, if you prefer, you can blend them with the other ingredients). Remove the loin from the fridge and cut it into thin slices. Arrange them on a platter and cover with the sauce.

I know, it's the same as veal tonné. But how many of you knew how to make a proper veal tonné?

Lamb with Pecorino

Do you want to know how I make it? I'll tell you. If my recipe is the same as yours, good for you; if not, get with the program.

I get a nice leg of lamb, preferably with the kidneys still attached. While still raw, I make some incisions across the thigh and fill them with pieces of garlic. Then I violently chop (I'm a tough guy) a large sprig of rosemary. I mix it with salt and pepper and spread it over the meat. In the meantime, I prepare an oven tray lightly coated with olive oil. I take the leg, place it on the tray, and you know what else I add? A generous handful of grated pecorino. That's right, pecorino. I put everything in the oven and, from time to time, I add a splash of dry white wine. After it's cooked a while, I thrown in some chopped potatoes. When it's ready you know what I do? I bring it to the table and eat it.

Now, tell the truth: you never thought of using pecorino, did you?

A Milanese In Rome

Don't tell me you don't know how to make cotoletta alla milanese (veal cutlet). Don't tell me you don't know how to make a basic tomato sauce ... Fine, I need to explain everything.

You'll need some veal cutlets (not beef but veal), 1 egg, white flour, breadcrumbs, lemon zest, salt & pepper.

For the tomato sauce: 1 pound of red tomatoes, 1 onion, 1 carrot, 1 celery stalk, basil, parsley, 1 teaspoon of sugar (you need sugar to balance the acidity of the tomatoes), salt & pepper.

Preparation: take the cutlets, pound them out a bit, lightly flour them, dredge them in an egg wash with salt, pepper, and lemon zest, then coat them in bread crumbs. Melt some butter in a pan, let it fry gently, add the cutlets and cook them without browning them too much.

In the meantime, put the tomatoes, onion, carrot, celery, basil, parsley, a generous teaspoon of sugar, salt & pepper in a pot. Cook for about 30 minutes, then pass the sauce through a food mill & there's your tomato sauce.

At this point, the nuptials: this will take place in another pan where you'll put a little more butter, then add the cutlets and then the tomato sauce. The happy union can also take place on the white bed of the serving platter, provided it's piping hot & that both sauce & cutlets are hot as well. Otherwise what kind of union would that be?

Raw Filet Mignon With 3 Sauces

This isn't the usual filet "alla Carpaccio" first created at the Harris Bar in Venice. In fact, I call mine "alla Guercino" after a completely different painter.

But before getting to the 3 sauces I use to dress my filet, I want to tell you a secret: how to cut it into thin slices, like prosciutto. Even the sharpest of knives can't do it, as the filet is rather soft. 3 hours before slicing it, put the whole filet in the freezer. Once frozen stiff, you'll see that the meat slicer will work its magic... Now that the "secretly" sliced filet is laid out on the plate, let's move on to the sauces.

The first. Make some mayo with 2 eggs. Add some red sauce, aka Ketchup, and mix until the mayo turns salmon color. Then add a tablespoon of mustard and a splash of Worcestershire. Spread the sauce over the fillet slices, in an artistic arabesque pattern, like Guercino would.

The second. ½ cup of olive oil, the juice of ½ a lemon, salt, pepper, then a dusting of Sardinian cheese or sharp pecorino. To top it off, a roof of truffle shavings.

The third. The same as the second, except no truffles. Instead, use finely chopped Cæsar's mushrooms or porcini. They cost about the same.

Bull Testicles In Pernod

I don't think any master of Italian cooking would have the courage to tell you about bull testicles in Pernod with my same nonchalance.

Frankly: what's the proper venue for such a recipe? On the radio, maybe, or TV? So let me, with "pen held high," take the opportunity to describe it for you here in this volume.

It's a recipe with historical precedents, even involving the Vatican. In fact, not long ago, there was a pope who was crazy about roasted bull testicles. He ate them from morning till night: six, eight slices, in butter and sage. Obviously this pope (whom I will not name in order to keep our "gastronomic state secrets") couldn't turn to his cooks and say: "Bring me the usual roasted bull testicles." Such behavior would have been unbecoming, especially for someone in his position. Therefore, the Holy Father re-baptized them as "granelli." And, since then, every respected maître'd in town recommends two nice big "roasted bull granelli" to his clientele.

I tested this recipe out 3 years ago when I held a tennis tournament at my house in Tor Vajanica.

30 contestants, 30 testicles in Pernod. Everybody mistook them for fried kidneys. But enough talk about balls, let's play.

Buy two nice bull testicles and skin them, making a longitudinal incision. With a knife, delicately cut the two

skinned testicles into slices (about the thickness of a pinky finger). Submerge the slices in a pan filled with Pernod: add a pinch of salt and let them soak for a good 30 minutes. When the testicles have absorbed as much Pernod as they can, toss them in breadcrumbs, and fry them, splashing them in more Pernod if the slices start drying up. Bring them to the table while keeping a straight face. Your guests will mistake them for your basic veal rump, or, like my friends in Tor Vajanica, for fried kidneys. Don't tell them otherwise until you serve coffee, then relish in revealing to your guests that they just swallowed about ½ a testicle each.

Enjoy their reactions. It'll be like a psychological test.

Chinese Duck

My culinary reputation is such that it stretches all the way to the Far East. A short time ago I was invited to pen the preface to a Chinese cookbook. I'm not crazy about it, I'm sure you know that. But I recognize it has style, an identity all its own. Chinese duck is my homage to one of the most renowned cuisines in the world.

Ingredients

3 pounds of duck (no surprises here)
4 tablespoons of honey
1 tablespoon of sherry, or dry white wine
1 tablespoon of vinegar
1 tablespoon of soy sauce
1 fistful of salt

Place the fistful of salt in a cast iron pan and heat it until it browns. Cover the duck in this salt, inside & out. Put it in a 400-degree oven for about 20 mins, or even a half hour. In the meantime, in a bowl, mix the honey, white wine, & vinegar then add the soy sauce, which will give the duck a darker color & that certain eastern taste.

Halve the duck and brush it inside and out with this mixture. Put it back in the oven, which you've lowered a bit, and leave it in there till it's completely cooked, brushing it every 30 minutes with the honey mixture & the drippings from the bottom of the pan.

Cut the duck into smaller portions, and serve it with scallions. If you don't like them, garden salad.

Banana Sweet

2 ¼ cups of all purpose flour
2 sticks of butter
1 ¼ cups of sugar
4 eggs
1 packet of yeast
2 bananas
A pinch of cinnamon.
Nothing else.

In a bowl, cream the butter and sugar together, mix well, slowly incorporate the flour, then the eggs, one at a time. Add the bananas, which you have previously blended, then the pinch of cinnamon, the yeast, and mix for 5 minutes.

Now it's ready. Grease a pan with butter and put in the mixture. Place in a 400-degree oven & bake for 45 minutes.

Bagnacavallo Cream

This is a desert from Bagnacavallo (a beautiful town in Romagna where I recently shot a film).

Buy ½ pound of mascarpone, 3 eggs, ½ cup of sugar, a box of amaretti cookies, dark chocolate, & whatever liquor you have on hand.

Take out 2 bowls and a whisk to whip the eggs. First of all, soak the amaretti in some liquor. Then use one of the bowls to mix the mascarpone with the yolks of the 3 eggs. In the other bowl, whip the 3 egg whites, adding in the sugar. Then delicately incorporate it into the mascarpone mixture until you get a fluffy mousse. In the meantime, grate the chocolate and dust it over the mascarpone cream.

Take out some serving cups: place 2 or 3 amaretti in each and top with a dollop of mascarpone.

100 of These Cream Puffs

With 1 quart of water, 3 tablespoons of sugar, 2 pounds of flour, ½ stick of butter, and 18 eggs, you'll get about 100 of these cream puffs. Naturally, if you want to make 50, all you need to do is cut the ingredients in half.

Put the water on to boil with sugar and butter. When it starts boiling add all the flour & stir vigorously for 5 minutes. Take it off the stove and let it cool. In a bowl, pour the mixture and add the 18 eggs. Mix until it turns into a stretchy cream. In the meantime, put a pot filled with oil on the stove. When the oil is piping hot, using a teaspoon, scoop out some of the mixture and drop it in the oil. In a matter of seconds the cream puff will be cooked. It will float to the surface. Fish it out with a skimmer and place it on the usual paper towel to take off the excess oil. Repeat until you run out of the mixture. At this point, you need some filling for the cream puffs. You can use anything. Cream, chocolate, zabaione, whipped cream. Use the proper pastry pouch and fill the puffs with whatever you like the best. Finally, dust them with vanilla flavored powdered sugar and call the kids to the table.

Fruit Flambé

Fresh fruit, a bit of alcohol, and olé! Fruit flambé! Let's call it a dessert.

The ingredients: green grapes, big black grapes, apples, pears, oranges, pineapples, bananas, shelled walnuts, a cup of pure alcohol, sugar, maraschino liqueur, and a bit of lemon juice.

Cut the fruit into pieces, roughly as big as the grapes. Dress as if making a regular fruit salad, that is, by adding sugar, maraschino liqueur, and a bit of lemon juice. Put everything in a large flat tray, so that the fruit can easily fit in one single layer. Warm up the alcohol on the stove and pour it over the fruit while still hot. Immediately light it on fire and bring it to the table. Remember to turn off the lights: the effect is marvelous, but that's not the best of it. The fruit will taste excellent since it's slightly cooked, caramelized, & irresistible. In fact, I can't resist it myself. Tonight, fruit flambé!

Strawberries In Vinegar

In 1946, every time I went to a restaurant that had strawberries on the menu, I would ask them to bring them to the table without any dressing and then I would tell the waiter, as if joking: "Could you bring some vinegar?"

When I would say "vinegar," both the waiter & the owner would think I was crazy and stood there in disbelief, wondering what I was up to.

I would splash the strawberries with a teaspoon of vinegar, sprinkle them with sugar, mix them well, then eat them.

Almost always the waiters would squint and grimace: but then they got curious and I would have to let them taste my strawberries. Almost everyone would then admit they were excellent. That's because strawberries cancel out the taste of the vinegar, leaving behind only a bit of acidity. In turn, the vinegar draws out the strawberries' juices, making them softer. Consequently, strawberries finally taste like strawberries.

After so many years, I've noticed that this invention of mine is on the menus of many restaurants, which present it as a refined dessert of their own creation. Yet those are the very restaurants where I, while on tour all over Italy, had asked for "my" strawberries, by now one of the most popular dessert items. I'm surprised they haven't called them "strawberries à la Ugo."

The Last Meal
(The Final Binge)

La Grande Bouffe

Let me start by saying that *La Grande Bouffe* was the most different, the most over the top, the most fantastic experience I've ever had in the world of cinema, not only for the atmosphere that was created while filming, but also for the film itself, one of the most unique films ever made, where food was part of our roles as actors, just as our acting was inextricably tied to food, & even perhaps directly determined by it.

When we arrived at the old villa in downtown Paris, you could see how it kept its distance from the other buildings, fully aware of its own decay; an old house whose neglected garden was like a faded ostrich boa wrapped around the walls to hide its wrinkles from prying eyes, so it could wither and die while holding onto a shred of dignity.

We immediately noticed the strange atmosphere of disrepair, for which the script had already primed us. We were going to die, one after the other, within those walls.

That didn't prevent us from inhabiting the space. Piccoli, Mastroianni, Noiret, and I asked for a couple of rooms on the top floor where we could gather during breaks to rest and, more importantly, digest.

During the first 3 days of filming we noticed that Ferreri, the director, asked us to say stuff that was nowhere to be found in the script. In fact, he would encourage us to make suggestions and come up with our own lines, scene after scene. This helped us overcome the barriers that an actor's ego inevitably erects.

We created a perfect climate, which might be impossible to ever replicate again. From then on, we never felt cheated if another had more lines. We got into a friendly competition based on perfectionism & selflessness. We got to a place where each of us cared more about our colleagues' performance than our own.

That's when we decided to tear up the script. While Ferreri was out in the garden setting up a scene, the 100-page script, torn into small pieces, rained above him.

The movie was being shot in chronological order, from beginning to end: it had become clear that we were going to make it up day by day, all together.

So for an 8 AM call, the cook Fauchon had sent us to prepare the day's menu needed to show up by 6: it would take at least 2 hours to make the gastronomic script we would later perform before the camera.[26]

Once on set, rather than discovering the scenes we were about to shoot using our eyes, we would see them with our noses. We would smell the aromas coming from the kitchens and we could tell what was in store for us. "Fellas, today, we're performing kidney bourguignon…" Mastroianni would say. Or: "Today's role is boiled meats…" And Noiret would add: "Too bad, today I could have really pulled off a great cheese soufflé!"

Our arrival on set was marked by aromas. Depending on the smells saturating the air, we knew what destiny awaited us in the scene we were about to shoot.

26. Fauchon is a French gourmet food & delicatessen company founded in 1886 & regarded as one of the temples of French cuisine.

Things were off to a great start. What's better than arriving at work in the morning and immediately smelling the food you would eat a few hours later? However, quite often, we would end up eating that fantastic food at 7 PM, rather than a few hours later, thus enduring a mortifying fast that we would often break by sneaking off to a nearby trattoria for a nice lunch. We rarely skipped a meal. Instead, we sacrificed our figures.

As the production moved forward, we felt as if we were hooked on food; excited at the need to constantly stuff our faces.

Yet the most extraordinary thing was this: the film, which is not a film about gastronomy but rather about consumer society, about existential crises, about human nature, about lack of faith, about everything, magically grew as if in a kind of parthenogenesis. A climate of desolation slowly overtook the set without us knowing it, a step at a time, day by day. At one point, all these aromas coming from the kitchen started to be less pleasant and, as time went on, they became quite nauseating.

All of us knew we were going to die. As the production continued, whenever a certain food was a harbinger of someone's death, the others were affected too: a purée no longer tasted like purée, in spite of having been impeccably prepared by Fauchon's cook; it started tasting like decomposition.

And then, without us realizing it, chaos ensued, that same chaos everyone can clearly see in the film. After so many scenes of pantagruelic meals, leftovers, half-eaten

cakes, & gnawed bones were strewn about everywhere. And the house was constantly visited by curious flocks of chickens, turkeys, and hens that came to feed on delicacies way more refined than their drab daily corn. No reason to be surprised; it's not like chickens & turkeys roam the streets of Paris like pigeons do elsewhere. It's just that we had, in a corner of the garden, our own reserve of generic animals, meant to perform, after make up & a quick trip to the oven, the most important scenes of the film.

All these animals running around the house, which we never bothered to shoo away, started to slowly turn our villa into some sort of country hovel. Halfway through the film, we had already started to unravel both physically & spiritually. Then another magical thing happened.

In the film, Mastroianni winds up frozen at the wheel of the Bugatti that he desperately wanted to start despite the polar temperature that night, and then we, at dawn, discovered he was dead, finding him there, stone cold, with an empty stare, covered in snow. Then the scene everybody remembers took place. After that, Marcello was done, since, as I already mentioned, the film was being shot chronologically, and that was its greatest strength. The next day, Marcello left early and, arriving on set, we couldn't find him anywhere. Noiret, Piccoli, and myself were the only ones left ... We couldn't help but feel a sense of loss, a certain angst... A few days later, as the production moved forward, it was Piccoli's turn, and he left us with that horribly physiological death. The next

morning, done with his scenes, Piccoli disappeared from the film's plot as well as physically from the set. In that room on the top floor he had shared with me, his bed was left untouched. His things disappeared, gathered by compassionate hands.

That day, Noiret and I, the two survivors, sadly did our make-up. And I asked, in the most natural tone: "What happened to Piccoli?... And Marcello? Where are they?" In a daze, Noiret answered: "Well, they died..." "Oh yeah, right..." I said. The atmosphere was straight out of a Pirandello play. And we couldn't help but fall into this strange mood which had slowly seized us and which we couldn't shake.

We would stare into each other's eyes and see the other's vague sense of fear. One day, Noiret whispered to me: "When are you going to die?" "Tomorrow..." I replied. He looked lost. "I'll be alone..." he said, as if to himself.

When we shot my last scene, Noiret was by my side, affectionately spoon feeding me, accompanying me to the very end. As he looked into my eyes, he seemed almost to implore: "Please, don't die... What will I do all alone?..."

I couldn't stay to keep him company on the set. Paris beckoned, with all its temptations & a hundred famous restaurants. He died alone, poor Noiret, and we were only allowed to see his final scene when the film was finished, during a screening about twenty days later. All four of us were together again. Our reactions were curious but also very human.

When we saw each other we hugged enthusiastically, perhaps too enthusiastically, given we had only been apart a few weeks. And we understood that in those effusions there was the strange joy, the unbelievable happiness, the primordial gaiety of being reunited with a friend we thought was dead.

Oysters
(scene 19)

This was certainly the most revolting feast of the film. Mastroianni and I, as we shot the scene, gobbled down at least 30 each.

It was a competition between Marcello and I to see who could eat the most in the shortest amount of time. I won't describe its disgusting conclusion. The film production provided a doctor & a vet on set.

The vet was there to check the oysters as they were being shucked, while the doctor checked the actors after they stuffed themselves. My suggestion to bring in a jeweler as well went unheard, in spite of my high hopes of finding a pearl or two. We ate the oysters raw, and that's what I recommend you do too. Remember the simple & well-known squirt of lemon juice.

It's true you can buy different kinds of aromatic vinaigrettes, but I wouldn't recommend using them, nor does Veronelli. However, I do use a little pepper, while Veronelli doesn't. I slurp them down between mouthfuls of whole wheat bread or, better yet, black German bread, lightly buttered. Veronelli doesn't.

For your edification, and to prove that when it comes to the kitchen I'm not a simpleton, I will now list the best oysters in the world: Armoricaines, Cancales, Belons, Ostende, Gravettes, Marennes, Arcachon.

Other more common oysters that are cheaper are Claires & Spéciales.

Our Mediterranean only produces the modest Tarantine, Lamellose, Adriatiche, & Cristate.

Pâté de Canard
(scene 89)

My "last supper" of *La Grande Bouffe*. In the fiction of the film I die swallowing the last spoonful of this pâté. In reality, I almost committed suicide three times after failing to prepare it.

Thus, without taking any responsibility for this recipe, I'll transcribe it here as it was given to me by the chef of a famous Parisian restaurant.

Ingredients (for 10 people)

a two-pound duck, possibly wild, or even a mallard
½ pound of lard
¾ pound of pork loin
1 cup of fortified wine (Port, Madera, or Marsala)
Some dry white wine
2 shots of cognac or a nice brandy
3 or 4 chicken livers
Some bouillon
Thyme, bay leaves, carrots
1 truffle
A tin of foie gras
An egg
Oil, salt, & pepper

For the pâté crust

2 cups of flour
2 ½ sticks of butter
2 eggs

And finally

enough packets to make ½ quart of gelatin

And now:

Debone the duck placing the bones in one oven dish, the meat in another, and, on a plate, the filleted breast, the duck liver, & the chicken liver, which you'll marinate overnight using part of the fortified wine and a shot of cognac or brandy. To the meat dish add the pork, cubed, the lard, chopped, the aromatics (thyme & bay leaves), splash generously with white wine, add the rest of the fortified wine as well as another shot of cognac or brandy. Let it marinate overnight and sleep on it. The next day, use the bones you set aside to make a broth; add the carrots, the bouillon, a bit of olive oil, salt & pepper. Let it cook for about 3 hours on low heat so as to obtain a bowl of "broth concentrate."

Meanwhile, prepare the dough for the pâté making a crust with the flour, the 2 eggs, melted butter, salt, & a little water. Let the dough rest for a couple of hours, wrapped in a humid towel.

Remove the meat from the marinade (not the livers) & pass it through a grinder twice. Set the marinade aside and after returning the minced meat to its dish, add, cautiously, a bit of the broth and the marinade, which you have previously passed through a sieve. I said cautiously because you don't want the dough to become too wet.

Roll it out into a rectangular shape big enough to fill the pâté mold (it's best to get one of those that has

a latch for easy opening) and so it rises about an inch above the sides.

Roll out another piece for the lid of the pâté. On the bottom, spread out a layer of the minced meat (about half of it); put in the duck filet, still dripping, the duck & chicken livers, mixed with the foie gras, and shape it into an even layer. Top it with the remaining minced meat and cover everything with the dough lid. Poke a hole in the center and insert a little funnel made of aluminum foil so the steam can escape. Beat an egg and brush it over the surface of the lid. Put it in the oven at 300 degrees & cook for about an hour. Be careful not to burn the crust. Before releasing it from the mold, let the pâté cool completely. Before putting it in the fridge for a few hours, don't forget to do the following: dilute the gelatin with a few drops of the fortified wine & delicately pour it into the vent you opened in the lid. Remove it from the form half an hour before serving, and bring it to the table with white toast & butter curls on the side.

Public Service Announcement
It'd be faster to catch a plane to Paris, go to Fauchon's, and return with a pre-made pâté.

Wild Boar Pâté
(scene 18)

This is the second time in the history of cinema that there's been an issue with boars' heads. At least as far as I know.

I read in an English cookbook, translated into Italian, that in 1935, during the production of *Henry VIII*, starring Charles Laughton, a must-see for the "youngsters" of my generation, a few "boars' heads" had to be prepared for the famous banquet scene.

In that film, as in *La Grande Bouffe*, the director demanded all dishes be real and the actors actually eat, during the scenes, the food indicated in the script. The production team managed to find only one chef in Paris who knew how to prepare a "stuffed boar's head." Due to a series of unforeseen circumstances, the chef had to prepare a half dozen of them, since they were repeatedly wasted or ruined, either during filming or while the cast was waiting to shoot. At that point the Parisian chef threw up his hands and so an English cook who had been working for the production came up with a semi-synthetic version, that is, an artistic rendition.

He asked a young sculptor (possibly the young Moore?) to model a magnificent boar's head. He used it as a mold which he filled with gelatin and stuffing. The resulting edible sculpture was a lot easier to prepare over & over again. And that's how they solved the problem of the most important and unforgettable scene in *Henry VIII*.

In our *Grande Bouffe* we settled for a wild boar pâté prepared by the cook of the famous Fauchon. Instead of using a boar's head, Michel Piccoli raised a calf's head to the sky reciting the famous monologue from *Hamlet*. If you want to prepare boar pâté without involving Marino Marini or Manzù, you can follow the same recipe as the duck pâté, substituting the poultry with boar, eliminating the foie gras but keeping the chicken livers.[27] You'll also need to cook the boar meat on low in its marinade for half an hour. To the whole thing, add pistachios and pieces of black truffle.

27. Marino Marini (1901–1980) & Giacomo Manzù (1908–1991) are two prominent Italian sculptors in the modernist figurative tradition.

Shrimp Cocktail
(scene 36)

For six people you'll need

¾ pound of shrimp tails (net weight naturally, that is,
    peeled)
4 red tomatoes
¾ cup of mayonnaise
About 3 tablespoons of ketchup
A piece of a sweet green bell pepper (optional)
Some grated horseradish
Juice of half a lemon
A tablespoon of chopped chervil (You couldn't find it,
    right? That's okay. Use chopped parsley instead)
Worcestershire sauce & tabasco: a few drops
A cup of unsweetened whipped cream
The heart of a lettuce

Using a wooden spoon & bowl, mix the mayo with
the grated horseradish, add the ketchup, lemon juice,
and the drops of Worcestershire sauce & tabasco. Then
fold in the whipped cream.

Meanwhile, cube the tomatoes, chop the bell pepper, and mix them with the shrimp. Finally, take out six
glass bowls, the kind with a false bottom for shaved ice,
and lay out the lettuce leaves to create a little cradle at
the bottom. Divide the shrimp mixture evenly amongst
the bowls, placing it on top of the leaves. Cover with the

sauce, without filling to the top. Sprinkle with chopped hard-boiled egg yolks, chervil or parsley, & serve cold. Perhaps accompanied by a lullaby.

Eggplant Caviar
(scene 45)

This is an eggplant mixture prepared the way I'll explain in a moment. It tastes nothing like caviar nor does it look like it nor does it cost as much. Why it's called eggplant caviar is beyond me. But I can assure you that that is its official name.

Roast some eggplant on a wood fire grill with the same care you'd give if you were roasting a steak. Once they're done and the purple skin begins to peel away, carefully remove it and chop the flesh, while still warm, using a wooden knife (wood, not metal; I know, not everyone owns a wooden knife). Start from one end of the eggplant & systemically make your way to the other to thoroughly mince it. During this operation you will also painstakingly remove all the filaments and fibers naturally present in this vegetable. The end result is a homogenous paste. Dress it with salt, pepper, & a spoonful of finely chopped onion. Then, using a fork (a wooden one; do you have a beater with wooden implements? No? In that case...), beat the paste as if to create an emulsion, adding some olive oil little by little.

The resulting spread is excellent and should be generously smeared over toasted bread, just like you'd do with caviar.

Niçoise Salad
(scene 48)

Nobody would dare accuse me of crimes against gas-tronomy if I make a few "seasonal" tweaks to the tradi-tional Niçoise Salad.

The classic version should be composed of

Green beans, boiled and cut
Potatoes, boiled & roughly chopped
Ripe tomatoes, quartered
Capers, as many as you like
Italian black olives, pitted
Olive oil, salt & pepper
Mix everything and garnish with anchovy fillets.

For the summer Niçoise, instead, you'll need

Lettuce
Tomatoes
Hardboiled eggs
Tuna
Cooked beets
Capers
Italian black olives
Everything mixed & dressed as above.

If you only use some of the ingredients of each of the two salads described, instead of a Niçoise, you'll get a "mixed" salad, although equally delicious.

Lasagna Andrea
(scene 20)

This is one of the few Italian dishes that was included in the menu of *La Grande Bouffe*.

For 6 to 8 people, the lasagna should be made with ½ pound of spinach, boiled & passed into a sieve to drain, 2 cups of white flour, 3 eggs, a drop of oil and, if necessary, a little water.

Kneed the dough well and roll it out into sheets that aren't too thin, which you will then fold & cut into strips about the thickness of a finger. That is to say, a little wider than tagliatelle.

For the sauce you'll need

One onion
Two cloves of garlic
Basil (a nice size bunch)
¼ pound of pancetta
2 chicken breasts
⅓ pound of pork
White wine
2 pounds of peeled tomatoes
½ cup of fortified wine (Marsala, Salento)
A generous amount of grated Parmigiano

Mince the onion; crush the 2 cloves of garlic with the palm of your hand; put a wide iron pan on the stove; melt a few spoonfuls of butter & olive oil; and add the onion and garlic, which you'll remove as soon as it browns; sauté the onion, splashing it with the white wine, salt and pepper.

Once you've cut the pancetta & other meats into strips or cubes, add them to the sofritto and let them brown. Pour in the fortified wine, let it evaporate, and then immediately add the peeled tomatoes, which you'll crush with a fork. Cook everything for about a half hour without letting it dry out too much, in which case you'll pour in a few spoonfuls of the pasta water. The sauce is ready & you'll use it to dress the boiled lasagna in a large bowl. Make sure to set aside 2 ladles of sauce.

Pour the dressed lasagna onto a warm serving platter. Cover it with a handful of Parmigiano and the basil cut in ribbons (with scissors). Top with the sauce you set aside.

Russian Borscht
(scene 55)

Ingredients (for 6 people)

3 pounds of beef (I prefer the rump, and I add 2
    bouillons to it)
1 onion and 1 leek or 2 onions
2 or 3 carrots
1 celery stalk and 1 bunch of parsley
3 large beets, weighing about 1 ½ pounds
1 bay leaf
2 tablespoons of butter
3 or 4 tablespoons of vinegar
1 tablespoon of white flour
A bowl of cream, to be served at the table
Salt & pepper

Start by boiling the beef in enough water to make a
nice broth. After 15 minutes add the onion & the celery,
both whole, the carrots, sliced in rounds, the bay leaf,
the leek, the 2 bouillons and adjust for salt.

As the meat cooks, sauté the beets in butter, naturally
after peeling and carefully cutting into thin slices. Add
the vinegar a spoonful at a time and continue to cook for
about 20 minutes on low heat. Only toward the end, add
the flour, after dissolving it in a ladle of broth.

Before it is completely cooked, remove the meat
from the broth, slice it thinly, and put it back in the pot

after removing the onion, leek, celery, and the bay leaf (leave the carrots).

To the broth, add the beets you've already cooked, & turn off the stove as soon as the meat is completely done.

Serve in a large bowl & add to each individual bowl a dollop of cream. Pepper to taste. I forgot: for the occasion you should think of hiring 4 ballerinas from the Bolshoi. They cost more than the borscht, but less than caviar.

Veal Kidneys Bourguignon
(scene 69)

Shallots delicately encompass the flavors of both onion & garlic. In France, they use them often. In Italy, they're hard to get (I found some excellent ones in Romagna, pickled). In any case, you can always substitute shallots with a bit of onion and a touch of garlic.

But let's get on with our kidneys bourguignon, which I personally prepared for *La Grande Bouffe* in the following manner.

Ingredients (for 4 to 6 people)

2 veal kidneys (which you'll submerge in water & vinegar for a half hour)
4 tablespoons of butter
1 glass of dry white wine
½ glass of red wine from Burgundy (but wine from Piedmont will also do)
3 shallots
Minced parsley
1 tablespoon of potato starch
Salt & pepper

Roughly chop the kidneys after draining them, and immediately place them in a pan. Cook for a few minutes to "evacuate" most of the water they hold.

Once that's done, in a different pan, sauté the kidneys with 2 tablespoons of butter, and the minced shallots. Salt and pepper. After a few minutes, remove the kidneys from the pan & add the white wine. Let it evaporate almost entirely then add the remaining butter and the red wine. Again, let it evaporate and then return the kidneys to the pan. Turn up the heat and let the sauce thicken, helping it along with a food mill & the potato starch. Stir gently. Serve piping hot.

Roasted Piglet Two Ways: On a Spit & in the Oven, Stuffed with Chestnuts
(scene 40)

In *La Grande Bouffe* we also ate 2 piglets: one roasted on a spit, the other roasted in the oven & stuffed with chestnuts. I'll describe them quickly.

Piglet on a spit

Prepare a rub made of minced garlic, rosemary, salt & pepper (in generous amounts), olive oil or, even better, lard. Mix these ingredients and rub them on the inside of the piglet. On the outside, grease it with oil or lard, salt & pepper. Roast on the spit.

The piglet stuffed with chestnuts, instead, must be cooked in the oven. Here are the ingredients for stuffing a piglet of about 6 pounds: 2 pounds of chestnuts, 1 ¾ pounds of sausage, a generous splash of brandy, a bit of lard, salt & plenty of pepper.

Cook the chestnuts & remove the skin. Puree about ⅓ of them in a food mill. In a bowl, place the purée, the whole chestnuts, and the sausage (skinned and roughly chopped). Mix everything and add salt, pepper, and a splash of brandy. The stuffing must be placed in the stomach cavity of the piglet, which you'll then seal with a large needle & twine. Grease the piglet with lard and

put it in the oven on a rotating spit. Remember to place a tray under it. Periodically check on it & keep it moist with the drippings from the tray. An occasional splash of white wine would not be unwise.

Potato Purée
(scene 41)

Forgive me if I use the French "purée" & not the Italian "purea." The word "purea" sounds ridiculous to me; plus everyone calls it "purée."

For this recipe, use Dutch yellow potatoes. For 2 pounds of potatoes, you'll need 1 ½ sticks of butter and about a glass of milk. Yes to salt, but no to pepper this time. Personally, I use a bit of cream and Parmigiano, instead of milk.

Roasted Guinea Hen
(scene 43)

We Italians on set cooked it our way, that is more or less like a chicken, although with the addition of a French "perfume" so as not to provoke the chauvinism of Michel Piccoli & Philip Noiret: a fistful of *estragon* (tarragon) at the very end.

So, besides a 2 pound guinea-hen, you'll need ¼ pound of cubed pancetta, the usual olive oil & butter (about 7 tablespoons in all), a good sized glass of dry white wine, salt, pepper, and the aforementioned *estragon* that, if you like, could be substituted with 3 cloves, which is what I usually do. Grab a nice sized pan with high sides, in which you'll place all the ingredients except the wine. Cook for a good hour with the lid on, so the guinea hen stays moist and doesn't dry out too much. Every now & then splash it with the white wine.

Cut it into pieces before laying it out on a nice round serving tray, pour the drippings on top, and don't forget to pair it with a nice fresh salad.

Nobody will call foul if halfway through cooking, you throw in a few roughly chopped potatoes, dressed with oil, salt, pepper, and a few sprigs of rosemary. Remove them when golden brown & throw them back into the pan with the guinea hen 5 minutes before it's done.

Pissaladière Provençale
(scene 52)

Let's get one thing out of the way. This is a kind of pizza made with bread dough; or, rather, a kind of bread made with pizza ingredients.

For 1 pound of bread dough you'll use

2 pounds of onions
A cup of olive oil
A dozen anchovy fillets
4 tomatoes
A handful of Italian black olives
Garlic, salt & pepper

Slice the onions and place them in a pan with the oil. Cook on low without stirring for about an hour. To prevent them from sticking, add a splash of water every now and then. Kneed the bread dough (you can buy it from your local baker) and incorporate some of the oil from the onion pan. Stretch it and put it in a round pie dish. Spread the cooked onions on top & garnish with the anchovy fillets in a star pattern; in the open spaces, place the garlic (chopped), the tomatoes (chopped), & the olives (pitted).

Add a bit more oil on top and place it at the bottom of the oven. Don't ask me for how long: I know nothing about your oven.

Veal Head Vinaigrette
(scene 57)

After carefully washing the veal head, you'll need to blanch it in salted water and then, while still warm, debone it and roll it up as if it were a giant salami, tying it with twine or, even better, wrapping it in a fine cloth.

Once you've completed this preliminary operation, pour an abundant amount of water in a pot, add a few tablespoons of white flour dissolved in warm water, 2 or 3 tablespoons of vinegar, a bouquet garni (parsley, thyme, bay leaves) and an onion. If you have you some beef suet handy (you can buy it along with the veal head) throw it in the water: it will prevent the head from turning a dark color.

Once everything's in place, add the veal head to the pot and cook thoroughly.

If you want, you can also add a veal tongue. When ready, slice everything, and dress it with a vinaigrette, that is oil, vinegar, salt, and pepper. Or, if you prefer, you can pair the meat with a nice *salsa verde*.[28]

28. See note № 20 on page 74.

Young Turkey Roast
(scene 91)

Can you tell a young turkey from an old turkey by its weight?

If it's an Italian turkey, a young one weighs 5 pounds. An old one 6. But if the turkey is American, it can reach as much as 36 pounds in a couple of years. However, the stuffed turkeys we ate in *La Grande Bouffe* were spring chickens, that is spring turkeys. And so they weighed about 4 pounds. We served 12, and ate 6 of them. The stuffing recipe that follows is meant for a bird that size. As you know, you'll have to insert it from the backside.

This kind of stuffing, which I call Bordeaux style, requires,

¼ pound of ground pork loin
¼ pound of veal liver
Turkey liver
2 eggs
2 ounces of cubed pancetta
A diced onion
A few drops of Madera & a bit of cognac
½ stick of butter
Salt, pepper, & nutmeg

In a large pan, sauté the butter, the diced onion, and the pancetta. Add the turkey liver, the veal liver (both finely minced), the pork, salt, pepper, & nutmeg. Splash

with a few drops of Madera &, if you can manage, flambé with the cognac. If not, don't bother. Remove from the stove, transfer into a bowl, let cool. Incorporate the 2 whole eggs (without the shells — hahaha) and stir until everything becomes smooth. Fill the birds with the stuffing, from the correct opening. Have a seamstress seal it & then roast the turkey. How?! Well, if you can't even roast some poultry... I usually put it in a tray with butter, oil, a clove of garlic, a sprig of rosemary, salt & pepper and add 2 glasses of a nice white wine. Do you want to put it in the oven? Who's stopping you?

Gigantic Ossobuchi
(scene 85)

In the film, we sucked on gigantic ossobuchi, emitting horrifying sounds. Entire shins cooked only in salted water. An operation that you too can easily replicate if you have our stomach and lungs, on the occasion of a great feast for men only.

But if you prefer a more "civilized" recipe for ossobuco, here's mine.

Ingredients

6 ossobuchi (veal shanks), which you'll ask your
    butcher to cut at least 2 ½ inches thick, from
    the two rear legs of a calf
1 pound of peeled tomatoes
1 onion
1 clove of garlic
1 carrot
1 celery stalk
Minced parsley
White flour
A strong red wine (not white, this is a chef's secret)
The zest of half a lemon
Broth, bouillon's okay too

Flour the ossobuchi and sauté them in butter in a large pan, big enough to accommodate all of them in one layer. Remove them from the pan and add the

onion, carrot, celery, & garlic, finely minced. Let it cook well, adding red wine every now and then. When these are fully cooked, remove them from the pan and pass them through a food mill. Return this purée to the pan, followed by the ossobuchi, salt and pepper to taste and pour in the rest of the wine. Let it cook on high until the wine evaporates completely. At this point, add the tomatoes to the pan, after running them through a sieve, and continue cooking with the lid on for about an hour and a half. If the sauce dries out, add a ladle or two of broth. 5 minutes before taking it off the stove, zest the lemon, mince the parsley, and sprinkle them on the ossobuchi.

I don't need to tell you that a side of risotto is almost mandatory.

Leg Of Lamb On A Spit à la Solognote
(scene 76)

Ingredients

Leg of lamb weighing about 5 pounds
Salt, peppercorns
4 carrots, 2 onions, 2 shallots (all finely minced)
Parsley, thyme, bay leaves
2 cloves of garlic, crushed
2 cloves
3 ¼ ounces of vinegar
1 bottle of dry red wine
¾ pound of lard roughly cubed
2 sticks of butter
3 pounds of steamed green beans
½ cup of capers

Place the lamb leg in a strong marinade, composed of: wine vinegar, carrots chopped in rounds, onions, parsley, thyme, cloves, bay leaves, crushed garlic, peppercorns, salt, dry white wine, and lard.

After 24 hours, remove the leg from the marinade & rub it with whatever lard you can fish out. Then carefully tie it up and set aside.

Pass the marinade through a sieve, smashing the vegetables and herbs, then cook them for about 20 minutes. Butter the leg well and roast it on a spit over an open fire. When it's almost done, add, to the drippings

you've been collecting in a tray, a few spoonfuls of the marinade, which you've fully cooked and puréed. Let it simmer as it collects the drippings from the leg above.

As a side, serve the steamed green beans quickly sautéed in butter and the rest of the marinade, finished with the capers.

Cassoulet de Castelnaudary
(scene 61)

In Italy, in Lombardy, we have the "cassœula"; in France, they have the cassoulet, which is a different thing entirely. To each their own...

To make a cassoulet, you'll need the following

1 pound of white beans from Cazères (but you can substitute them with our own Toscanelli, which might actually be an improvement)

2 ¼ ounces of pancetta
2 pounds of goose
5 ounces of garlic sausage
1 pound of pork butt
4 sausages
4 tablespoons of tomato purée
2 onions, 8 cloves of garlic, a bouquet garni, cloves, 2 carrots
Pork skin & a pig foot

Soak the beans overnight. The next day, in a clay pot, cook them in salted water with: 1 onion, 3 cloves, a few pieces of pork skin, the pig foot, 1 carrot, the bouquet garni, 1 clove of garlic, and the pancetta. In the pot, find room for the garlic sausage as well.

Now make a goose ragout. That is: chop the goose into pieces and cook in a sofritto of onion & garlic, and

then the tomato purée. Cook until the goose is completely done. If the sauce dries out, add a few spoonfuls of the liquid from the beans.

Make another ragout with the pork butt using the same procedure as the goose.

In a pan, cook, with the addition of a little white wine, the sausages but remove them before they're completely done.

Mix the two ragouts; drain the beans, put them in the double ragout, and add the pigskins cut in ribbons, the cubed pancetta, and the deboned foot. You're not done yet! In a terracotta oven dish, which you've rubbed with garlic, place a layer of beans, the goose, the pork meat, the garlic sausage (all chopped) *&* the sausages (whole). Add another layer of beans and top it with the ragout sauce. Finish au gratin in the oven.

Between the Milanese "cassœula" *&* this cassoulet I'm not sure who'd win a contest for the world's heaviest dish.

Grand Marnier Crêpes
(scene 58)

Ingredients

White flour, 1 cup
Powdered sugar, 1 tablespoon
1 sugar cube for each diner
1 stick of butter
1 glass of cold milk
3 egg yolks
Salt
Orange zest & orange juice
Grand Marnier

Mix the flour, sugar, yolks, salt, and, little by little, the milk. You'll get a rather watery batter. Using a wooden spoon, mix in ⅕ of the butter, melted, and a few drops of the Grand Marnier.

As you're waiting to get started on the crêpes (that's going to be the hard part: did you see how effortlessly I flipped them in that scene?), as you're waiting for the crêpes, as I was saying, hurry up and do the following: using the orange skin, rub each sugar cube & squeeze out as much oil as you can from that skin; watch out for your eyes, they might look fabulous. Pour the orange juice onto the sugar cubes and let them sit.

Prepare the crêpes. How? Oh well! You'll need the proper pan (better if you buy one in Paris) and some

good flipping skills. Just so you know, I could do it better than Fauchon's chef. Stack them one on top of the other & get a silver pan (that's right, silver) and a "lamp." The lamp is that contraption our grandparents would have called an alcohol burner, which all high-end restaurants have, along with silver pans & elegant maître d's. It costs about 150,000 liras. For years Paolo Villaggio has been promising me one for all sorts of occasions (birthdays, Christmas, Easter), but he never bought me one, so I don't have it & neither do you.[29]

So let's forget the burner & the silver pan and make do with a non-stick one.

In it, melt the butter (whatever's left) and the sugar cubes drenched in orange juice; stir, add the remaining orange juice. Keep stirring and, every now and then, splash with some Grand Marnier. How much? As much as needed.

Now grab the crêpes, one at a time… haha! You'll never get them with a fork, use tongs instead. You don't have any? Then buy some! Do you want to make crêpes with nothing but dried figs?! Using the tongs, flip the crêpes and heat both sides: it'll be a breeze. Less easy, however, is folding them in four, like a handkerchief. Using the tongs, place them at the edges of the pan.

29. Paolo Villaggio (1932–2017) was a very famous and beloved Italian actor, writer, director and comedian. One of his recurring characters, the Ragioniere Ugo Fantozzi, has become a national icon, so much so that "fantozziano" has officially entered the Italian vocabulary.

At this point, before serving, I should tell you to use a little more Grand Marnier or, better yet, some cognac or Armagnac & flambé!

However, if Carnacina, the great gastronome, was among your guests, he would probably refuse to eat them, since he believes the true crêpes suzette should not be caramelized. Perhaps he's right, since flambé is a way of caramelizing, but it's also true that looks are important, especially if you spent 200,000 liras (gosh, the price keeps going up) for a lamp and a silver pan.

Andrea Cake
(scene 72)

Make a large short crust about half the size of a woman's bottom.

Roll it out into a circle on a wooden table. Pick up a woman from just under her armpits, set her onto the shortcrust (bare assed), and push down a little.

To keep her warm, kiss the woman while waiting for her form to be impressed into the dough.

Remove her butt, let the dough rest a half hour. Don't let the woman rest at all.

Place the dough with its new shape on a large plate greased with either lard or butter, sprinkle it with bread crumbs, cover the whole thing with wax paper and then place some dried beans on top. Put it in the oven for about 15 minutes.

Then add: pitted plums, pitted cherries, pitted and chopped apricots, cooked in a little syrup made of sugar and water.

Put it back in the oven for about another 20 minutes. On the stove, thicken the syrup used for cooking the fruit and pour it over the cake after taking it out of the oven.

While it cools, continue to keep the woman warm.

Boobs Bavarois
(final scene)

Ingredients

Milk, just over a cup
Vanilla extract
5 ¼ ounces of strawberry purée
1 cup of sugar
5 egg yolks
2 sheets of gelatin

In a saucepan, slowly boil the milk with a few drops of vanilla.

Put the sugar in a different bowl & add, little by little, the egg yolks, mixing them with a wooden spoon. Pour in the boiling milk, stirring as you go.

Put the mixture back on the stove, but make sure you don't let it boil. When the cream begins to stick to the spoon, that is when it "coats" it, take the pan off the flame & throw in the gelatin, which you previously dissolved in water for 15 minutes and wrung out with your hands.

Stir everything well, add the strawberry purée, mix again, pour it into two round bowls and put them in the fridge.

Take them out of the fridge, overturn the two bowls one next to the other.

The only thing left are the nipples. You could use two candied cherries or, if you prefer something more "moist," chocolates filled with liqueur.

Images

Ugo Tognazzi preparing spaghetti
during the Cannes Film Festival.

❋

Ugo Tognazzi walking in a cheese factory
in Bernardo Bertolucci's *Tragedy of a Ridiculous Man.*

Philippe Noiret, Ugo Tognazzi, Michel Piccoli, &
Marcello Mastroianni at the Gala De L'Union Des Artistes.

Ugo Tognazzi & Andrea Ferreol in *La Grande Bouffe*.

Photo by ullstein bild (1973) / Getty Images

Postface

Rabelais' Grandchild
A note by Alberto Bevilacqua

❋ This new edition of the book calls for a long essay. Its main theme has to do with food but is not exactly food; it points to overindulgence, but it's not just about eating. This text is a short breviary in which Ugo sketched a map of his personality, in a sly and sprawling manner, grabbing here and there: memories, impressions, realities drawn with an ironic pencil. I'll say it again: a long essay is needed. Many years have passed since the first edition, *&* time has brought more clarity to Ugo's psychological profile: the coexistence of light and shadows, extreme reticence *&* intolerant reactions, a slight laziness coupled with a poetic intuition that would have required a sustained effort to become reality.

Ugo could be considered Rabelais' grandchild. His dreams were instinctual offshoots of his masterpiece: *Gargantua*. If you look for them, there are many similarities between Ugo and the French author. First is their love for France. Second is their light-hearted tone. Third is the comic effect born out of the enlargement, to a gigantic scale, of all physiological functions. Fourth is their sarcasm used as a spice to be sprinkled over a love for food. But was it love or just a performance? Ugo was not a big eater, but rather a keen observer of those who eat. He was a raconteur-mime who, due to his unconscious nausea of politics *&* societal pleasantries, preferred to speak "in code," as they say, using the language of the

table, with its stories and rituals, as well as other tales more closely connected to sexual delights.

"Delights," that's the right word. However, such delights were never an end in and of themselves, but were always juxtaposed against the shadows I mentioned earlier. They loomed large over his deep psychology, at times making him aware of the ultimate end of all things. This juxtaposition found an ideal refuge in his home in Velletri, where Ceroli's wooden sculptures managed to reconcile their extravagance with the evanescence of the Etruscan penumbra. There's a lot to say about Ugo's sense of religion, even though such a thing would seem paradoxical to many. I mean a popular form of religion, one that didn't require sacred images or devotional rites, but rather praised a clear spring sky, the colors of a well-made dish (the *colors*, the colors of food, that's the whole point) notwithstanding the inevitability of sunsets.

I directed Ugo in two films. In one of them, he managed to play three different characters at the same time: an old father, a young father, and a son. How could he have pulled that off had the music of the various human ages not resonated in his blood? I truly regret that Ugo, after his death, was tied to a stereotype that doesn't capture his true essence. We should have done more, better. He shouldn't have been tied to the *Commedia all'italiana* (he couldn't have cared less, I repeat, about social commentary); he shouldn't have been tied to his reputation as a *bon vivre*. Ugo was made of sarcastic nostalgia; of sincere compassion for certain aspects of life. This ex-

tended to women, whom he didn't pursue with relentless greed. I heard him say: "I feel sorry for them, their beauty is condemned to a cycle of blood that has enslaved them, for millions of years, as blind instruments to the preservation of the Species."

My wish is that this book (where "making food," with its rules and customs, is interspersed with anecdotes from his life) may correct some misapprehensions regarding the man's true nature & his vocation as an artist. But as I said, this would really require a long essay...

The Contra Mundum Press Agrodolce Series

Agrodolce, the sweet *&* sour, two opposite elements that create a tangy contrast, evoke the agon, *Innigkeit*, the *coincidentia oppositorum*, unsuspected *&* surprising amalgamations. Spurred by this, one thinks of the two primary opposing elements of the universe, as conceived by Empedocles: love *&* strife. The philosopher that hails out of Akragas (Agrigento), Sicilia, the surrogate birthplace of philosophy, the philosopher's true home. Separate from any mainland, separate from nationalism. A culture born of centuries *&* centuries of amalgamations. More exigently, its mythic site is Mt. Etna, the volcano that, as legend has it, Empedocles leapt into. Etna, the agricultural home of apiaries, vineyards, olive and citrus groves, pistachio *&* hazel trees, wild herbs *&* far more. In erupting over 12 times a year, the landscape of Etna is one that undergoes continual metamorphosis, with eternally-evolving soil comprised of basalt, pumice, and ash. The Agrodolce Series, a source of unorthodox books on food.

Curated by Emile Plateau

Contra Mundum *&* the translators of this book
dedicate *The Injester* to Anthony Bourdain
(1956–2018)

COLOPHON

THE INJESTER:
LAUGH OUT LOUD STORIES
& RECIPES TO DIE FOR
was handset in InDesign CC.

The text font is *Auroc Text Quart*.
The display font is *vc Henrietta*.

Book design & typesetting: Alessandro Segalini

Cover design: Alessandro Segalini & CMP, based
on Jean-Marc Reiser's original French film poster
for *La Grande Bouffe*.

THE INJESTER:
LAUGH OUT LOUD STORIES
& RECIPES TO DIE FOR
is published by Contra Mundum Press.

Contra Mundum Press   New York · London · Melbourne

CONTRA MUNDUM PRESS

Dedicated to the value & the indispensable importance of the individual voice, to works that test the boundaries of thought & experience.

The primary aim of Contra Mundum is to publish translations of writers who in their use of form and style are *à rebours*, or who deviate significantly from more programmatic & spurious forms of experimentation. Such writing attests to the volatile nature of modernism. Our preference is for works that have not yet been translated into English, are out of print, or are poorly translated, for writers whose thinking & æsthetics are in opposition to timely or mainstream currents of thought, value systems, or moralities. We also reprint obscure and out-of-print works we consider significant but which have been forgotten, neglected, or overshadowed.

There are many works of fundamental significance to *Weltliteratur* (& *Weltkultur*) that still remain in relative oblivion, works that alter and disrupt standard circuits of thought — these warrant being encountered by the world at large. It is our aim to render them more visible.

For the complete list of forthcoming publications, please visit our website. To be added to our mailing list, send your name and email address to: info@contramundum.net

Contra Mundum Press
P.O. Box 1326
New York, NY 10276
USA

OTHER CONTRA MUNDUM PRESS TITLES

SOME FORTHCOMING TITLES

THE FUTURE OF KULCHUR
A PATRONAGE PROJECT

LEND CONTRA MUNDUM PRESS (CMP) YOUR SUPPORT

With bookstores and presses around the world struggling to survive, and many actually closing, we are forming this patronage project as a means for establishing a continuous & stable foundation to safeguard our longevity. Through this patronage project we would be able to remain free of having to rely upon government support &/or other official funding bodies, not to speak of their timelines & impositions. It would also free CMP from suffering the vagaries of the publishing industry, as well as the risk of submitting to commercial pressures in order to persist, thereby potentially compromising the integrity of our catalog.

CAN YOU SACRIFICE $10 A WEEK FOR KULCHUR?

For the equivalent of merely 2–3 coffees a week, you can help sustain CMP and contribute to the future of kulchur. To participate in our patronage program we are asking individuals to donate $500 per year, which amounts to $42/month, or $10/week. Larger donations are of course welcome and beneficial. All donations are tax-deductible through our fiscal sponsor Fractured Atlas. If preferred, donations can be made in two installments. We are seeking a minimum of 300 patrons per year and would like for them to commit to giving the above amount for a period of three years.

WHAT WE OFFER

Part tax-deductible donation, part exchange, for your contribution you will receive every CMP book published during the patronage period as well as 20 books from our back catalog. When possible, signed or limited editions of books will be offered as well.

WHAT WILL CMP DO WITH YOUR CONTRIBUTIONS?

Your contribution will help with basic general operating expenses, yearly production expenses (book printing, warehouse & catalog fees, etc.), advertising and outreach, and editorial, proofreading, translation, typography, design and copyright fees. Funds may also be used for participating in book fairs and staging events. Additionally, we hope to rebuild the *Hyperion* section of the website in order to modernize it.

From Pericles to Mæcenas & the Renaissance patrons, it is the magnanimity of such individuals that have helped the arts to flourish. Be a part of helping your kulchur flourish; be a part of history.

HOW

To lend your support & become a patron, please visit the subscription page of our website: contramundum.net/subscription

For any questions, write us at: info@contramundum.net

CPSIA information can be obtained
at www.ICGtesting.com
Printed in the USA
JSHW012246091122
32908JS00001B/74

Library of Congress Cataloguing-in-Publication Data

Tognazzi, Ugo, 1922–1990

[L'Abbuffone. English.]

The Injester: Laugh Out Loud Stories & Recipes To Die For / Ugo Tognazzi; Translated from the Italian by Dominic Siracusa & Gianluca Rizzo

—1st Contra Mundum Press Edition

258 pp., 5 × 8 in.

ISBN 9781940625553

   I. Tognazzi, Ugo.
  II. Title.
 III. Siracusa, Dominic & Rizzo, Gianluca.
 IV. Translators.

2022939401

UGO TOGNAZZI

The Injester

Laugh Out Loud Stories
& Recipes To Die For

Translated by

Dominic Siracusa *&* Gianluca Rizzo

Contra Mundum Press   New York · London · Melbourne

The Injester

UGO TOGNAZZI

Ugo Tognazzi feeding a white goose
& some ducks in his farm, Velletri.

✺

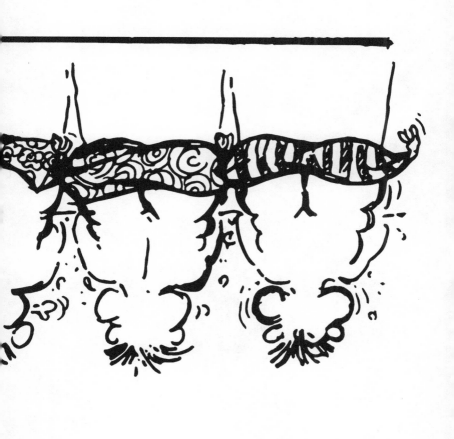

FOREWORD

VIRGIL P. NEMOIANU

One of the outstanding successes of the secularist Left during the last few decades has been the way in which it has seized control of *translations*. By virtually monopolizing this domain, a motley but numerous army of half-literate ideologues, critics, and intimidated publishers have managed to give the impression that outside the Anglo-American world leftist thinkers have emerged the intellectual victors by simple default. Thus, American (and, largely, British) conservatives are often persuaded that all Continental thinkers are ranged against them, Anglo-American conservatives being thus reduced in their own eyes to a tiny idiosyncratic group of rear-guard grumblers. In turn, Continental readers have been bombarded with Keynes, Rawls, Rorty and the like, making conservatives look like hopeless reactionaries or else pushing them toward extreme positions. The sheer laziness of conservatives on both sides of the pond has led to their disadvantage. Fortunately, the Left exercises no monopoly on intellectual life either here or on the Continent, and it only takes some energizing in order to re-establish a healthy balance in the arena of translations.

A few short examples will suffice to illustrate my thesis. Jean Baudrillard, a major contemporary thinker, is known in Anglo-

American and German lands for his early leftist and deconstructionist writings. Few, if any, are aware that his more recent productions are toughly satirical against globalist hegemonism and shrewdly critical of media manipulation. The name of the younger and brilliant Philippe Muray, with his equally playful and substantial ironies against "the Empire of the Good" or *homo festivus*, is all but unknown in English circles. The whole "school" of critics of the media's deleterious impact on politics (Paul Virilio, Ignacio Ramonet, Paul Valadier, S.J., and a number of others—my list is far from complete) are almost totally ignored in English and German. Only the cautious moves of Pierre Manent and Marcel Gauchet toward conservatism have been given some attention. The situation is similar when we think of other countries: the great Colombian Nicolás Gómez Dávila is unknown in America and in England; absolutely major figures such as the Germans Luhmann and Spaemann have not been translated; the complex Italian Bobbio is certainly not a household name; and neither is Peter Slotedijk (although he *has* been translated). The list could go on and on.

A most significant name on any list of unjustly ignored thinkers is that of Chantal Delsol. Prominent and creative women in "political science" are about as frequent as women in astrophysics. Hence, one would have expected feminists to exult at the sight of such a distinguished exception, but of course their hypocrisy always overtakes our naïveté. It so happens that this remarkable woman does not toe the line of "political correctness" in any way and therefore does not enjoy the approval of the hegemonic Left.

Delsol is a prolific writer and a professor at a major French university. Among her more than a dozen excellent works let us mention here *Les Idées politiques au XXe siècle* ("Political Thought in the Twentieth Century," 1991), a masterpiece of clarity and competence that has been translated into at least eight languages. This work places her in the neighborhood of such luminaries as Martin Malia and Paul Hollander. Her classifications are exemplary, as are her distinctions between socialism and communism, racism and corporatist-fascism.

Among other things the work is historically ingenious in that it ana-
lyzes the theories of René de La Tour du Pin, a French thinker who,
well before World War I, had outlined the doctrines that were to be
implemented several decades later in various countries, not excluding
Portugal or the Austria of the 1930s. The fifth and last chapter of this
book argues in favor of "l'état-garant," something in the tradition of
Montesquieu and Michael Oakeshott.

Perhaps Delsol's best book is *L'État subsidiaire: Ingérence et non-
ingérence de l'État: le principe de subsidiarité aux fondements de l'his-
toire européene* ("The Subsidiary State: Governmental Intervention
and Non-intervention: The Principle of Subsidiarity as Cornerstone
of European History," 1992), if for no other reason than that here
she tackles a topic that is much bandied about nowadays. The term
"subsidiarity" was probably coined by the socio-Catholic essayist
Bishop von Ketteler (a towering figure, now unjustly forgotten)
soon after the middle of the nineteenth century. The concept was
used (but, I believe, not named) in Leo XIII's celebrated encyclical
Rerum Novarum and then defined limpidly by Pius XI in 1931 in
his *Quadragesimo Anno*. To simplify as much as possible, "subsidiarity" was meant to suggest that any social task ought to be fulfilled at the lowest possible level. If something could be done by the
individual or the family, it must not be pushed up toward a more
complex level of society; if something could be implemented by the
city or the county, the central government had no business dealing
with it. Thus, the number of issues that "superior" powers are entitled to handle turns out to be severely limited. And "supranational"
authorities can intervene only in extraordinary situations.

Chantal Delsol traces the concept of subsidiarity to its
Aristotelian roots and explains in detail its development in the
works of Montesquieu and Tocqueville. (I for one would have
added to her analysis the likes of Peel and Guizot.) She also discusses
the contributions of the sixteenth-century Calvinist theorist
Althusius (alas, long ignored!) and, even more unusually, rescues
Hegel from the almost unanimously accepted accusation that he

was merely an apologist of the centralized state. The "School of Freiburg" that flowered later in the nineteenth century is regarded in her book as the seed-bed for later developments, and the contributions of Pesch, Röpke, Maritain, and Hayek are given pride of place. Solidarist harmony, personalism, ordo-liberalism are, according to Delsol, modes of social functioning that circle around subsidiarity. Consensus and common good are no longer "values" to be imposed but draw their legitimacy and desirability from their own eloquence and ability to convince others. A "subsidiarist" system differs from a "providentialist" one in that it rejects any kind of equalitarian ideology and in that it ignores the direct exigency of subjective rights. Needs and rights are sharply separated and judiciously balanced in a subsidiarist state. Within such a state, dignity and liberty have a clear priority over equality; the latter might be a consequence of the system, but in no case is it a target or purpose. The increasing intervention of the state into family relations (the practices of Sweden are offered by Delsol as a typical example, but we know very well that Sweden is not the only villain here) is a perfect example of the violation of the principle of subsidiarity. Federalization is admissible by the subsidiarity principle, but it ought to be regarded as complementary: a tool to help out when the original units are at a loss. For Delsol, subsidiarity is the road to be taken if one wants to overcome the tension between "classical" (i.e., in her terminology, strictly individualistic) liberalism and centralizing socialism.

"Authority" as such is and must remain secondary in as far as it has no finality in itself; it ought to remain a kind of helpful strategy for the free functioning of society. Its main role is a palliative one, whenever society is insufficient; it is merely a supplement at *all* levels. Subsidiarity is meant to bolster the indispensable diversities, dignities, and rights of the component parts, rather than to justify trampling on them by centralizing and leveling forces.

These two major works (which have now been translated into almost a dozen languages) are surrounded and strengthened by a series of spectacular book-length essays by Delsol that apply general principles to specific situations, or, better said, to the political horizons of the contemporary world in general.

I am not going to insult my readers by "explaining" what the present work wants to say. Suffice it to say that *Éloge de la singularité: Essai sur la modernité tardive* (which will be published in English by ISI Books in 2004) and the present volume, its predecessor, are remarkable works. Chantal Delsol has the very special knack of explaining current events and tendencies in theoretical terms. She combines masterfully the insight of the cultural commentator with the discourse of the philosopher. Introducing these outstanding writings, with their energetic zest and their scholarly erudition, to the English-speaking reader is a pleasure and an honor, but above all, a genuine intellectual duty.

TRANSLATOR'S PREFACE

Any amateur, no matter how thoroughly he masters a foreign tongue, knows that translation can be a perilous, tedious, and humbling enterprise. The seasoned professional efficiently resists the temptation to linger on a crucial word or on the nuances of an idea, making his living by perfecting and applying his technique in as detached a manner as possible. The text *per se* may not even interest him. For the rest of us, the translation of a book can never be anything less than a labor of love.

Shortly after *Le souci contemporain* appeared in 1996, I came upon an interview with Chantal Delsol in a French weekly and immediately knew I must have the book. There I hoped to encounter in more complete form the author's keen insights and deep humanity, which shone through already in the magazine article. I was not disappointed. Hardly a specialist in French political theory, although an ardent follower of thinkers who bravely pursue the quest for meaning in the contemporary world, I was profoundly impressed by Delsol's understanding and articulation of the thought processes that seemed to be at the root of so many current attitudes and opinions, attitudes and opinions I recognized not only in my colleagues and students but also in myself. It became clear to me that the work simply had to be translated. And so the adventure began.

I could scarcely have anticipated the enthusiasm with which the partially completed manuscript was received at ISI Books, however. It was thrilling to learn that others, with a much broader perspective than my own, recognized that the translation of authors like Chantal Delsol was essential if a more balanced view of French philosophical thought was to be attained in the English-speaking world. In a culture obsessed with globalization, how unfortunate it is that much of the best of what other cultures have to offer never seems to find its way into our own. In this respect, *Icarus Fallen* represents a humble attempt to work towards remedying that situation.

The cultural "translation" of Delsol's work is remarkably easy, a sign not only of just how pervasively a spiritual malaise has settled over the Western world, but also of the author's almost uncanny ability to express this state of mind in genuinely inclusive terms. Her explicit preoccupation is European, and her illustrations are naturally drawn from the social reality most familiar to her. In some cases, this requires explanation, but American readers should have no difficulty seeing the obvious parallels, even if, for example, the Marxist intellectual currents Delsol often reacts to have never been as influential in the Anglo-Saxon world as they have been in the French. As Charles Taylor has observed, the "mainstream academic cultures aren't all that different."*

The author's use of language, on the other hand, represents a particular challenge for the translator. As a widely translated and successful novelist, she has developed a rather literary style and does not hesitate to use literary devices when they suit her purposes. Her sentences are often long and complex, and are not always easy to render faithfully in English without sounding awkward. The greatest challenge, however, and one that I'm not convinced has always been met, was to keep the work from sounding overly

---

* *A Catholic Modernity?* James L. Heft, ed. (New York: Oxford, 1999), p. 119.

academic, an effect that Latinate words (always the first to come to mind when moving from French to English) inevitably have in our language. The text in French is highly readable and engaging. I can only hope that much of that quality is retained in the English rendering.

As key figures in the achievement of that end, a few important collaborators must be acknowledged. Professor Virgil Nemoianu supplied many invaluable observations. Jeremy Beer, at ISI Books, who has been unfailingly patient and encouraging, was able to ferret out more imprecisions and ambiguities than I would care to admit. Barbara Negley did a superb job of proofreading the text and helpfully suggested a number of alternative translations. Chantal Delsol, who for me has gone from a mere name on a book cover to a dear friend, was always prompt to help in clarifying any points particular to the French context in which the book was written. My colleagues in the English department at Collège Lionel-Groulx, Jeffrey Nethercott, Lynne Gaetz, Heather Yorston, and Bessie Zoubris, were always willing to give feedback, provide moral support, and do some preliminary proofreading. I also owe an immense debt to my wife Suzanne, who opened up the whole French world to me, and made this undertaking, like so many others, possible.

AUTHOR'S PREFACE TO THE ENGLISH EDITION

If it is true that the philosophical enterprise is one of astonishment, then one might say that writing this book was a response to the astonishment I felt as I contemplated contemporary Western society, which in a more recent work I have called the society of *late modernity*, as there once was a *late antiquity*.

This society indeed seemed surprising to the forty year old I was when I wrote this book. I experienced this puzzlement as I listened to what I was hearing from the media, from my students and friends, and from my own children. I realized that, in comparison with the postwar period in which I had grown up, a different society was taking shape, one characterized by the flight from meaning, the need for absolute security, the shrinking of personal time, and many other factors that I have attempted to analyze in this book and its sequel, *Éloge de la singularité*. Of course it is not by chance that these diverse but interrelated phenomena have made their appearance in societies that for fifty years have undergone none of the three great catastrophes known to befall human societies: economic hardship, war, and political oppression. These phenomena have come about in what are probably the most fortunate societies in history—that is, if common good fortune can be defined in terms of objective characteristics.

I thus attempted to understand what was going on in the minds of my contemporaries, and in this sense this book is very much a *sociology of the mind*, perhaps the most appropriate category in which to place it. I obviously do not feel that I am essentially any different from the contemporary man of which I write (Rousseau clung to the pretense of being the only human being to have survived the transformation he deplored; I have tried to avoid this error), and I was only able to undertake this work because I am a child of my time, although somewhat removed from it by the demands of philosophical reflection.

While I was writing this book, I regularly did work in the eastern European countries that had just recently been freed from totalitarian communism, and I gradually came to realize that these peoples were absolutely untouched by the phenomena that had provoked my astonishment at home. Having just emerged from a period in which economic hardship, daily political oppression, and the spectre of Russian tanks had not been spared them, these peoples were stunned at our behavior and our ways of thinking—so much so that as they grew to know us better, they increasingly considered us as creatures from another planet, even while at a different level they dreamed of becoming like us. Naturally, the growth of economic and political liberty in these countries has been progressively closing the gap between their culture and ours, transforming warriors into merchants. A difference nonetheless persists, a difference so flagrant that I later became convinced that it was in these eastern European societies that I should seek some answers to our questions. This quest provided the material for several chapters in *Éloge de la singularité*. Seeing firsthand the divergences between us and them led me to the belief that the last fifty years of good fortune had entirely erased our sense of the tragic dimension of life. And the loss of this tragic dimension lies at the heart of the phenomena commented upon in the present book.

It would not be an exaggeration to say that *Icarus Fallen* has earned me both many enemies and many friends. The hundreds of lectures I have given in France and elsewhere since its publication have at times sparked harsh criticism and at times enthusiastic debates. On the one hand, it is sometimes painful to hear, for example, that the sacralization and multiplication of rights ends up undermining the very human dignity that the concept of human rights is supposed to promote. On the other hand, many of our fellow citizens have felt the malaise I have described without conceptualizing its components, and it is with a sort of relief that they have welcomed analyses that clarify their own intuitions. Few have reacted with indifference, which at the very least means that the book is not tepid.

At the same time, the views presented here may be thought of as reflecting a larger movement, albeit one represented by a minority of European thinkers. These thinkers do not really constitute a "current of thought" because they are indeterminate in number, but they do echo analogous intuitions from one country to another. It is important here for the American reader to note that the "Old Continent" is not entirely given over to deconstructionist thinking, nor to the sad nihilism that succeeded the joyous nihilism of Nietzsche, even if these intellectual currents are the ones that attract media attention and attempt to dominate public opinion. European thought is also represented by writers who believe in the existence of a "human condition," who refuse to equate man with animals, things, or machines—in short, by thinkers who take life seriously.

In spite of my fragmented and insufficient knowledge of North America, I am convinced that there is a similarity between your societies and our own, at least as far as this "sociology of the mind" is concerned. Nevertheless, it is perhaps true that the events of September 11, 2001, have opened up a new era in American ways of thinking, a possibility that the future will reveal to us. In the warm and cozy world of democratic consumption and certain peace, September 11 marks the brutal and unexpected resurgence of life's tragic dimension.

It is thus possible that the processes described here will ultimately turn out to be inconsequential, that they concern only a brief historical interlude, one linked to the postwar boom and the fall of the twentieth-century ideologies. In this case, the return of wars after the fall of communism of 1989, the balkanization of the world, and the doubt cast upon the idea of progress will lead Western societies to "return to history," to reintegrate the philosophy of finitude that, for a short time, they believed they could do without.

And yet it just may be that, on the contrary, the malaise described here is the sign of a definitive metamorphosis in our societies. If this is the case, they will increasingly resemble Asian societies: for example, the flight from personal responsibility will slowly draw them from individualism to holism, the substitution of immortality for eternity will render them pantheistic (a future that Tocqueville predicted a century and a half ago), and the lack of an anthropology of the human subject will gradually efface human rights thinking.

We do not know where this malaise will take us. We can, however, say from whence it comes, and perceive some of its consequences.

It is not just to satisfy our intellectual curiosity that we should reflect on the spirit of our time. This reflection can arm us for the future. What kind of society do we want our children to live in? Ultimately this is the essential question, one that eminently deserves to be asked.

— Chantal Delsol
February 10, 2003

INTRODUCTION

Does anyone not know the story of Icarus? To escape from the labyrinth he flies up on a pair of waxen wings but, in spite of the warnings he receives, comes too close to the sun. The wax melts, throwing him into the sea, where he drowns. Now let us imagine that young Icarus manages to actually live through this ordeal: he falls back into the labyrinth, where he finds himself horribly bruised but still alive. And let us try to imagine what goes on in his head after this adventure. He has to go back to a normal life after having thought himself capable of attaining the sun, the supreme good. How will he get over his disappointment?

Today we find ourselves in a similar situation. For the past two centuries, in order to escape from the labyrinth of mediocrity, we have believed ourselves capable of radically transforming man and society. Since Condorcet, the philosophy of Progress has promised to eliminate war, disease, and need, and various ideologies have announced a radiant future. We have just come to the realization—because of the revelation of human disasters in Eastern Europe,*

* The author is referring here to the discovery, after 1989, of just how catastrophic an effect the communist regimes in Eastern Europe had had. Cf. Stéphane Courtois et al., *The Black Book of Communism* (Cambridge, Mass.: Harvard University Press, 1999). *Trans.*

and in the West through the reappearance of poverty, illiteracy, war, and epidemics—that these hopes were finally in vain. We have fallen back to earth, where we must re-appropriate our human condition. But along the way we have lost the keys of understanding, and we no longer recognize this mediocre world, nor do we know its meaning.

Western man at the beginning of the twenty-first century is the descendant of Icarus. He wonders into what world he has fallen. It is as if someone has thrown him into a game without giving him the rules. When he asks around for instructions, he is invariably told that they have been lost. He is amazed that everyone is content to live in a world without meaning and without identity, where no one seems to know either why he lives or why he dies.

This type of existential questioning usually occurs in young minds, agile enough to ask the questions but too inexperienced to be able to answer them. We observe today, however, that adults and even the elderly are haunted by these dizzying questions. And this seems historically abnormal, especially since after the initial question, a whole series of other questions comes tumbling out. Why has Progress failed to prevent the re-emergence of endemic poverty, AIDS, and medieval wars in the heart of Europe? How is it that "correct" thinking has been imposed on us at the very moment we proclaim the sovereignty of the individual conscience? Why do people seem so dissatisfied when so many, in the West at least, have acquired everything they reasonably need to be happy? Why has equality produced such unexpected inequalities? Or why are we now obliged to rehabilitate the market economy and individual profit, which so many of us despise?

Icarus was obviously guilty of a terrible error in judgment. But more than this, he is a character who has lost hope. Having, in spite of himself, tumbled back down into the labyrinth where the Minotaur is lurking, he sums up the spirit of the times.

Events shape men, and so does the lack of events. The spirit of the times—the collection of ideas, beliefs, moods, and ways of life particular to an era—singularly reflects the actions and the passions of the recent past. In this sense, men are at once both the fathers and the sons of their common history. An era of combat gives rise to magnanimity, enthusiasm, and sometimes madness. Tragic events allow heroism, of both the wholesome and unwholesome variety, to flourish. High hopes feed the sense of the sublime and call forth leaders of deep faith. Totalitarian society stifles the creative energies and the dynamism of human solidarity. A society of facile comfort produces narrow, petty people, not because, through some kind of spontaneous generation, they are born without character, but because, in the absence of conditions that would allow it to develop, their character remains latent. A society that fears greatness silences its expansive personalities. Incapable of eliminating them, it forgets or shunts them off to the margins. A very long and prosperous peace devoted entirely to material comfort engenders a superficial kind of happiness, the passion for routine, the fierce protection of small advantages. With no other hope than the perpetuation of the ordinary, a people gives itself colorless elites. By what miracle could it be any different?

And so it is that the *zeitgeist* puts its signature on an era. Because we have just emerged from pointless epochs like the stylish revolt of the late '60s, followed by years of glitz and money, the spiritual tone of our society is one of idle recreation. No wonder we consider it empty and superficial. There are, however, collective ventures that men undertake together that go unnamed because they do not fit into standard categories—they resonate within individual consciousness alone. Only a spiritual sociology could capture their essence.

Certain pessimistic observers sometimes wonder if what characterizes our era is not simply that it has no spirit whatsoever. But this would be unfair. Contemporary man is not a being who stands in the crosswinds of history, passively reflecting their effects but incapable of forming any judgments about them. Nor is he the project-less man described by Roger Nimier as being "the enemy of humankind." In fact, the drama of Western society may sometimes seem to lead to such conclusions, but I would like to demonstrate that this observation is superficial, and that our contemporary is rather a being who is actually suffering from an illness of which he is not even aware. He perceives the consequences of this illness as being disorders that suddenly and inexplicably appear in his personal and social life with all the treachery of unexplained misfortunes. He is more aware of evil in all its forms, but is less prepared to understand it, and therefore to fight against it, than perhaps any of his predecessors. He is disappointed by discourses and theories, but is unlikely to accept any new theory or to find any suitable discourse. He has rejected, often justifiably, prophets, theologians, and thinkers, but is incapable of living without them. He seeks heroes at random but quickly perceives their lack of greatness. He is a misanthrope, yet one who is perfectly aware of the vanity of self-infatuation. In other words, modern man is not a zombie or a monster, but a drifter with an unhappy conscience,* because, having a right to everything, he is fulfilled with nothing, and due to this dissatisfaction, he does not even know the name of what he is looking for.

Our time seems to be characterized by a feeling of being locked in, a feeling that typifies physical or moral suffering. It asks the question not of where to go, but of how to get out. This spiritual discomfort holds the promise of metamorphosis, but no one can yet imagine what will come of it all. Nevertheless, by its very existence, this discomfort is an essential element, and points in an obscure way to the yet unknown future. As is always the case in periods of transition, most of us have moved to the sidelines, waiting to latch onto some newly legitimized reference. After all, not all members of a society can be seekers of meaning. Religions, which are rooted in habit, naturally attract far greater followings than does the skeptical questioning that occurs in periods of change. When, for various reasons,

---

* The French word *conscience*, depending on the context, can be translated as either "conscience" or "consciousness." In this case, both might be appropriate, since the weight of meaningless is felt on both the moral and intellectual levels. *Trans.*

religions, ideologies, and traditional values are tossed aside, one can be sure that a countless mass of people will deliberately opt to wait the period out.

Since this wait seems to be self-contented and impassive, some have concluded that our society is also brainless, which, I believe, would be to seriously misjudge it. Obviously a lively spirit is to be preferred to a dull one, or the act preferred to the potential, as Aristotle said. But periods of metamorphosis hold within themselves, albeit in a veiled fashion, the hope of meaning, which they nourish unawares. We find ourselves today not so much in a brainless society as in a slumbering society, that is, in a society waiting for certainties to appear. One might wonder how to distinguish this gestation, which is after all invisible, from the total "desertification" that diagnosticians of decadence describe with such complacency. To affirm the existence of this virtuality might seem gratuitous; it might simply express the desire to see something that is not there. This expectant spirituality, however, is oozing out of every pore, and one must deny it outright in order not to see it for what it is. Of course we are dealing here with a hope, the hope of somehow going beyond the technical-minded and banausic world in which we live. Hope, when it exists, already indicates a sort of pre-knowledge, even more poignant than actual knowledge, which tends to become too quickly self-satisfied. We find ourselves in a society that is waiting, but does not know what it is waiting for. The feeling of being locked in implies the dream of liberation and implies, too, the suspicion of something hidden beyond the confines of daily life, however adequate daily life is claimed to be.

I hope to show here that the loss of meaning is related to the particular situation of contemporary man, who finds himself back from exile. I hope to describe what this exile consists of and the circumstances of his return. There are, after all, many reasons, both good and bad, to go back home. My main interest, however, lies in the description of this returnee. Haggard and surprised, like the prisoner or the escapee come home, he wakes up in a world he no longer recognizes. This is very much the situation of Icarus fallen back to earth.

Modern man wanted to cut his mooring, to transform the givens of his "condition." The phenomenon we call modernity appears to be multiple and plural. It encompasses the most diverse currents of thought and is expressed through different achievements. A hidden thread, however, ties these diversities together: the ever-present rejection of circumstances or properties whose permanence has marked humanity since its origins. Modern man threw himself eagerly into the Promethean culture, but he made no distinction between the permanent and the circumstantial. To fight against fate he had to eliminate the structures of his own existence. He tried to rid himself of political authority, of the oppositions between good and evil, of God, and of imperfection in general.

By rejecting the structuring givens of his condition, modern man believed it possible to discard his world and replace it with another. This hope expresses itself at different stages, and international communism represented the monstrous excesses of the Enlightenment, which it continued while altering their nature. Modern man here ostracized his own universe, which he held to be undesirable, and ultimately replaceable. But since 1989—a symbolic date and a rupture in time—he has realized that he ostracized himself from an irreplaceable universe.

Catastrophes of every kind have accompanied the totalitarian attempts to re-create the world, while here in the West, our fervent expectations of achieving Enlightenment ideals through Progress have resulted in one disappointment after another. These discouraging relapses reveal the persistence of a condition that is woven into our being and which no desire or volition could ever abolish. The present age is an age in which man has come to realize that he cannot get out of his own skin. One certainty imposes itself on us: he who cuts his moorings chooses not to restore his natural world, but rather to live in exile. The rejected universe has come back and is taking shape within the very wake it left behind.

How could Icarus not be overcome with an inconsolable nostalgia for his extinguished hope? How might he newly apprehend the world of the labyrinth that he thought he would forever be able to forget? This self re-appropriation is happening amidst unhappiness and incomprehension: unhappiness, because of the reappearance of properties of existence that signify a fallen hope; incomprehension, because the human condition no longer makes sense, since its foundational narratives, mythical or religious, have been eliminated. The return from exile is being experienced within an unhappy conscience. Contemporary man wanted this exile, and intellectually at least, he liked it; he refuses to view himself as constrained by a condition he has not designed himself. At the same time, he finds himself in the grip of necessities that impose themselves on him from without, against his will, and he is caught in the trap of what he is no longer able to name or interpret.

The present phase, experienced as a transition towards something yet unknown, does not express the gaping hole of a missing conscience or the hesitations of a rambling conscience that does not know where it is headed. It expresses rather the tragedy of a conscience torn between the desire to conquer everything, the recently acquired certainty of the limits of this conquest, and the inability to understand these newly revealed limits.

The unhappy conscience here resembles the dove that Noah saw in the sky. It pointed to coming certainties but did so in a negative way, by pointing to insufficiency alone. It contains almost nothing more than its own admission of resignation: it considers itself deprived, but does not know of what. But it does latch onto the half-truths it manages to find in the desert. If our time is ill, its illness just might be an illness of hope, as certain symptoms seem to suggest. This is why we can now begin to vaguely make out, through the misdeeds of an era guided by a clouded conscience, the features of a familiar face, that of the prodigal son who has just experienced a flash of doubt. And this doubt changes everything. As yet, it has resulted in almost nothing, but it is a sign of things to come.

The challenge facing the contemporary mind could be compared to that of walking on a glacier. When the climbing party slips from a wind-carved ledge, it is useless to reach for a hand, the guide rope, or the pickaxe in the snow: everything flies away at once. It is a world with no fixed points. In high altitudes, the fixed point, the certainty of rock or ice, reassures the adventurers and makes the undertaking possible. In the cultural and social realm, meaning takes the place of fixed points. The man who has meaning firmly in his grasp can allow himself to wander and explore. He who knows the why, as Nietzsche said, can tolerate any how.

PART ONE

A CONDITION
DEPRIVED
OF MEANING

CHAPTER 1
EXISTENCE AS SIGN

In general our contemporary cannot imagine for what cause he would sacrifice his life because he does not know what his life means. One cannot accept death if one does not know why one lives.

This is an entirely new phenomenon and represents a profound break with the past. The two previous centuries, having rejected religion, gave rise, for the first time in history, to societies which no longer wanted to be structured by religious meaning. If modern man distanced himself from God, however, he found meaning in the ideals of modernity. Twentieth-century man in general no longer devoted himself to the quest for saintliness or to preparation for eternity. Instead, he gave himself over to the construction of an ideal society, described in different ways according to the worldview to which he subscribed. Therefore, even if the abandonment of a structuring religion constituted a change of seismic proportions, the ways of considering existence never changed much, since the content of one just replaced the content of the other. In both the former and the latter, the existence of man meant something, pointed to something beyond itself.

On the other hand, the age that is now dawning constitutes a dramatic break: ideals of every kind have more or less disappeared.

Contemporary man observes with a suspicious eye the certainties he once held or the institutions he maintained—institutions are very often the extensions, guarantees, and tabernacles of certainties. His existence no longer means anything. Hence, we see unfolding before our eyes a strange phenomenon: a world without signposts.

How can one describe the "meaning of life"? The individual one meets in daily life says, "My life has lost its meaning" (by "my life" he actually means "my existence"). In saying this, with a voice wrought with regret, he clearly indicates that meaning is the salt of existence; or, if one prefers, what makes it palatable, digestible. Without it, life becomes no more than a colorless, bland thing accepted out of habit, routinely. Existence that "is no longer worth living" indicates a rupture with an object outside of oneself, a fallen fervor, a downcast look, a pointless act. Such an existence signifies nothing; it is no longer the *sign* of anything. It does not stand for anything to which it can bear witness or for which it can be a guarantee. It remains within itself, as if a thread had been snapped, or a vital link suddenly broken.

To have meaning, to signify, is to stand for something other than oneself, to establish a link with a value, an idea, an ideal beyond oneself. Life has meaning, for example, for those who spend their time and energy in search of a cure for a disease, or in the struggle against injustice, or just to show every day that society can be more than a jungle. The link one establishes with this value or idea confers a higher value on life.

A life that has meaning recognizes certain references. One might say that existence takes on meaning insofar as it enters into a relationship with exterior referents that go beyond it and outlive it. In other words, it is paradoxically worth something only to the extent that it admits itself not to be of supreme value, by recognizing what is worth more that itself, by its ability to organize itself around something else.

Everyone will admit that existence is at once both finite and deficient. We consider society to be mediocre, love insufficient, a lifespan too narrow. The person whose life has meaning is the one who, instead of remaining complacently in the midst of his regrets, decides to strive for perfection, however imperfectly, to express the absolute, even through his own deficiencies, to seek eternity, even if only temporarily. If he spends his life making peace in society or rendering justice to victims, he is effectively pointing, even if it is with a trembling finger, to the existence of peace or justice as such. If he spends his life raising his children, that is, in teaching them a way of life, it is because he thinks that his way of life is worthy of immortality, that it deserves to be perpetuated because it brings happiness. In raising his children, he seeks to give concreteness to values that he deems essential.

He *seeks*, since his world is too narrow and too imperfect to completely realize his ideals. By pursuing his referents, he points to them. He awkwardly expresses these impalpable, immaterial figures of hope or expectancy. His existence never entirely realizes justice or peace, but it partially draws them out of the nothingness of abstraction and makes them appear in outline, which is a great victory in itself. Individual existence, when it means something, points to its referent through its day-to-day actions and behaviors, the sacrifices it accepts and the risks it dares to take. It is well known that those who fight for peace or justice are capable of taking extraordinary risks, of making extraordinary sacrifices.

In such cases, and no matter what the nature of its referents, existence then seems to deny itself, since it compares itself to something greater, wanting to be the expression of what goes beyond it. It is a sign or witness: it alone does not say everything, but rather grows by saying what it is not. It seems to know, however, that it is thereby worth more. A pale reflection of the referents it points to, this existence considers itself greater than an existence for and of itself. The contemporary man whose life no longer has meaning envies the freedom fighters who are capable of self-denial because he considers them greater for this very ability.

So it is that what is commonly called an ideal in its different modalities guarantees the value of existence. The converse, however, is also true. Ideals themselves survive and are realized only by the existence that guarantees and bears witness to them. Liberty would never have acquired any reality at all if no one had ever become its servant. It took shape and form through the combat of its heroes, from Brutus to Solzhenitsyn, and the countless other anonymous heroes that reveal it to the world. One might well wonder what wisdom would be without philosophers, peace without the infinite patience of those constantly seeking truce, solidarity without militants, saintliness without seekers of God. These ideas take shape in a groping sort of way through the miraculous efforts that some devote their lives to in order to show that such ideas are real. How many men live and die only to convince others of the possibility that an idea might break through the weight of being—to simply demonstrate that justice or love exists? It happens that certain men are identified so strongly with their ideals that they become the living symbols of them, as were Gandhi, Walesa, or Sakharov in the twentieth century. They make the earth yield unhoped-for flowers. Conversely, an ideal dies when its advocates fall into disarray. A society that methodically quashes wise men ends up taking delight in insanity, to the point where it can no longer see this insanity for what it really is, since there is nothing to compare it against. Thus, man carries full responsibility for his ideals, which, without him, remain strangers to the world.

Man's existence and the reference he points to, therefore, are intertwined and grow from each other. The difference lies in the fact that the reference does not die, or rather, that it only dies when it is forgotten. Every man knows his existence to be mortal. By embracing a project, a philosophy, a God, he steals a small piece of immortality. He escapes the fate of his own fleetingness. By identifying what goes before him, he identifies himself. But in spite of his precariousness, it is he, and he alone, who guarantees the survival of his ideals and confers a reality upon them.

To say that existence has meaning is to affirm the distance between existence and its references, to affirm their irreducibility, their inability to be one and the same thing. This is how we must understand the dynamic of existence toward the ideal, its feverish impatience to make the ideal real and thereby make itself still more real, that is, suffused with a sort of immortality.

This distance is expressed in the restlessness of an existence given over to the never-ending quest for those figures that are not immediately attainable but rather take on concrete form over the course of a lifetime. The seeker moves forward, all the while wondering, "What is worth serving?" Individual existence structures itself through the call for meaning. Existence is shaped by questions and expectations. By defining its questions—by describing the justice or peace it longs for—it becomes the author of its own destiny.

Man can manage to live without thinking about meaning, contenting himself with raw existence. It is like a musical lyric one keeps turning over in one's head that finally becomes reduced to the song's melody. The lyric loses its intrinsic interest and the words get lost in the tones. Existence, in a similar way, can become reduced to its ephemeral joys and interior troubles, spinning round within the walls of selfhood, sinking in the sand instead of marching toward its dream, without an echo to its cry. This is indeed the situation of Generation X, a generation that has nothing to do, does not know what to do, nor to what it should devote itself—a generation without a sense of purpose.

In general, however, this closed-off existence is not satisfying, because man defines himself, on the contrary, in the adventure of the quest for meaning. A life that seeks meaning throws itself into the adventure. Existence calls out for references in an epic journey rich with meanderings. Or rather, when it has meaning, existence signifies an object that evades and escapes its grasp. It knows it wants to signify something but does not know exactly what. What is more, it is ignorant of the shape and form, of the face of what it claims to signify. This adventure represents the way of being of an existence in the perilous pursuit of a reference it desires and intuits but has no idea where to find. Someone may seek to make liberty real, but not only does its realization elude him, its very definition also escapes him. He manages with difficulty to give some shape and form to liberty, but cannot help but notice that this liberty gives rise to abuses. In other words, he seeks what he does not entirely comprehend, and so in his quest defines his object more clearly.

Hence, the pursuit of an ideal feeds on our sense of futility by making us aware of the distance that keeps it from reach. It also feeds on our anxiety, but an anxiety armed and comforted by the certainty of being. No one can be without being *for a reason*. This is clearly seen in the physical and mental decline associated with old age, when we become useless to the world, incapable of serving anyone or anything. Deprived of his vitality, man becomes distraught. The dynamism of existence cannot be found solely within the self. Paradoxically, existence that signifies something saves itself by going outside of itself. By seeking and realizing the ideal through the actions it engages in, existence unfolds and confirms itself in time.

The deprivation of dynamism corresponds to the situation of the free man as generally defined by contemporary man. He willingly considers freedom as an end in itself, to the point that he measures the good life according to the level of liberty he enjoys. But freedom is nothing but an empty form awaiting content. The freedom to be oneself, to define one's own norms, is not sufficient to structure the subject, since it is mere openness and condition. It opens up possibilities but does not define them. It is the atmosphere, the backdrop, the framework in which the individual can shape himself, but it does not itself shape him. In fact, it is not the *freedom to be* that the individual wants, which would make him merely a subject in the world who knows himself. The axis around which the subject shapes himself positively is, rather, *responsibility*. In choosing what he will "answer" for, the subject is mobilized and shapes himself into a whole being. Modern freedom signifies only that the subject is free to choose what he will be responsible for. To the extent that this freedom is taken to mean that he will be responsible for nothing, the subject destroys himself by mistaking the means for an end. However, the man who must answer to, or be responsible for, even a reference he himself has chosen is no longer entirely free in the sense of this objectless adventure. He can no longer be absent, cheat, or call in sick. He must remain steadfastly present, and this presence carries with it the weight of attention. It is precisely this carefree-ness that contemporary man fears he will lose by giving a meaning to his life.

The question of the meaning of existence is naturally related to the question of what man is doing here on this earth. One is tempted to ask what purpose man can possibly serve in this world. In fact, he *serves* no purpose at all, but rather *signifies*. He is the sign of something that he is often unaware of himself, of something he seeks and occasionally believes he has discovered. He is not a useful structure indistinguishable from its task, but a sign, and in him can be detected everything that is uncertain about a sign, which never *de-sign-ates* with certainty, and which can never be confused with what it is meant to be a sign of. He is a subject because he himself decides what he will signify—in other words, what is worth more than himself.

We speak of a *useless* machine, but of a man we say he is *insignificant*. The difference is clear. An insignificant person is unworthy of our consideration; he signifies nothing, designates nothing, remains imprisoned within his own narrow limits. Thus, common parlance expresses the blandness and nothingness of an existence that does not refer to something outside itself.

Furthermore, and paradoxically, existence actually finds true happiness in the anxiety of unresolved questions, and suffocates in the identification of itself with the object of its expectations. Freedom fighters, those who combat poverty—in fact, all tormented watchdogs of change—bear the unmistakable mark of meaning. Those who are bloated with freedom and abundance bear nothing in their self-satisfied connivance with the world, where hollowness and emptiness are manifest. The man whose desires are satisfied is characterized by a feeling of wandering even though he has achieved an enviable stability. Utopias that describe a man who has at last arrived home, also describe him as distraught, deprived of both history and hope. If the postwar period did indeed give rise to a kind of utopia made real, with the emergence of societies for the first time free from the threat of war, oppression, and want, it still does not seem that the satisfied individual really achieved the happiness he longed for.

Is it really necessary that man remain unsatisfied in order to be happy? Can he only find happiness when engaged in a quest? Or does he, through this quest, actually seek something other than what he believes he is looking for? No doubt both questions have the same answer, albeit a problematic one: the intuition of an ontological, as opposed to a circumstantial, insufficiency. If not, why would men, whose needs have all been met, still feel that something is missing? What is it that is still missing when nothing is missing?

Our contemporary asks the question, "What is worth serving?" and worries that he might not find anything. To regret the elusiveness of meaning is to contemplate in sorrow the unrecoverable distance between oneself and the object of one's hopes. Existence that points to nothing beyond itself is doomed to die. If nothing is worth more than my *self*, how can I survive myself? This question is written in capital letters throughout our books and individual consciences. All the epics of our society evoke it and remind us of it. It epitomizes the major torment of our time.

The dissolution of meaning, understood as the dissolution of ideals, seems to announce the death of the individual—not his biological death, but the absolute death that now seems to be his through biological death. Existence that fails to signify devalues itself, or rather, underestimates its value. It thereby becomes equated with life, that is, reduced to the narrow frontiers of biological life. He whose existence points to nothing, owns nothing more than his own life. Of course, no one owns anything more than his own life, but existence that signifies gives value to a project that goes beyond itself. On the other hand, if there is nothing that existence points to, everything of value in existence lies exclusively at the biological level. As a result, biological life becomes overvalued, in the sense that it eclipses all other values, to the point of becoming the only entity that is sacred and untouchable. So it is that the present era has a tendency to protect life at any cost. The frenetic efforts we undertake in order to conserve the physical health of individuals, the struggle to prolong life and, increasingly, to portray death as an unexpected catastrophe obviously reflect only laudable aims. They nonetheless clearly express the desertion of meaning.

There can be no path from oneself to oneself. That is why the desertion of meaning announces the arrival of a bland and disconnected existence, that is, an existence deprived of its pathway. The man whose existence is deprived of meaning finds himself left on his own. In other words, he does not have the courage to really be himself, having nothing to demonstrate or to call into existence. Nothing extends beyond him and nothing calls to him from without. He neither expects nor hopes for anything more than himself. And paradoxically he finds himself abandoned in this independence. One has but to look around to see evidence of this feeling of abandonment, even if we are not yet ready to understand the hidden spirit behind it, and even if this obvious fact offends and upsets us.

Having attempted the experiment of internalizing referents, having wanted to produce an individual with no reference other than himself, we now know that existence wants to bear the mark of more than just what it reveals as it stumbles along, and that only this hope nourishes it. And we also know that existence fails in its attempt to bear its own mark. We are emerging from an era that considered man to be alienated by his ideals. This era saw man as servile and enslaved, relegated to the shadow of ideals, which, it was thought, inevitably devoured him and deprived him of his own creativity and complete happiness. It was thought that he who remained expectant lacked something and was for this very reason unhappy. In order to make existence accessible to itself, then, we set for ourselves ideals that were realizable, capable of being appropriated. Our ideals became historicized, achievable in time, when before they had always remained on the horizon: in other words, complete freedom or perfect justice became realizable in historical time. This is how our referents, while not losing their content, lost their status as referents. They ceased to represent an unattainable horizon. They were, in fact, transformed into programs to be carried out.

In the era preceding our own man did not suppress ideals. He attempted rather to internalize them. He did not abolish that which had value, but rather the distance between existence and what had always given value to it. He accomplished this movement—in which the self and the expected object were equated—by believing himself capable of transforming into reality all the virtualities he had once been content to inadequately point to. He believed that soon he would no longer be just a freedom fighter, but a truly free man; he held the conviction that he could do more than forever point to a hoped-for solidarity, that he would soon be totally and truly united. He was no longer a man engaged in a quest for the good, but the very inventor of the good. He would no longer be a lover of wisdom, since the lover is never satisfied, but the actual proprietor of wisdom. And on and on. In this way, he ceased to be a being who stood for something, and became instead a being who tried to take possession of what he stood for, with the ultimate purpose of someday having no longer to stand for anything at all.

Thus, we lived with the certainty that ideals were condemned to disappear, since the time for them to be fully realized had finally come. Henceforth they would cease to be referents, at last taking their place in concrete existence. This is no doubt why the previous era was a period so full of meaning, during which men knew very well why they lived and what causes they were willing to die for. For what greater or more exalting work could there be than to solve the enigma of mankind, to cut through the Gordian knot of existence? Where might man's unhappiness lie if not in the distance that separates him from the object of his desires, a distance he had never been able to overcome? Could his misfortune arise from anything other than his failure to fully bring liberty, solidarity, or wisdom into reality?

Naturally, we know today that this effort to totally turn our ideals into reality has not been successful, and has in fact produced some very bitter fruit indeed. We have attained neither concrete liberty, nor peace, nor justice. The world in which we live seems to us to be as insufficient as ever, but this fact has not convinced us to redraw the figures of hope. On the contrary, the fall of ideologies now casts a deadly shadow over every ideal. Ideologies were systems of reference structured like cathedrals, and our memory is long. We have watched all the cathedrals fall into ruin, one after the other. And we have come to realize that we have too often nourished hopes that were not only false but shameful as well. Over the centuries, countless men have died for nothing—or rather, for evil—without their being aware of it. One thinks of the disciples of fanatical religion, the fascist youth, the Komsomol in their starred caps.* Could it be that the dynamic itself was perverse? Consequently, our contemporary remains immobile, riveted to himself.

Some hope that these terrible experiences will bring forth a new era, extinguishing once and for all man's call to the absolute, failing his ability to equate himself with it. This reasoning is, however, faulty. To banish from the mind of man the call to meaning has been revealed to be in no man's power. Our contemporary, freed from what constrained him to run ever further, continues desperately to run, but without knowing where he is headed. He continues to engage in all the actions that used to correspond to some

* The author is referring to the Soviet youth league, founded in 1918, which was used to socialize youths between 14 and 28 in the thought and ways of the Communist Party. *Trans.*

meaning and in doing so he bears a grotesque resemblance to the headless chicken. Activities without meaning occupy his existence. He exhausts himself for no defined purpose. He creates anti-heroes. He invents arts made to express nothing other than his inner silence. He runs risks with nothing at stake, leaving behind not happiness over the disappearance of meaning, as one might expect, but the troublesome traces of meaninglessness.

Through this lost message, through this broken cord, the subject finds himself relegated to his own inner self. He is like a messenger without a message. He knows vaguely that he was thrown into the world to carry the messages of his hope. If this were not true, he would not be so distraught, now that he has finally been relieved of his task. But this is the very source of his worry when, hurrying towards nothing, he by chance catches a glimpse of himself in the mirror and must ask himself: Just what am I doing here?

The previous understanding of man as a designator of referents corresponded to a specific understanding of the human condition. How did this understanding come apart? Icarus, having fallen back to earth, no longer understands the world he has rediscovered. Under what conditions, and at what cost, will he be able to apprehend it anew?

CHAPTER 2
THE REJECTION OF THE FIGURES OF EXISTENCE

When existence signifies something, it expresses its own poverty. In any case, it lacks precisely that which it is trying to signify. Such an existence can be recognized by its modesty: it places ahead of itself that which it signifies, even before it introduces itself. It is unsatisfied and discontent because it indicates what it is not and what it does not have. It knows no peace since it is constantly engaged in the combat of witnessing to something that remains improbable and expected.

It is precisely this dissatisfaction and this distance that modernity has attempted to suppress by seeking to liberate man from the anxiety engendered by a necessarily indefinite quest. And indeed, how could anyone be opposed to the praiseworthy effort to eliminate torment, to invent an individual who feels nice and cozy, who has become the very object of his own desires, and therefore has ceased his endless longing and is at last at peace with himself?

This process of assimilation was only made possible through a reinterpretation of the human condition.

Let us for a moment consider an individual existence devoted to the quest for charity. This quest testifies to the possibility of love, and its aspiration is only made possible by a distinction between good and evil. If this distinction disappears, the good immediately disappears as a possible reference. Another individual existence might be devoted to the elimination of scarcity. He believes a state of well-being is possible that does not yet exist. This person's ambition is conditioned only by the struggle between need and scarcity, since if all desirable goods were as abundant as pure water in a mountain stream—or, on the other hand, if scarcity were not perceived as a lack—the referent would immediately vanish and there would no longer be an object to the quest. Similarly, what reason for being would the countless fighters for political freedom have if those in power did not routinely engage in subjugation of one kind or another? Could the untiring servants of peace find their way in a world characterized by the absence of conflict and a perfect harmony of all hearts and minds? Would men whose lives are spent trying to convince others of the reality of eternity not cease their quest if, by some miracle, man became immortal?

From man's very beginning until the nineteenth century, the meaning of existence depended entirely on a specific understanding of the human condition. Because man understood himself to be tormented by the contradictions between his imperative needs and his incapacity to fulfill them entirely, he could devote his existence not to "accomplishing" in any complete sense what could never be perfectly accomplished, but to bearing witness to the legitimacy of his hopes through modest, less-than-perfect achievements.

The meaning of existence hinged on the permanent presence of the opposition, or antinomy, between good and evil, need and scarcity, power and freedom: in other words, on the perception of these oppositions as figures of human existence, or even as forms of our condition. In seeking a life beyond the inevitability of death, in seeking good beyond the inevitability of evil, existence acquired meaning. These figures of our condition, because of their persistence, in fact immortalized meaning. The dynamic impulse was unstoppable, since death, evil, and need could never reasonably be expected to disappear. The insecurity that weighed upon man amidst these contradictions went hand-in-hand with the perennial nature of meaning, which always connoted distance and incompleteness. These antinomies—good/evil, need/scarcity, freedom/power—represented the figures of being in the world, man's means of accessing the world, in other words, the irreducible terms of existence. The presence of man in the world is expressed through the conflicts between need and scarcity, authority and freedom, good and evil, life and death. And the cross-threads of economics, politics, morality, and religion take shape through them. We are dealing here with the very structures of the human world, its constituent oppositions. Julien Freund, who identified six (religion, morality, politics, economics, science, art) called them *essences* in order to underscore their significance.[1] These are the essential structures with which the question of the meaning of existence is directly related, since they express the condition of a being that finds itself torn between what it is and what it wishes to be, between what it has and wishes to have, between the real world it finds itself in and the world it hopes for.

One of the crucial questions that haunted the past two centuries regarded the legitimacy of these antinomies, or more precisely, the validity of their claim to last indefinitely. After all, why should man remain mired in these particular modes of being? Who could certify their necessary permanence and justify their future? How could their past permanence demonstrate their constituent character? No one could answer these questions. At least, any answers that were proposed remained debatable: in order to find out, one would have to verify, and take concrete steps to abolish, these so-called invincible figures. And in fact, modernity has done just that. It has experimented, sometimes in systematic fashion, sometimes in a veiled or incomplete way, with the suppression of the economy, politics, morality, and religion, an experiment never attempted before.

In this respect, the modern era might seem to be a period of unprecedented lucidity. Antinomies once considered unalterable were historicized, and their so-called necessity reduced to that of circumstance. That they were manifestations of a condition woven into human nature came to be seen as a subterfuge that was reassuring but false. For two centuries man has attempted to refashion his condition and, in a sense, to separate himself from his former self. The major discovery of modernity consists in affirming that man invented transcendence, morality, and politics from top to bottom. The reasons that might have possessed him to invent these things are multiple, and vary according to who interprets them: to reassure himself, to escape from his natural anguish, to satisfy his desire for power or glory. In any case, what is essential here is the idea of *invention*. The figures of the human condition are thus seen in modernity as the products of culture and therefore destructible. The lucidity of modernity, then, consists in our awareness that, until now, these figures of existence were thought of as products of nature; as such, they dominated us, when all the while we could have dominated them, if only we had known better. This is an incredible insight into an ancient error, and brings with it the power to recommence history.

Economic reality is rooted in the immemorial conflict between need and scarcity. The word "conflict" is appropriate because what is specifically human here is that man's desires are never completely fulfilled. The attempt to create well-being by combating scarcity constitutes one of the meanings of existence, not only because individually each person seeks to "live better" in the future, but because generations and peoples make it a point of honor to demonstrate that humanity can grow by freeing itself, at least partially or temporarily, from poverty. In this regard, the West during the twentieth century has accomplished incredible feats in combating immemorial misery.

In attempting to end this permanent dissatisfaction, this exhausting struggle between need and scarcity, many modern currents of thought have tried to suppress one or both of the terms of this antinomy, which in effect would be sufficient to abolish it altogether. Marx's successors hoped to eliminate scarcity by creating a society of abundance. Western socialism hoped for a kind of happy austerity, in which desires would be limited in proportion to the available goods, imagining that people would be content with a bare minimum made palatable by the attainment of equality for all. Here again the aim was to reconcile man with himself, to seek the ever-elusive unity by restricting desire.

In defining man as a political animal, Aristotle gave politics the status of a figure of being. And one might say that the present era has brought with it for the very first time the experimental demonstration of Aristotle's presentiment. It was necessary to try to get rid of politics in order to learn that politics is woven into the very fabric of society. Because human society cannot do without leaders, and because power seems disagreeable if not completely intolerable to a normally constituted man, politics is the arena of an unhappy contradiction. And from this stems the temptation to reject it as a constitutive property of human existence. Thus, modernism has taken up, in many ways, the huge and unusual task of transcending the age-old relationship between command and obedience. By describing government as a phenomenon that appeared historically, social contract theories let us imagine that it might also one day completely disappear. Of course, such theories can also justify the necessity of an all-powerful state, as does Hobbes, if they postulate the solitude of the individual and his complete vulnerability at the inception of the contract. The contract theory may, as it does in Locke, open up the possibility of negotiations, in which a necessary yet fearsome state finds itself constrained to ratify and even guarantee its citizens' freedom. But the historicization of political authority begs the question of its real necessity, even if historical time is lost here in mythical time. The contract theories may lead to the subjugation of politics to circumstance, and thus to the detachment of politics from the human condition, of which it had been considered a constitutional part since Aristotle. Politics can from this point on cease to be seen as a properly human phenomenon and become the arena for a controversy which may go so far as to question the legitimacy of its very existence. Instead of merely asking how it is possible to tame political authority in order to make it palatable, one may now wonder what kind of progress would make it possible to suppress political authority altogether, thereby ridding humankind of the permanent conflict it supposes.

In spite of their popularity in the nineteenth century, anarchistic currents of thought, by seeking to suppress one of the terms of the antinomy between power and freedom, are really only a backdrop to more sophisticated thinking. Anarchy offers no solution to the dilemma because it immediately appears to be too easy to be true, and we are rightly suspicious of what is too simple. In fact, it is not so much a question of suppressing those who govern as it is of identifying the governed with the governors, and of reducing the one to the other. In this sense, Rousseau is clearly the father of modern attempts to suppress politics; indeed he represents their point of reference. Mere collaboration or mutual confidence between the governors and the governed is not enough: they must be identical. It is no longer a question of democracy, in which each member governs in turn, as in ancient Greece, but of a democracy in which each member finds himself at once in the role of governed and governor. The rejection of political representation embodied in this position indicates a rejection of politics as a figure of existence. The notion of government disappears as soon as he who obeys and he who commands are one and the same person. Rousseau's direct democracy aims at nothing less than the abolition of order-giving, since if everyone can give orders, no one is really in command. Politics can only exist as a dialectic.

The nineteenth century is ridden with anti-statist currents of thought, all aiming in their own ways to eliminate politics. For Proudhon, the individual citizen is to be replaced by the group, but this group, like Rousseau's citizen, is at the same time both governed and governor. Political authority is neutralized. The state, or in other words, the body that commands without having to obey, fades away before the law. By wanting to "let law rule alone,"[2] Proudhon tries to suppress the political. He in fact considers it useless, to the extent that the guarantee of rights is sufficient to avoid conflict both without and within. Politics disappears when the age-old conflicts that made it legitimate disappear.

It is as true of certain nineteenth-century liberals as it is of Marxists that one of their aims consists in the elimination of the state, not only as a modern centralized level of government, since politics can exist without a state, but as a level of command. The Marxist idea of the "withering away" of the state responds to the hope of creating a society of equals in which the distinction between governors and governed disappears. Marx's successors expect to eliminate not only the governments of their time, but government as such. Certain liberals since John Stuart Mill have hoped for a progressive and painless fading away of governing authority as the inevitable progress of the Enlightenment rendered it useless. This idea correlates with another: that despotism is legitimate among less advanced peoples. "Authority must diminish as civilization advances," writes Jules Simon in *La liberté politique.*[3] The ideology of progress holds up the promise of a consensual society achieved through the discovery of self-evident truths that make differing opinions obsolete. Diversity of opinion is good only "while mankind are imperfect," writes Mill in *On Liberty.*[4] Thus the politics of debate, which tames the conflict between power and freedom and makes it tolerable, is really only a step along the way to the elimination of politics altogether. As in Marx—albeit, obviously, in a different way—liberal progressivism boils down to the expectation that politics will ultimately be abolished entirely.

This hope goes far beyond the two schools of thought mentioned above. It seeks its realization in various forms throughout the nineteenth and twentieth centuries. Whether politics seeks to dissolve itself into law (Hans Kelsen and his successors) or in the science of management (as in contemporary technocratic thinking), it is just waiting to disappear.

The past two centuries have also seen the development of the hope that morality, conceived as the opposition of good and evil, will be suppressed. By placing the appearance of the criteria of goodness in historical, even primeval, time, Rousseau describes certain ancients as being beneath good and evil. As a historicized phenomenon, morality can henceforth be imagined as potentially disappearing. The same idea is clearly expressed by Engels. Evil is the result of bad structures. It is sufficient to abolish these structures to save us from evil. Nietzsche places man not beneath, but rather above moral criteria. The philosophy of values, and the resultant era of dogmatic relativism we have entered, ratifies the disappearance of morality. The conflict between good and evil is stricken down not by the disappearance of its terms, but by their relativization.

If the designation of goodness is valid for no one but oneself, then goodness can be found everywhere—and consequently, nowhere. Of course, the antinomy is still to be found in the heart of the subject himself, but it no longer gives rise to conflict, nor does it spur a quest for the good, since the good is, in advance, identified with what the subject himself chooses. And the subject has no hope of ever conquering a good that he is not yet capable of obtaining, for on what basis outside of himself would he be able to judge the value of this good? At this point, the antinomy dissolves. The contemporary era, as the end-product of the modern attempt to suppress morality, has created individuals who no longer raise the question of good or evil, and who are entirely ignorant of what used to be called "the examination of conscience."

The effacement of the religious antinomy finds expression in the "death of God" and at the same time in the hope of the advent of the man-god. Religion attempts to respond to the contradiction between finitude and the desire for infinitude. And it is just such infinitude that the prophets of modernism, in various forms, promised: biologically, as Condorcet once wrote, we are to enjoy a lifespan approaching ever closer to being unlimited.[5] Intellectually and psychologically, we can expect advances so decisive that they entail a transformation of human nature.

The previous era was filled with the notion of completion, in the sense that it felt itself to be preparing for the advent of a new world. This outcome called out for a qualitative metamorphosis of human matter: history could no longer be the ground on which conflicts were fought out. It was necessary to somehow get out of the human condition as it had always been experienced and described. In a more or less near future, the setbacks and the paradoxes of our condition, with all their consequences, would to the new man seem like petty quarrels, questions from a bygone age. Attempts at abolition were multiple and diverse. They involved all of Europe, from West to East. In fact, these attempts established a powerful link between the regimes of so-called real socialism and the regimes of liberty. Everywhere, they marked the territory of modernism. Sovietism broke down religion by using terror, while in the West, religion was relegated to the realm of subjectivity, a particularly debonair way of getting rid of it. Sovietism attempted to abolish the economic and political antinomies, while in the West we were dreaming about either happy austerity or unlimited abundance, or, as is still the case, about a politics reduced to science, law, or a moral code.

Man once found the meaning of his existence in the heart of these antinomies. He sought the good despite immemorial imperfection and his discouraging and repeated falls into barbarism. He sought God in the midst of doubt. He pointed to a possible freedom in the midst of political conflict, and in this always indecisive battle, his status as citizen took on meaning. Man in the modern era, by raising his pretensions a notch upward, found the meaning of his existence in the hope of forever abolishing the antinomies between which his ancestors had always struggled. This could only be the work of a titan, and as such it has given our era an air of capital importance. This is why our age has become the meeting-place of all manner of fanaticisms and unheard-of sacrifices. At stake was the abolition of the quest for meaning, seen as the pursuit of what is lacking and as a dissatisfaction with the imperfection of reality. We are now arriving at the historic moment when, before our very eyes, the consequences of this unprecedented adventure are being revealed.

CHAPTER 3
BLACK MARKETS

We know now that modern man did not win the Faustian wager in which he had hoped to free himself entirely from his condition. He was unable to inaugurate a new era free from the conflicts between good and evil, need and scarcity. Although he did make a serious attempt to lift all peoples out of the scorned categories of the human condition, the failure of this attempt can be seen in the spontaneous and unexpected re-emergence of everything we had rejected. The figures of human existence are again developing in spite of their illegitimacy. Ban the economy and the black market will blossom. Decree that religions are obsolete and you will have sects. Deny that human beings seek the good, and the ghost of the good will appear surreptitiously under the guise of *correct* thinking. Societies that attempt to rid themselves of the figures of economics, religion, and morality must put up with them in their black market form. We are witnessing the emergence of a low-profile world that defies conceptualization because it is forbidden, repressed; it is illegal or illegitimate, or both at the same time.

The figures of existence, rejected by public opinion and sometimes also by institutions, have reappeared in the obscurity of daily life. No one has called them back. They have not been rehabilitated since, on the contrary, common opinion justifies their abolition. They have few defenders. Rather, they seem to have appeared from out of nowhere.

What is unique about the black market is that it fulfills the functions of an official market that has disappeared or has become too demanding by the sheer weight of its own rules. Although this is most apparent in the economic sphere, it can be seen in the other spheres as well, as soon as a vital human function is discredited or forbidden. This reappearance alone indicates that the function was indeed vital.

Lenin's New Economic Policy (NEP) constitutes the first significant historic instance of a response to the official quashing of a human paradox.* The Soviets, as we now know, were hoping that collectivization would answer all needs and thus eliminate scarcity. In other words, their ultimate goal consisted not only in abolishing the market economy, but in abolishing the economy as well. Realizing just how serious was the damage caused by the institutional prohibition of the most stubborn human behavioral patterns (working to get ahead, buying and selling), Lenin decided to allow the market to redeploy itself, at least temporarily. Though this policy's real purpose was concealed by various pretexts, with the introduction of the NEP Lenin admitted, regretfully but with a keen political intuition, the persistence of the economic "condition," although he continued to believe it was perishable (and even on this last point his later writings seem to indicate a flash of disquieting doubt).

The twentieth century is the century of NEPs, peopled by NEP men of all sorts, still dreaming of a humanity unhindered by any framework, yet reinstating the old, denigrated humanity in hidden

---

* Lenin's NEP was a "partly experimental economic system introduced [in 1921]. . . . The system privatized some small-scale business, decentralized major parts of industry, and encouraged foreign investment. Stalin abandoned it in 1928. . . ." *Chambers Dictionary of World History* (Chambers Harrap, 2000), p. 580. *Trans.*

catacombs. Throughout the century private gardens have flourished, in both the literal and figurative senses, gardens that societies spontaneously plant out of a survival instinct.

Any refusal to acknowledge the political merely forces it underground. A government that denies the existence of exceptional situations finds itself one day at the mercy of a powerful group, either internal or external, that, in a way, makes politics in its stead. Suppressing conflicts does not make them go away, but rather allows them to come back in less visible and more perverse forms. Such "black market" political forces may be fanatics, in those cases in which the government has denied the legitimacy of the conflict between worldviews, or they may be respectable citizens who support the common good, in those cases in which the government has refused to open its eyes to crucial needs. But in either case, such political agents put society in danger because they act covertly. And in both cases, through blindness to the facts, and through the inappropriateness of the means used to the reality of the situation, government has its fate imposed on it instead of being fate's master.

The attempt to eliminate the antinomy between good and evil through a denial of their differences should logically lead to carefree indifference towards these categories. Modernity has replaced the objective category of the good with what it calls *values*, that is, a smattering of subjective goods, each of which derives from individual judgment. By their subjectivity, values spell the death of the good, even if language confers upon them the majesty of the defunct good. Put to the fore with no other criterion than that of the sovereignty of individual judgment, values are a form of solipsism or mere whim, depending upon the degree of clarity of thought one may find in them. A purely subjective "good" is binding on no one but oneself, and can be differentiated only with some difficulty from sentiments, affections, or self-interest. In this light, total war may be a good according to Zhirinovsky, and no one can say anything to the contrary.

We might well have got along without a "good," in the sense of an objective referent that brooks no challenge. But this did not happen. Not that the old distinction between good and evil has withstood the test. On the contrary. But within the philosophy of values itself the certainty of an absolute good has reappeared. It is expressed first of all in the rejection of totalitarian terrors, and secondly in the importance now conferred on the different expressions of human dignity. We are here in the realm of a "black market" moral code, one that operates without clearly declaring itself, hiding behind the mask of the philosophy of values. It proposes an objective good while at the same time rejecting the objectivity of the good. It ostracizes those who contest it even while it proclaims subjectivism. In short, it grows beneath the surface in spite of being prohibited.

Similarly, the religious spirit reappears behind the certainty that God and the gods are dead. The stupefying sects that flourish in the desert represent ersatz religions. A growing number of our contemporaries are refusing to resign themselves any longer to ignoring the question of life and death. They are reluctant to seek answers in the traditional religions, which have been hard hit by modernity, and have yet to recover. Indeed, the churches have responded to modernity's fundamental questioning of their validity sometimes with compromises that have bordered on complete sellouts, rendering them virtually unrecognizable and making them look so much like their adversaries that they no longer offered any real help; in other cases by a brutal refusal to listen, belying a fortress mentality and provoking a negative reaction from anyone who did not wish to reject everything modernity represents, which is to say, almost everyone. In other words, the churches have not been able to meet the expectations of an era tormented by the return of the eternal questions and weakened by the feeling of having made horrible mistakes, but also convinced, and with good reason, that something has been gained in the venture. This is why our contemporary is turning to ersatz religions fashioned in his own image and suited to his own use—doctrines without tradition, far removed from historical quarrels—invented by the first prophet who happens to come along.

It is inconsequential here whether the question of the existence of an objective good or of transcendence can be answered true or false: perhaps God does not exist and perhaps the objective good is sheer fantasy. We can only observe that we are dealing here with inescapable questions. Although this may not tell us much about the eternal truths, it at least tells us something fundamental about the human condition. The return of the obstinate questions, in their "black market" form, shows just how relevant they are, even if this return tells us nothing about the truth of any answer in particular. As soon as a clandestine form of thought or existence, opposite to its official or legal counterpart, appears and develops with any degree of tenacity, we can be sure that something essential is involved. There is every reason to suspect that our dominant thinking and institutions must therefore be based on a misguided, if not downright false, anthropology. As soon as an underground world becomes organized on a large scale beneath the official world, as soon as a vast unspoken world develops behind the dominant discourse, one can be sure that a profound disequilibrium looms.

These substitutes, however, can of course never be entirely sufficient, in the sense that, as we all know, a replacement product is never quite the real thing, and cannot help but call to mind what it is a replacement for. Wherever it develops, the underground economy protects its unpunished abuses from the prohibition that is meant to strike it down. It responds to a vital need, but does so under a reign of violence and therefore in an inhumane way, even though its very presence points to entirely human needs. In the same way, the political underground is characterized by the brutality of its conflicts, which by definition played out under the cover of darkness. Nothing could be more savage than the politics of the Soviets, who claimed to be beyond politics. That underground replacements are much more dangerous than their official and accepted counterparts is in fact not very difficult to understand.

Something that cannot be done in broad daylight obviously cannot lay claim to any laws. And one does not regulate an activity that does not exist, either on paper or by public acknowledgement. Any hidden activity therefore, in any area of existence, gives rise to venomous excesses. Thus, the rejection of the antinomies, far from bringing about their demise, actually gives rise to ersatz phenomena that grow out of the same necessities, but express the human condition in a wildly distorted way.

Deprived of the moderating forces that the mere recognition of them once allowed, the human paradoxes each fall into the excesses particular to their nature. The black market economy gives rise to the merciless battle of wealth against poverty. Clandestine politics engenders the raw violence of power struggles. The underground moral code is saturated with sentimentality yet arbitrarily intolerant. Occult religions are fanatical and manipulate individuals like crude machines programmed to obey.

The figures of existence have reappeared here and there because their suffocation brought about distress. Some forms of this distress, however, are less visible than others. The religious dimension can disappear for relatively long periods of time without seeming to cause any damage. This is so because the questions that religion asks do not touch the events of daily existence, but rather concern existence's fundamental relationship with itself, which it is quite possible to cease thinking about without ceasing to eat or to be involved in public debate. Economics and politics, on the other hand, directly create the concrete, material links of a society in such a way that a society officially deprived of an economy immediately sinks into poverty, while a society officially deprived of politics immediately falls into anarchy or terror. The moral code and religion also contribute to individual and social survival, but do so indirectly, such that the effects of their suppression only appear in the long term and often remain debatable. A society undermined by corruption and by the desertion of moral conscience can remain standing for a long time, even if its life is permeated by anxiety and it is haunted by an uneasiness it cannot fully explain. A society deprived of transcendence may in fact even be proud of what it calls its lucidity, overcoming centuries of aimless wandering through history as soon as it stops thinking about death. The moral code and religions contribute neither food nor laws, and men live above all by food and laws. However, a culture that understands humanity only through its political and economic aspects can never be more than a truncated culture.

Contemporary man has needed the evidence of totalitarian terror in order to be able to identify an objective evil, a sure sign of the reappearance of a moral code. We had to reach the point of extreme spiritual disarray in order for certain individuals among us to feel drawn to the discourse of hallucinating gurus, who, through their often shameful success, bear witness to the permanence of the desire for the absolute. In center stage, there is a renewed perception of the world as being riven by contradictions and therefore intrinsically finite. In recent years, these certainties have spread into the writings of intellectuals and into ordinary conversations. They reveal nothing new, since premodern thinking integrated them naturally into its worldviews. But their reemergence does reflect an entirely new lucidity with regard to mankind; one might even speak of the return of an exile to his native land.[1]

CHAPTER 4

The return of the good, religion, and the economy leaves us perplexed. Previous eras gave meaning to the antinomies through the mediation of worldviews that we have since abandoned. In general, religious thought explained the permanence of temporal imperfection and thereby legitimized the necessity of a moral code, politics, and all the other structuring antinomies through which human destiny is wrought. The will to radically transform our condition, or to eliminate it as "that which conditions," very naturally coincided with the withdrawal of the religious thought that gave meaning to these fundamental demands of being in the world. That is why these figures now seem to appear in their raw form and without justification. We now have to live with the inexplicable: Why must any society rely on the profit motive, which invariably generates injustices, in order to survive economically? Why does the well-being of a child necessarily depend on the family, crucible of inequalities? Faced with these questions, contemporary man remains petrified. He knows from hard experience that the profit motive and the family are indispensable, but he no longer knows why. And because these demands contradict the values he continues to promote—justice, equality—he is both distraught and revolted by the idea of constraints from which he thought he was free.

It is as if we no longer speak the language of the world into which we have returned.

The drama of the present age does not lie so much in the return of certain figures of existence as it does in the fact that these figures were—and in many cases, still are—despised. If modernity attempted to abolish them, it was with the intention of delivering humankind from them. The reappearance of the political, moral, and economic antinomies does not in any way lessen their despicable character. As stowaways they are not any more desirable than they were as legitimate passengers. This is why no one would have thought of imposing them on us with rational arguments. No, it came about through wordless necessity. And so contemporary man seems convinced of his misfortune: demoted to the rank he so much wanted to go beyond, forced to deal anew with reasoning he despised.

This is especially true since these figures of existence are forcing themselves on us with greater force than ever before. In the premodern era, they remained the fruit of an immemorial observation, such as when Aristotle described man as a "political animal." One could only ensure their force and stability, however, by calling upon either the hypothesis of "human nature," or by positing a transcendence that acted as their guarantor, sometimes with both hypotheses working in conjunction. In other words, until the modern era, the figures of existence contained within themselves the question of their own necessity, or of their ontological truth. After all, the fact that a property has always existed in various forms throughout history does not guarantee its radical necessity. And thought about man's "nature" and transcendence could always be called into question by other ways of thinking penetrated by the hope of delivering man from his condition. It was the gargantuan project of the modern era to recast the age-old as temporary, and to banish the certainties that rooted these figures in a so-called eternity. Today, however, we are forced to speak of the human condition without recourse to either a tradition or transcendence, or indeed any philosophy of human "nature." The experiment to abolish the human condition has been attempted, and this experiment, in which no means were spared, opens the door to a new era. The catastrophes in which it resulted are more persuasive than any argument or tradition could ever be. We now know with acute certitude that we cannot renew our attempts to rid ourselves of the former man, since the terrible consequences of doing so immediately become apparent. All the same, we do not know why our new condition obligates us as it does. It is the combination of this conviction of necessity and our ignorance about just what this necessity is based on that shapes our present angst.

It makes one think of someone with an incurable disease who had been promised a cure, but now realizes it will never happen, or of Icarus, brought back down to earth forever, after an adventure filled with high hopes. How will he live now, without knowing what power reduced him to his present state? Contemporary man looks at himself in the mirror and is painfully astonished. Politics is an eternal conflict. Evil persists. Man, who had been delivered from his "opiums," gropes for a religion. The world we have rediscovered will have to be re-thought, for it is indeed ours, whether we like it or not.

Thus, the return from exile does not imply a return to square one. The scar of disappointment will never go away. We will live in the same world as before, but we will not live the same way. A certain innocence has left us, and lost innocence can never be recovered. We must re-inhabit our condition, but we must, at the same time, both get used to it again and understand it. It is very difficult indeed to re-accustom oneself out of pure necessity to demands that one had not only hoped to jettison, but that no longer come with any self-justification. We are being forced to relearn politics as conflict, morality as a never-ending quest for a good that goes beyond subjective values, and existence itself in its tragic dimension—it is after all the tragic element in life that ideologies had hoped to abolish. So how is it possible to understand these necessities after their former justifications have disappeared? In this regard, we really have burned our bridges. No one would now dream of invoking religious references to legitimize the fullness of the human condition. How might one then make sense of this anthropology, which cries out its self-evidence yet comes out of nowhere? In what soil could it take root?

The question of justification is related to other questions that are even more discomforting. If these figures of existence, which we mistook for phantoms or shams, represent the very framework of being in the world, just how far do they go in determining what we are? If they are models, in the sense that they are part of the fabric of existence and not merely passing historical fads dependent only on circumstance—if they are states and not stages—then must we understand them as being inescapable destinies? Will we again have to subscribe to the notion that fate awaits us, that a history lies traced out ahead of us about which we can do nothing? If they fashion our social existence, without our even knowing it and against our will, what power over the future do we have left?

At the dawn of a new century, we know that Kant's question, "What am I allowed to hope for?," calls for an infinitely more modest answer than the answer our fathers gave. But just where shall we put the limits on this necessary modesty? One might well ask what kind of expectation is reasonable in the face of insurmountable contradictions. Thinking in the coming era will have to focus on the relevance and status of hope, as well as the foundations of a rediscovered anthropology.

The modern will to re-create man was a reaction against the previous dominant way of thinking, often an anthem in praise of the status quo. Confronted with the apparently stable figures of human existence, the first temptation is to set these determinations in stone, to deny humanity any ability to shape, let alone defy, them, or to make them a part of "nature" because of their necessity, as if the necessary were the same as a norm. In other words, this way of thinking took the stability of the figures of existence and forged an essentialism out of it. This effectively imprisoned humanity, forgetting that man is an animal that cannot help but want to break his chains—that he is Promethean—defined more by a history than by a status, by evolution as much as by static nature. This fundamental characteristic was at the root of the modern revolt. And if modern man attempted to destroy the figures of existence, it is because no room was left between essentialism and nihilism, since it was impossible to alter essentialism. It either had to be accepted or completely eliminated. Could Proudhon have amended the deified authority of Joseph de Maistre? Could Engels have amended the divinely rooted figure of the bourgeois family? And so it was that one excess generated another; through its own vanity, essentialism doomed itself by programming its mortal enemy.

Essentialism, having grown out of a clear perception of the figures of being in the world, was the extreme, grotesque, sometimes fanatical conclusion drawn from this perception. Absent from this perception, though, were humanity's tenacious efforts to come to terms with the necessities, and, failing to eliminate them, to restrain them within the limits assigned to them by culture and hope. Essentialism never once recognized the success of these efforts. On the contrary, it stigmatized them as insults to the divine Destiny, which was guided by the hand of God himself.

The contemporary era then leaves us with the following choice: to return to essentialism, or to discover that the figures of being in the world are at once both structural and flexible. The first alternative is a reassuring refuge for thought in want of a reference, and at the same time an easy victory for those anti-moderns who savor the defeat of the prophets who foretold the advent of the reinvented man. As the somber twentieth century fades, it is tempting to hail the victory of a kind of fatality that resembles ancient Greek destiny: since we have not been able to rid ourselves of politics, the economy, a moral code, or religion, we will have to resign ourselves to arbitrary power, to endemic poverty, to moral order, and the tyranny of the clergy. The resurgence of new corporatisms and new fascisms, of the partisans of a moral order, of a Church that brandishes the furious finger of God are responses to the failure of the modern attempts to eliminate the structure-giving figures. But must the defeat of Marx mean the return of Bonald? This is why so many of us, aware of the chasms that lie behind as well as ahead of us, prefer to live with the chaotic ambiguity of meaninglessness rather than rally behind some new avatar of the old fatalisms.

Having concretely experienced every imaginable excess, we find ourselves in the ideal position of the sage, whose clear vision of opposing errors enables him to trace the way of truth. Yet it is not enough to just be in a good position, since we could always choose the solution of waiting things out, which essentially is only a solution for those who refuse to make a choice at all: we could remain expectant, terrorized both by what we have just emerged from and by what lies ahead. It is indeed very discomforting to perceive so clearly, after such high hopes, that the complete annihilation of evil is not within the power of this world. Thus, rather than deepening our understanding in order to find out exactly what we must forever tolerate, we could choose to hide our heads in the sand. However, it is only by reflecting on what we have just discovered that we will be able to move forward with the Promethean enterprise. If we really do find ourselves forced to give up the hope of reinventing mankind, we may yet find hope for mankind in the rediscovered structures of existence. After all, we have proof that this hope is not vain: in recent history we have destroyed and terrorized every time we have attempted to recreate our social world, but on the other hand, we have accomplished miracles every time we have attempted to limit conflicts, to come to terms with contradictions—in fact, liberal democracy is nothing less than one of these miracles.

These forms of being in the world reveal the basis of a new anthropology, in the sense that, as it turns out, man always exists in this way—and we may now say "always" because we have observed the resurgence of the structures of his existence. Indeed, it is a question of his very being, not of his expected, awaited being, since there is nothing normative about these forms, which inspire more regret than anything else. Maybe it is after all a question of "nature" in the strict sense of "essence." In any case, we will have to delineate this anthropology, now that we know we cannot actually invent it. We can hope that sincere analysis, seeking to define that which is imposed on us, will one day open the door to the why of it all. We will have to find that which is hard and fast in the history of existence and separate it from that which gives way when scrutinized in light of our recent and distant past experience. We cannot entirely move beyond our contradictions, nor can we resolve or eliminate them. But how and to what extent can we fight them and thereby limit their perversions and push back their constraint?

An initial observation is in order: The fact that we immediately ask how we might combat the determining factors which have come back to haunt us tells us that anthropology cannot be reduced to the reality of those determining factors. What we can know today about man is at once the demand placed on us by what simply will not yield and the demand we find within ourselves to resist this very thing. Hope is part of this anthropology, since it judges the forms of being in the world that it would like to eliminate. We are not only wrought with contradiction, but with unhappy contradiction. Most important here is not so much human tragedy as the sense of unhappiness that accompanies it. The torment that seeks to find a "solution" to the paradoxes in order to achieve an impossible one-ness tells us more about man than do all the analyses of irresistible determination, or of "nature" in its old sense.

This is why modernity, in spite of its failures and especially because of them, reveals humanity to itself much more surely than any religion or world system ever could. Through an unexpected paradox, modernity has unveiled a human "nature" that it would have preferred to leave unveiled, wishing rather that it could forever be reinvented. It has revealed a truth about man in its very attempt to do away with that truth. And what it reveals, it reveals with a brilliant self-evidence: the emergence of realities that have returned from nothingness—not realities reinforced and, so to speak, protected by affirmations rooted in the uncertainty of a religious faith or ideological system. At the same time, however, in telling the story of the most radical attempt to overcome the human condition it reveals more clearly than ever, and in spite of the colossal failure of its attempts, that the Promethean hope is an anthropological property. In this respect, it would not be an exaggeration to say that the ideological enterprises of the twentieth century were the first ontological experiments in history. Our concrete experiences, for the first time, have struck so deeply that they bluntly reveal to us what we really are.

Contemporary thinking, at least if it is honest with itself and does not become mired in disappointment and resentment, will have as its mission to define the intangible contours of our condition, but even further, to define the sense of hope that judges them. Our recent experiences have opened a vast world for us to explore. In this respect, it is false to proclaim the emergence of an empty world in which there is nothing to retain our gaze. The discomfort of contemporary man no doubt comes less from a feeling of nothingness than from a world that is in fact too full, full of what was never willfully called back into being. It is the dull discomfort of perceiving exactly what modern fervor had hoped to get rid of, the inability to give it meaning, and the inability to tell to what extent fighting against it is worthwhile. The contemporary world is not a simple void in which the mind explores its limits; on the contrary, it is a labyrinth of contradictions from which unanswerable questions arise. There is a pervasive sense of casual indifference that mimics emptiness or the futility of everything, but it is not the reality of the times, merely its appearance. The reality is, rather, the suffering caused by the questions that have reappeared without legitimization. The man of the ideological era was ready for anything and drunk with the possibilities his boundless space seemed to offer him. Contemporary man lives in a walled-in space. The former is the character on an empty stage waiting for Godot: nothing is necessary or determinative any longer; everything is possible. The latter, having fallen into the very real ruins of Sarajevo, wonders why war has struck here, and what to do with the fact of war, which his mind can make no sense of.

The near future will probably depend on our ability to judge the limit of the invincible properties of our condition and its possible transformations, dictated by hope. It will depend on our ability to separate the possible from the inevitable, for we now know that by trying to abolish the inevitable, we destroy the entire world, and with it, its inhabitants. But we also know that by being contented with the inevitable, we will descend into a less-than-human existence. We cannot remain mired in ignorance, oppression, and the certainty of death, but neither can we definitively triumph over them. If there is a human destiny, it is not the everlastingness of the figures of existence, but the struggle to tame them—a struggle that recognizes the perennial nature of these figures in that it is never-ending. Man's condition is not to live in want or await detested death, but to struggle—without ever being defeated or victorious, but never discouraged—to come to terms with his contradictions. This is probably the only struggle that "makes sense," with the caveat, however, that it must be rooted in the recognized truth about what man's vocation and status are.

PART TWO

THE REVELATIONS OF
THE DEVIL

CHAPTER 5
THE GOOD WITHOUT THE TRUE

One of the particularities of our time consists of the fear of truth. We hold dearly to the good, but we are suspicious of truth. Ethics survives in spite of the fading of religions, world systems, and ideologies, which are structures of truths. Contemporary man is no longer sure if the world is infinite, if there is life after death, or if human society can hope for perfection in this world. In this sense, he is very different from his ancestors, who prided themselves in having certain, albeit diverse, answers to all these questions. Contemporary man will hear nothing of it. Furthermore, these questions do not really interest him. What does interest him, however, is ridding the world of its monsters—and not becoming one himself. In other words, he does not fear what is false, but what is evil.

Yet this observation begs a whole series of questions. What are the reasons for this indifference to truth? Where did the idea of the good without truth come from? What possible meaning can be assigned to this phenomenon? And what kind of morality does one build on a notion of the good without truth?

The present situation, which can be compared to no other in history, does not reveal a generalized relativism or the disappearance of all points of reference. The disappearance of truth, understood as *objective* truth, and its replacement by "points of view" or *subjective* "truths," does not stop contemporary man from identifying moral imperatives that he would not abandon under any circumstances. Where do these moral imperatives come from, seemingly born out of nihilism, like trees flourishing in a desert?

One observes that the collapse of great ideals often draws in its wake a kind of cynicism: if all hope is lost, then let us at least have fun! This is precisely what happened to the Soviet rulers, who became a privileged elite devoid of scruples as soon as the faith was lost. Our situation, however, is different from theirs, since for us it is not only the impossibility of achieving our various certainties that led us to abandon them. Nor is it because we understand our errors, as we might have done. In fact, what has driven us to abandon our ideals is the perception of the evil into which they inevitably seemed to lead. And so, having become suspicious of "truths," we have not become cynics. One might say that it is the very cynicism of truths that we find repulsive.

We will have to examine the convulsion by which we passed so quickly from the age of great certitudes to the age of indifference to truth. And indeed, a veritable convulsion was needed to cause so many men to abandon their reasons for hope, as well as the causes for which they were once prepared to give their lives. One need only consider writers, who always reveal the heart of a society: before and after World War II, very few were not somehow socially "engaged"; today, this concept is unfamiliar.

Worldviews did not lose their credibility as result of the analysis of their contradictions, the perception of their erroneous foundations, or their obvious misapprehensions of reality. We never saw the disciples of National Socialism admit that they had founded their reasoning on perverted science; we never saw intellectual Marxists doubt the innocence of the proletariat; we never saw either of them sit in critical judgment of their utopias. The convulsion was not intellectual, nor was it rational; no, it was uniquely *moral*. By observing the consequences that the realization of their worldview had in certain societies, the ideological zealots themselves pointed to the evil of it all. They did not show that it was false, but that it was bad. Today, these former ideologues are sickened, having witnessed the gradual revelation of the heretofore hidden consequences of what they had so ardently defended. It is not the mind that recoils, but the heart.

This instinctive nausea, so compelling that it has brought into question even the most solidly anchored certainties, is the undergirding, however negative and frightful it may be, of contemporary thought. Nevertheless, it is also the first hint of a new beginning. The twenty-first century, which began in 1989, started not with enthusiasm or understanding, but with a sort of indignation. A moral imperative has appeared that contradicts the certainties: it cries out that the fruits of certainties are repulsive and intolerable.

This rejection of ideological truths through moral intuition has two consequences: the fear of truth, and the redeployment of a new imperative through the intuition of an objective evil.

The analysis of totalitarian mechanisms has allowed us to compare ideologies to one another, and specifically to ferret out their historical premises. The Inquisition is taken to be the ancestor of all modern totalitarianisms, which have always involved sacrificing men to a dogma, or to a triumphant truth. And if we must find a common denominator shared by forms of totalitarianism, it must be certitude itself: this is what we believe we have learned. Certitude kills, irrespective of whether it is truth or error that nourishes it. Great certainties terrorize in great ways. Truth, or rather the belief that one possesses the truth, is inherently dangerous. He who believes he knows wishes to impose his certainty on others. He will not leave others in peace until he has convinced them. He kills in order to convince, which is certainly a strange method indeed.

The tyrannies of truth succeed one another and resemble each other: tyranny of heaven or of earth, tyranny of clergy or of commissars are essentially the same. Contrary to what certain critics of modernity might think, it is not mindlessness that has led us to relativism, but an overloaded memory. We have a long experience of the excesses of certainty. As soon as a group believes itself to be in possession of a certainty, it will impose this certainty on others to the extent that it has means to do so. That is the lesson we have learned. In a sense, if we do not seek truth, it is precisely because we are afraid we might actually find it. In its excesses it engenders everything we hate. It is as though truth—or what is deemed truth—will inevitably lead to evil.

There is, however, something contradictory in rejecting all certainties in the name of a hatred for fanaticism, since this rejection itself indicates an obscure conviction of sorts. Thus, we are rushing headlong into an era of unconscious certainties. We know they have not been eliminated since the belief in evil reveals to us their underground presence. A pervasive moralism, reduced essentially to bad conscience, that is, to an anemic moral code, has replaced the search for truth. Contemporary man is satisfied to merely reject the objects of his disgust. His only compass in the general disorder of his thoughts is the consensus of repugnance—towards Nazism, totalitarianism in general, anti-Semitism, apartheid. There is no other solid ground to stand on.

This disgust indicates an anxious search for the good. But because it is unaware of its own origin, it drifts about aimlessly and does a poor job of serving its own ends. A wrong remains unknown as such when revealed through pangs of conscience rather than ethical reflection, which would identify an underpinning truth—a bad conscience is, after all, no more than an emotion. Although systems may be recognized as being bad, they are not recognized as being false. Rather, one does in fact obscurely deduce that they are false but only by sensing the unhappiness they cause. The kind of intelligent argument, however, that would destroy their premises would also inevitably bring positive truths to the fore, which no one wants. And so henceforth, moral sentiment keeps error below the surface without actually destroying it. The dangerous wanderings of the mind remain beneath the surface, ready to spring up again at the slightest sign of weakness in the consensus of disgust. Eugenics has been beaten and rendered impossible because it gave birth to Nazism, and Nazism is intolerable to us. But a deepened understanding of human nature, which is in fact the only basis of a refutation of eugenics, would lead us to the recognition of some indubitable truths, where our errant liberty could no longer reign supreme. It would be necessary, for example, to re-evaluate the discourse about eugenics in light of these discovered truths. Hence, without any real contrary arguments, eugenics lurks in the shadows, ready to resurface if, for example, the question of the number of aging handicapped persons arises.

Rather than simply exposing evil, quashing it once and for all by falsifying its presuppositions, and then replacing them, our fear of the truth prevents us from replacing anything. We *should* in fact be considering whether only some kinds of certainties engender fanaticism, and which ones, or whether they all do, and why. We should be asking ourselves by means of what wisdom or precautions we might temper our certainties. In other words, we should be trying to stake out a middle ground between relativism and an absolute moral order.

In any case, the criterion of disgust is only able to impose itself on what has already proved to be unacceptable. In order to denounce a great wrong, we must wait until it produces virtually irreparable human disasters. This is exactly what happened with eugenics, and also with communism. Horrible destruction had to occur before we agreed to open our eyes. Before the Second World War, and for more than a century, a chorus of innumerable voices, and some of the most talented ones, indirectly legitimized the validity of such-and-such a massacre. But the extreme consequences of this habit of mind had to be reached before it was finally disavowed. In a similar way, the communist massacres around the globe were for a long time considered to be the unfortunate but necessary corollaries of the overall process of social transformation. In fact, the number of intellectuals who indirectly prepared the way for Nazism or who later legitimized Sovietism was legion. And we must not think that our fear of truth protects us henceforth from human disasters. Even if we are no longer governed by great certainties, we live under the domination of shared assumptions that have taken the place of those certainties. For example, the individualistic style of life, which has thrust its legitimacy upon us, could very well drive us to disaster. Will a disaster have to occur before we understand? Would it not be preferable to undo the mechanisms of error before they cause a grave deterioration of society? In order to do this, we will have to reflect on the consensus of disgust and explore its foundations.

Indignation—which is after all merely a gust of anger, and one unaware of its sources—reveals the only certainties, however modest they may be, that are left in a time otherwise completely deprived of certainties. In the era of the philosophy of values, of moral relativism, we are still able to point to an absolute evil. This Evil expresses the rebirth of a moral absolute, albeit in a disoriented and empty form. Apartheid, for example, has become taboo, ordained in advance to be rejected: those who defend it are condemned to silence and must skulk about in the shadows. Henceforth, the existence of something intolerable in and of itself, and no longer merely for some, snatches thought out from the grip of relativism. No one has the right to come to the rescue of moral monsters such as apartheid. And objective monsters do indeed exist, even if the kind of objectivity we are dealing with here is unclear, and even if the idea of objective certitude is also rejected. In a groping fashion, and in utter darkness, thought has thus recognized a universal moral principle, irrefutable both in space and time.

Contemporary man hunts down neo-fascism, neo-Nazism, racism, wherever he finds them, on every continent. In doing so he is at the very least armed with great indignation, if he has no other means at his disposal. He pronounces posthumous judgments on the perpetrators of racism or Nazism, even if the objects of these judgments were only indirectly responsible, for even if they did not commit crimes themselves, they participated in the venomous

THE GOOD WITHOUT THE TRUE

atmosphere of the times. This shows just how objective, how universal, contemporary man believes Evil to be, since it extends beyond temporal and circumstantial limits. Our contemporary therefore admits the existence of an absolute anti-value in spite of what this admission might cost his pride as the sole creator of values. In fact, objective evil is no longer a value, even a negative one, since any value is relative only to oneself and one's circumstances. Rather, it resembles a reality, huge in its irreducibility, imposing itself from without, against all expectations, objective in its obsessive presence. Here finally is something that transcends the sovereign individual.

From the discovery of an objective evil, however, we cannot deduce the existence of an objective good, since in our time it is precisely the relativity of the good that guards against falsifications of the Good, and against the Good's great temptation to reign by terror. After all, does absolute good not inevitably seek to bend its subjects to its own will when it fails to convince? One might well ask if the Church would have abandoned its oppressive practices in the absence of modern relativism. One might also wonder whether modern Pyrronian skepticism, in spite of its harmful consequences, does not at the same time protect our conscience from the tyranny of the clergy and from the rebirth of dominating ideologies. Henceforth, morality must prevent, but not bind. Its norms are exclusively negative. This, then, is how we are able to reconcile everything that is dear to us, that is, by erecting barriers that protect us from the unacceptable, while allowing each person to choose his own good.

Of course there is a kind of inherent dishonesty in this refusal to designate the good. Or perhaps intellectual cowardice would be more accurate, since by antithesis, absolute evil, once it has been recognized, cannot fail to evoke the existence of an absolute good, which is also objective. An absolute good, however, would naturally entail obligation, and this would necessarily limit individual freedom. Thus, morality has been reduced primarily to the act of identifying evil. The only moral faculty that contemporary man considers valid is a bad conscience. Vague and unreasoned sentiments, in brute form and with purposely indefinite contours, are considered sufficient to avoid the worst. This morality of the requisite minimum keeps intelligence at bay. It fears that the intellect might invade forbidden zones.

The good, however, imposes its presence through a rejection of the intolerable, and this double negation reveals a positive affirmation. A negation requires a foundation, since the certainty of a rejection is something positive. To denounce an evil essentially means to identify a good under attack. And this is true even if we merely react to evil and refuse to look for the good. In this deliberately maintained haze, it is as though the good manifests itself by its lack of presence. Its intolerable absence shows that it is impossible for it not to be. The good is understood to exist even while it is denied. It lives, albeit as a nebulous presence, in the very heart of its desertion.

Contemporary man, who perceives absolute evil, finds himself stricken with anguish, not by the mere perception of evil but by his inability to comprehend the presence of evil, which rises up unbidden and fills his field of vision. Without the means to identify the good, he remains ignorant of just how the evil he is able to identify has come about, and also remains ignorant of why his intuition is telling him that what he sees is evil. The examples of incredible human destruction in the twentieth century seem somehow to be provocations, since in principle we were supposed to be creators of good and evil. So what went wrong, exactly?

The deeply rooted feeling of having caused destruction indicates that we have upset an order of some kind, but which order? We simply do not know. We find the very idea of an "order," in this sense, completely unbearable. Our contemporary imperiously refuses to recognize an objective disposition of things, a hierarchy of references organized and situated outside of himself and that is binding on his conscience. He has convinced himself over the past two centuries that anything he does not fashion himself cannot be real. A world that is not his own brainchild seems to him to be no more than an imaginary phantom, which is precisely what he thinks of a supposedly objective order revealed to him without regard to his will.

The identification of an absolute evil forces us to believe that an order exists beyond our will, beyond our capacity as creators of order. This identification puts into doubt not only the subjective morality of our times, but the very possibility of its being. We cannot decree that each individual has the sovereignty to invent his own values and at the same time point our finger at an intolerable and permanent universal. We cannot proclaim, "To each his own morality," and at the same time decry racism and apartheid. There is a flaw in this reasoning that we will inevitably have to confront. We can remain faithful to subjectivism and accept everything, including the unacceptable, which then simply becomes unacceptable "for some," or we can hold on to our absolute judgment about evil, and thus cast aside our subjectivism.

Some might say that a reconciliation between the identification of an absolute evil and relativism is indeed possible, since we only identify as "evil" those thoughts or behaviors that deny individual sovereignty by imposing certainties on us. We thus reject exclusively totalitarian or intolerant thoughts. This would imply that we are libertarians who allow everyone to define for himself what is good. But this is clearly not the case. On the contrary, our era is singularly dogmatic, in spite of its slogans of relativism and tolerance. It not only forbids certain opinions but mandates the acceptance of certain ideas. One might well wonder how to explain the fact that in a world where each is free to decree his own good, strange unanimities have developed that function as categorical imperatives and have the power to function as a veritable moral terrorism. Orthodox thinking does indeed exist today, in spite of the banishment of all objective truth and of an objective good. The source of this orthodoxy, however, raises an important question. Just where does it come from when, in principle at least, we were so relieved to be rid of it?

Simultaneously with the rejection of any idea of the objective good, a discourse of the *obligatory* good has developed. The idea of social solidarity, for example, will tolerate no opposition. It has become an objective reference that admits of no controversy. We feel that we must share. Similarly, we are under an obligation to protect the earth. No one can defend the destruction of the environment or manifest his indifference to such destruction. At the same time that totalitarianism has become taboo, the philosophy of rights has become sacred. This is entirely new, since as recently as the '50s, intellectual currents as different as those found among post-Marxists and in the Vatican were opposed to the philosophy of rights, or at least expressed serious misgivings about it. Today, however, every current of thought is required, under threat of ostracism, to defend human dignity in the idiom of the philosophy of rights. Does this mean that an objective good does after all exist, independently of opinion, and is rooted in a truth or a reality that does not depend on us? The mandatory discourse against absolute Evil—in the sense of the absolute as independent—can be justified by relativism or by tolerance. The mandatory discourse about objective good, on the other hand, seeks its justifications in vain, for why must we show solidarity with our contemporaries, or even, according to the environmentalist discourse, with future generations.

In the society that proclaims "to each his own morality and truth," a question asked by one of Dostoyevsky's characters comes to mind, "Why must we love our fellow men?" Why indeed does xenophobia seem to us to present a mortal danger? Why does our contemporary demand respect for others across the globe? Why does he require that the living protect the planet for future generations and thereby advocate respect for beings that are not only virtual but perhaps undesirable as well? Why does he ask that poor nations make their institutions more humane in exchange for his aid? Why does he worry about the effect the international drug trade has on the younger generation? Why is he indignant in the face of government corruption? Why does he get upset about despair in the ghettos? Why does he resolutely reject the idea of a society in which people would never show up for appointments, would break contracts on a whim, or would get ahead on the backs of the weak? And how is it that these affirmations, in the form of judgments, take the shape of imperatives, ostracizing contrary affirmations to the point that their proponents accuse their opponents of being cynics, and fight against them with every means at their disposal?

Our contemporary would be amazed to be asked such questions. He considers it completely natural to denigrate xenophobia and to promote solidarity. Furthermore, he considers that simply raising these questions is somehow suspicious; he is so sure of being right that the question itself seems to him to indicate the presence of a doubt: might it not emanate from one of his dirty opponents? This peaceful certainty is nevertheless striking: where might such absolute certitude come from, in a world characterized by subjectivity? The "good," reduced to a collage of values, and as such relative to time, place, and the individual, could never claim the status of an absolute. In the world of values, there is no absolute. Absolute good rests on objective realities, it takes root in truth, in the knowledge of a good from which one cannot escape. What is truly astonishing today is the emergence of messages that function like truths, mimicking an objective good in their intransigence and triumphant assertiveness—at the very moment when subjective values and the rejection of the idea of the objective good have reached their peak.

Thus, amidst the disorder of a world in which each man creates his own morality, we are witnessing the enigmatic and silent resurgence of an absolute good of whose roots and justifications we are ignorant. The very possibility of an absolute good remains incomprehensible to the modern intellect. Our entire recent history objects to its existence. Nothing in our present discourse legitimizes it. And yet it pours through all the cracks in the hull, submerging us in unexpected places. Its presence calls modern relativism into doubt and foretells a different way of thinking. It is as if a bolt of lightning had flashed in a darkened sky. The unknowing mind could never have invented the certainty it possesses, because all its habits and prejudices reject the very idea of certainty. On the contrary, our contemporary's mind seeks out the subjective and the relative; we fear above all that we will find ourselves once again caught in the trap of an imposed universal. And the image of the absolute good *does* impose itself, and does so upon those who do not want to see it. It imposes itself even upon the conscience that wants so badly to have the right to choose everything. It subjugates against all expectations. It functions as a belief, equated here with the mind, in the sense that Ortega y Gasset has written that we *have* ideas, but we *are* our beliefs.[1]

Contemporary man finds himself incapable of distancing himself from these certainties. In the era prior to our own, he learned to question his convictions by unmasking the underlying needs or desires that kept them in the realm of the unspoken. It would, however, now seem incongruous to invoke the philosophies of suspicion in order to question our certainties. It would not occur to contemporary man to engage in psychoanalysis in order to explain his anti-racism or his desire for solidarity by their insidious and shameful causes. In fact, he would most certainly recoil in horror from anyone who proposed such an inquiry, and would undoubtedly suspect him of being in the camp of the adversary, or rather, of the enemy, since in these matters he shows no tolerance. And so it is that man, having spent two centuries examining his own certainties with a critical eye and then unmasking them, finds himself caught in a trap. The certainty of absolute Good and Evil has slipped into his mind in spite of himself. It has repossessed him, in spite of his having spent so much effort in dispossessing himself of everything.

Must we then conclude that we cannot do without the certitude of an objective good, even without prejudging its content? And that, in the current relativist atmosphere, this certitude reappears in a black market fashion, in other words, in the form of an unconceptualized intuition that nevertheless effectively reigns over thoughts and mores in the same way that the objective good did before the advent of the philosophy of values? Dogmatic relativism suits our independence-hungry spirit perfectly well. Its presuppositions, though, and also its consequences, contradict our common vision of humanity. To say "to each his own morality" means, apart from the enviable freedom to name one's own values, that the same criteria of the good do not apply to everyone. Humanity thus becomes fragmented into individuals radically differentiated from one another by their divergent paths—each person's "good" being nothing more than the destination he has set for himself. Through this very divergence, the *other* is kept from becoming one's fellow man. Relativism takes away all meaning and the *raison d'être* of sympathetic consideration or compassion in the sense of "suffering-with," which seems so natural. However, each of us experiences the suffering and the joy of a fellow human being as a sign of sympathetic solidarity (*complicité*), and *fraternité* is not a dogma invented by some ideology, but an undying intuition. We have no defense against the inner certitude that "fellow man" is an inherent part of the "other." This inner certitude obscurely convinces us that a valid "good" does exist for the entire species, that is, independent of our sovereign will. Relativism, which makes of each of us a species unto himself, as if to be preserved on Noah's ark, contradicts our most profound convictions. This is why it is not viable. Nevertheless, we are reluctant to openly question relativism, because it represents a victory for the individual, and so we let its internal contradiction play out in the shadows. Absolute evil and absolute good thus do not enter our conceptual universe. We are unable to understand them as objective entities because we remain captive within a relativist conceptual framework.

The emergence of an evil and a good independent of us should tell us that the subjective world is not the only world. The absolute, if it does exist, seems not to come from within. We are now aware of the tremendous price that has to be paid by turning relative entities, such as peoplehood, race, class, nation, or community, into absolutes. Absolute good and evil cannot be eradicated from our mediocre, chaotic world. Perhaps the intuition of radical evil gives some insight into the idea of the absolute. Radical evil, as an irreducible event transplanted into the heart of what is never-radical, forever middle-of-the-road reality, reveals the presence of forces for which our world has no name. This revelation constitutes a rupture in the banal, gray, horizontal world we inhabit.

In short, the contemporary era cannot be defined by the absence of moral references, but by the rejection of an Evil and the apologetics of a Good that are taken for granted and detached from any idea of objective truth that might give them legitimacy. It would not be right, however, to see in this attitude an inability of the mind to discover their foundations. Rather, this attitude signals a refusal to even go looking for such foundations, for fear of actually discovering them. Contemporary man postulates not the emptiness of truth, but the danger of truth. His agnosticism is of a new sort, born not of conviction but of fear. The contemporary moral code establishes itself within a timid mode of thinking. If this mode of thought fears truth,[2] it is precisely in order to safeguard the morality. It is as if today the emptiness of truth, or in any case, silence about truth, were alone enough to guarantee the good. Every certitude eventually creates obligations, while the recognized good is equated with freedom and respect for others. This is why we feel we must be careful not to go looking for the foundations of these moral certitudes. For we might very quickly find, or believe we have found, universal truths, ready to call into question the very things they were supposed to legitimize.

We know that truth compels, and we do not want to be compelled. Classic truth—the Greeks' "unveiling"—imposes itself on the perceiver.[3] So it is that the contemporary era tells the tale of a veritable flight from truth.

We may reasonably wonder, then, on what basis the certitude of a good might rest in the absence of a genuine discourse about truth. Why, and on what basis, for example, should the freedom associated with democracy be accepted without question? In reality, the good gains legitimacy through the happiness, or well-being, with which it is associated. We simply agree that men are happier when they are free. The good without the true is thus justified by satisfaction. It finds "authentification" in the happiness it produces but forbids itself from understanding that happiness. This is a good that has been reduced to a smile, a good that refuses to think out of fear that it just might lose its smile.

The good, understood here as a particular understanding of human rights, finds itself destined to perpetuate and glorify itself. It is satisfaction made sacred but incapable of self-knowledge, by definition. It is a morality not only without philosophy but hateful of philosophy. It is a politics that establishes its perfection by suppressing philosophy.

In this respect, our time cavalierly ignores the maxim "Know thyself." It refuses to get to know this man for whom satisfaction suffices to determine both personal and political action. Our era rejects both philosophical "astonishment" and the culture of doubt it has inherited. Europe has in fact always doubted itself. Over the centuries, Europe has attempted to seek knowledge even at the expense of happiness; it is a land of persecuted truth-seekers, symbolized by Galileo. Today, however, we refuse to even ask ourselves the question, "What is true?" so that the only question that remains for us to ask is, "How can we live well?"

One would like to believe that this is unimportant, since ultimately what really matters, at least if one wants to remain human, is the ability to separate the good from the bad and act accordingly. Our contemporary thinks that we do not really need to know why freedom is desirable, or why man is worthy of respect, as long as these certitudes remain anchored in our minds as unshakable axioms. Little does it matter whether these axioms come to us from a creator, or from a sort of human nature, or from an unwritten metaphysics. Let us live first and philosophize later. Given the damage that philosophical certitudes are capable of causing, living without philosophy seems much preferable. Thus, since democracy holds in high regard the ethics of human rights, our era tends to prefer a democracy without philosophy—precisely in order to save democracy.

We are far enough along, though, that this enviable position of suspended thought, which enables us to live with both certitude of the good and indifference to truth, is becoming increasingly untenable. Our absolute certitude allows for no contradiction. Our ethical intuitions claim to be universal, illustrated by our conviction that we may justly impose the idea of human rights on other countries from without, or forbid terrorist or racist ideas within our own territory. Our ethics functions like an ensemble of objective certainties. However, to the extent that these certainties are based solely on intuitions, we are incapable of really persuading anyone of their rightness, even if they are shared by countless numbers of people. Piling up solipsisms in no way alters their nature as solipsisms, objects of unreasoned certitude, and as such, incommunicable.

To persuade its opponents of its rightness, an ethical code must refer to its foundations. But since our only argument is that of satisfaction, what can we say when others claim that they find their satisfaction elsewhere? Our certitude is founded on the most intimate subjectivity, a basis on which persuasion is impossible. Naturally, we are profoundly convinced that our satisfaction expresses something even more fundamental, and this is why we decree that some of our "values" are universal. Yet, until we are willing to unveil its foundation, this universal will convince no one but us. We are reduced to simply imposing it without argument. We brandish the arms of invective, disdain, repetition, and force, for we simply have nothing else to say.

In the desert now uninhabited by truths, ethical universals create obligations only because most people share them. The "good" appears as a necessity without a reason for being. It is everywhere at once even if it has been deprived of legitimacy and imposes itself self-righteously. We may therefore quite appropriately speak of a common agreement about certain values, without their being at all

THE GOOD WITHOUT THE TRUE

objective. In Western societies we see a convergence of subjective norms. A certain moral consensus is emerging, without reference to truth. The indefinite repetition of the same subjective intuitions is creating an ersatz objectivity. The repetition of sincere feelings is creating a substitute for moral truth.

One cannot, however, say that contemporary man actually founds his morality on consensus, since he is fully aware that an entire people can be wrong. It is not general agreement that sovereignly dictates what is right and wrong, but rather an intimate certitude, which, in fact, has not sprung up from out of nowhere. If we look closely at its content, we see that it resembles previous moral codes, once again taking up the immemorial figures of good and evil.

The Greek *diabolos* literally means "he who separates," he who divides through aversion and hate; he who makes unjust accusations, denigrates, slanders; he who envies, admits his repugnancy. The absolute Evil identified by our contemporary takes the form of racism, exclusion, or totalitarianism. This last in fact appears as the epitome of separation, since it atomizes societies, functions by means of terror and denouncement, and is determined to destroy human bonds. Apartheid and xenophobia of all varieties are champions of separation.

In other words, contemporary Evil expresses, in a modern form, the Evil of antiquity and Christianity. The criteria are the same. Satan has not changed faces. Separation is as popular as it always has been, but its concrete manifestations still call for remorse. Cain is still being pursued by the terrible eye of a troubled conscience. Ever since Auschwitz, we have been turning over in our minds the remorse of cowardly and passive complicity. Hate for others has not been abolished, yet it always carries with it the stigma of something that should never have happened, of something that has no place in the human world.

The Good, in a similar way, has a face we find familiar. For contemporary man, the notions of solidarity and fraternity, and the different expressions of harmony between classes, age groups, and peoples, are still associated with goodness. The man of our time is similar to the man of any time insofar as he prefers friendship to hate and indifference, social harmony to internal strife, peace to war, and the united family to the fragmented family. In other words, he seeks relationship, union, agreement, and love, and fears distrust, ostracism, contempt, and the destruction of his fellow men.

The "good," even when it is deprived of its traditional or religious foundation, still possesses a status that is given to it intuitively and is shared by almost everyone without discussion. This good has the face of fellowship, no matter what name it is given, be it love, the god of Aristotle, or the God of the Bible.

The certitude of the good finds its guarantee in the attraction it induces. The separation of the *diabolos* occurs constantly, but one day or another it will be pursued by mortal shame. *Complicité*, on the other hand, never gives rise to remorse. On the contrary, it mysteriously survives as hope, even within the movements of Evil. Berdyaev, in describing the Russian terrorists of the nineteenth century, wrote that in these minds totally deprived of any point of reference and devoted to nothingness itself, one certitude remained: love for one's fellow man. The brotherhood of man and solidarity need no justification. They are simply given.

Evil as separation and goodness as *complicité* take on the appearance of moral truths, or realities that cannot be equated with opinions. Their very permanence makes them a part of what might be called "natural morality."

We nevertheless fear having to recognize this permanence and having to confer upon these notions the status of truth. We hesitate for a perfectly understandable reason. As soon as the "good," recognized as *complicité* and relationship among men, is conceptualized as truth and becomes institutionalized and thereby perpetuated, it creates the *obligation* of relationship. The former religious morality pushed this obligation to the point where, at times, it was intolerable. What we now denounce as moral order is nothing other than a facet of this compulsory relationship. The past century has taught us nothing if it has not taught us that the good can become oppressive, not only through the totalitarian temptation to impose perfection but through the institutionalization of a morality that is paradoxically capable of becoming inhuman. By experience, we know that evil lies in the excesses of the good. This is why we refuse to search for the rational foundations of the good, why we voluntarily allow our conception of the good to remain purely instinctual.

CHAPTER 6
THE MORALITY OF COMPLACENCY

The morality of our time could be defined as a morality of complacency. Contrary to what one might at first think, there is no contradiction in terms here, since complacency does after all have its norms, and even its demands, to which society ultimately submits. Complacency is an overall penchant, an *art de vivre*. It could even be considered an ethical system, in the sense that it can eventually become a practice that establishes norms for itself. What interests the contemporary individual is less the accomplishment of a "good," which he does not know how to define in objective terms, as self-fulfillment in the short term, which has now become the ultimate criterion of the "good." An act is considered to be good if it allows the individual to fulfill himself. The question of criteria remains unresolved, however, for how is one to define self-fulfillment? In fact, it can be measured only by the standard of satisfaction.

Complacency indicates a predisposition to seek pleasure. Raised to the level of a principle, it supposes the permanent identification of the good with that which pleases. To be complacent means to be easily accommodating, to admit whatever is convenient, or to look kindly on whatever comes one's way. It indicates an open or easily obtained indulgence, without any judgment attached. It accepts things in advance.* It can become a sort of selfish servility. All this is true of present morals in general—in the relationships contemporary man has with his work, with money, with authority, and with others.

The complacent man is, in a manner of speaking, a slave to what pleases him, in the sense that he has trouble stepping back from what pleases him and examining it with a critical eye. He is therefore just as accepting of the unhappiness associated with what displeases him. He is complacent in sorrow and discouragement, and readily complains about what has befallen him, for he is unable to distance himself from his own ego, to lift himself above his displeasure.

The ethics of complacency legitimizes and recognizes all thought, all behavior, and all ways of life—on the condition, of course, that they do not oppose complacency itself. In doing so, this ethics constitutes a worldview, for it is not merely the attitude of the smiling sage, or of the fool who takes what comes without regard to its consequences. The ethics of complacency's indulgent accommodation of everything corresponds to a refusal to accept any established limits, or to a refusal to refuse, which brings to mind the the catchphrase of the 1968 generation, "It is forbidden to forbid." The sweeping away of moral taboos during the preceding two decades was probably due less to a fading of the previously dominant religious thinking as to an inability of traditional thought to justify the barriers that, in the end, were being propped up only by the force of habit. Traditional thought had come to live more through its institutions than through its points of reference. We know that institutions, created to embody and perpetuate the certitude of these points of reference, often ended up abusively replacing what they were supposed to protect, and became mere hollow shells in the process. Thus, the ethics of complacency never had to impose itself by arguing for its legitimacy. On the contrary, it was able to imposeitself without any argument at all, filling the vacuum left by other itself without any argument at all,

---

* We might say that it is quintessentially "laid back." *Trans.*

filling the vacuum left by other ethical systems whose points of reference had been lost along the way.

The ethics of complacency is an openness to all that is possible, which it justifies in advance. It closes no doors. Thus, the highest virtue of our time is open-mindedness. Our contemporary has said it all when he speaks of an open-minded person. We are not dealing here with the humanist who has pointed out errors and misdeeds but, without legitimizing them, is able to see the suffering humanity behind them. Rather, this is the man of accommodation, who has decided in advance that nothing can be called deviant or unnatural because he does not recognize any criteria according to which an idea or a behavior might be considered deviant. Unaware of any criteria of the good apart from that of well-being and pleasantness, he rejects any and all judgment: above all, "do not judge"—this is the obsession of our contemporary.

It is significant that this "open-minded" man is, as a social model, the heir to the Greek *kaloskagathos* and the *honnête homme* of a bygone era.* These men were characterized by their devotion to external, objective points of reference. Our "open-minded" man, in contrast, is characterized by his disowning of any exterior point of reference. This is what makes him historically unique. And it is precisely this absence of reference that makes him a modern model.

His behavior, which is at the same time a way of thinking, corresponds to what his detractors call "easiness," "indulgence," and overall weakness. These pejorative appellations, however, are entirely insufficient as critiques of complacency. For why should "easiness" be in itself reprehensible? There is certainly something vain about seeking difficulty for difficulty's sake. Complacency might appear worthy of contempt to an ideology of force or virility—to an ideology of the superman. Some might even find a hint of lowness in complacency, which is what we sense in the expression *the wink of complacency*. But here we are in the realm of

* Or the English gentleman of the seventeenth and eighteenth centuries. *Trans.*

sentiments or even passions, not rational argument. It is difficult to see on what basis the rigor or intransigence of established limits is more legitimate than well-being or pleasantness. We find ourselves here in an area of debate where the only exchanges occur at the level of anathema—and no amount of anathema has ever constituted an argument.

The identification of the good with what pleases amounts to an extreme constriction of the imagination's conception of time. The good, whatever its foundations, generally extends over the long term. How is it possible to seek the good today without wondering if it does not compromise the good of the future? How can one aim for a result without being interested in what are its consequences? The "good," in the sense of what leads to happiness, encompasses the individual in time, melding the present and the future, and in the space of his human and natural environment. This is why we distinguish it from capriciousness, which we generally associate with children because of the lack of a broader vision it supposes. What is essential about caprice is less its arbitrary nature than its "primal" character. The contemporary individual thinks that well-being is happiness; however, well-being is short-term pleasure, whereas happiness is a "good" anchored in a given time and place.

The ethics of complacency deals only in what immediately seems obvious. And in doing so, it indicates a short-term vision, a narrow conception of time and space. It simultaneously denies the temporal dimension of personal life and of social history. Complacency dismisses all futures. The virtue of what pleases cannot be judged in the present by the measure of a religious or ideological good, but by a good that lasts in time. If the vertical criteria are no longer accessible to our contemporary, the horizontal criteria cannot be avoided.

Contrary to what some pessimists might believe, we do not find ourselves in an era without "values," but rather in an era characterized by the appearance of an unstructured, erratic, and deficient ethics. Of course whether we are in fact dealing here with an ethics or not remains open to discussion. Nonetheless, contemporary man has not abandoned the idea of the good, even if he talks so much about it that his logorrhea raises suspicions. Of course, he does not actually seek the good, since he is without the necessary criteria to accomplish this quest and in fact rejects any such criteria in advance. He seizes anything at hand that pleases him, anything that moves him or stimulates his emotions, and calls it good. In doing so, he believes he has discovered a new pragmatic outlook, one free from his former prejudices, and a way to provide for his general happiness, which is the purpose of any ethics.

The appearance of the ethics of complacency marks a complete rupture with what we knew before, not only concerning the source of norms, but also concerning the spectrum that the identified "good" covers. As we know, modernity is the era where the determinant of what is good is no longer an authority or doctrine, but the individual himself. But everything is happening as if the rise of subjectivism had conjured up not only a new source of the good, but also, and probably in a related way, a good that serves a different purpose.

The break with the notion of an objective "good," which specifically characterizes modernity, allows the rise of a "good" defined by each individual within the sovereignty of his own conscience. The "good," as something objective and given from the exterior, was the product of a religious or ideological worldview and brought with it a hierarchy of norms that rested upon a truth. It proposed, or imposed, not only the meaning of existence—it identified what existence can expect—but the very blueprint of a "good" existence. It brought with it the architecture or model of a respectable human life that was generally esteemed and devoted to happiness. Ancient morality, and later, Christianity—and even modern ideologies—spoke less of a series of piecemeal collection of "goods" as of a "good life."

The individual who has now been left to himself to determine his own "good" has not only been "liberated," in the modern sense, from this truth that weighed upon him. He has at the same time lost the overarching rationale by which the idea of the "good life" is made intelligible. We might expect that the sovereign individual would become the creator of his ethics. After all, he is not supposed to receive anything from anyone, and must find within himself everything he needs to exist with dignity, which corresponds here to an idea of the good.

However, if the human subject defines himself by the ability to create norms, each individual cannot really be expected to be able to create his own ethical blueprint. In an earlier time, each individual's birthright was an ethical blueprint given him along with the first smile of his mother. He could of course later modify it or reject it altogether, but he then had to bear the marginalization that this choice would inevitably bring. In this respect, each individual was blessed at birth with an ethics, and it is uniquely modern to have understood this blessing as a form of slavery, since, for modern man, to have to accept an ethics from someone other than oneself is oppressive. This is why contemporary man is born into a shapeless, soundproof, de-clawed, and innocuous world, and why it is up to him to give it direction. He has to assign a name to his own dynamic impulse in the darkened absence of signs, and he has to do this alone.

Each person is henceforth called upon to choose his own values, or even to invent them. Furthermore, these values are for internal use only; that is, they must not be imposed on others. The ethical project each man invents is valid only for himself, from which follows a twofold difficulty that inevitably serves to confirm the individual's place within the destructuring ethics of complacency.

The first difficulty is that each individual must in principle be able to discover or invent the alpha and omega on his own, for no one is going to rush to his side to propose an alternative ethical project. On the contrary, such a gift would be understood as a form of alienation. Contemporary man is supposed to find due north without a compass. Or rather, he is expected to use himself as a compass to find his own north. However, we have to have the courage to recognize that no society is made up of millions of theologians, avant-garde moralists, inspiring visionaries, and prophets. The kind of heroes who bring with them points of reference, or who are able to shine a light on previously unseen points of reference, are few and far between. The vast uninspired mass of people finds its moral blueprint through the mediation of a Moses, Socrates, Saint Paul, Luther, or Solzhenitsyn. No egalitarian theory, however sophisticated, will ever be able to hide the obvious: not all Greeks are Socrates, but the existence of Socrates allows other Greeks to name their own existence, and to assign a reason for it. Our contemporary has rejected prophets, but has great difficulty formulating his own moral blueprint; at the same time he cannot do away with the idea of the good. He therefore contents himself with an erratic good, jumbled norms, and a succession of incoherent "goods," which are inevitably tied to the immediate present since no moral project binds them together.

The second difficulty our contemporary faces is the following: even if he does possess an ethical project able to structure his existence, taken from himself or from elsewhere, he must keep it to himself. Whoever holds the key to a life-giving hope normally seeks to share his convictions. And anyone would naturally prefer to uphold a universal conviction rather than a uniquely personal value. But our contemporary distrusts those who defend values, that is, those who want to found values in truth. He suspects that values will transform themselves into absolute truths as soon as they find proponents to defend them. He fears nothing more than the fanatical domination of a moral project. And because of this fear, he circumscribes the defenders of certitude within a perimeter of safety, where he can cautiously watch over them.

So it is that the individual who develops a moral project and decides to equate his destiny with it becomes dangerous. He is suspected of judging others by his decision, and of secretly harboring the desire to force others to imitate him. It is true that every individual choice implicates all of humanity by forging—even unconsciously—

a model that becomes a standard, or a sort of unofficial point of reference. Moreover, any coherent ethical project takes on overblown proportions in the face of the deconstructed nature of contemporary ethics, and immediately threatens it, for chaos is uncomfortable, and nothing is more reassuring than certitude. He who deliberately embarks on a project of this nature—he who chooses meaning—implicates, like it or not, the whole of society, and tends to transform a value into truth, which revolts contemporary man. This is why our contemporary so conscientiously tries to protect himself from the dangerous whisperings of seekers of meaning and strives to conserve a smooth and colorless society peaceful in its indetermination. The only defendable ethics is the ethics of complacency.

Enjoined to invent for himself his own norms, and forbidden to speak about them once he has found them, the contemporary individual is finally reduced to doing without a structured ethics at all, either because he finds that he is not clear-sighted or patient enough to invent one, or because he becomes discouraged by a project that is valid only for himself and derided as soon as it has universal pretensions. Subjectivism does not in fact engender the end of all striving after the good, nor does it produce cynical men. It engenders the end of a structured good, of projects that lead to the "good life." The desire for the good, characteristic of man as a moral being, must then express itself in an impulsive way, and so it finds a place for itself in the ethics of complacency. The good can no longer manifest itself through global and long-term visions, rather only through fragmented intuitions.

CHAPTER 7
A MORALITY OF EMOTION AND INDIGNATION

The fragmented ethics of our time is partially the result of a fear of being tied down. Yet there is something strange about this since the characteristic of ethics specifically consists of uniting the conscience to a norm, which we find in the expression "you must." In fact this bond has not completely disappeared—otherwise we could not speak about an ethics at all—but it is in every instance subject to the discretion of the individual, which is to say that it can be moved and transformed at will.

So just what are the criteria for good and evil in this ethics without any fixed points of reference, characterized at once by both its subjectivity and instability (for even if this ethics does have norms, there is no longer any structure to them)? How does the individual recognize good and evil?

The ethics of complacency corresponds to an ethics of indignation. The good, equated with what pleases the subject at the moment, finds its antagonist in an evil equated with what displeases or terrifies.

Evil, deduced from successive moments of indignation yet not conceptualized, finds expression in a plurality of evils identified by a feeling of disgust. Moral judgment is founded on the reaction, or one might almost say, the reflex one has when confronted with what seems revolting or scandalous. Contemporary morality is reactive and non-rational. And this is precisely why it is still morality, no matter what the traditionalists and the harbingers of decline say, for amorality implies the inability to distinguish good from evil. In spite of this, however, the difference between the present and the former morality is enormous. Thoughtful moral judgment establishes a relationship between a situation and certain points of reference. It compares, weighs, and doubts. Every situation takes its place on a scale and is compared to a pre-existing model. Reactive moral judgment, on the other hand, is all that remains—and it is not nothing—after the collapse of scales and models. It instinctively rejects evil, as if it were blinded by it. Its only scale is emotion. Reflective judgment is constantly on the lookout for the evil it fears it might find hidden behind the apparent good, for it considers emotion insufficient, and often hypocritical. The previous morality was forever examining itself, and calling up the memory of its points of reference, while reactive judgment does without such internal debates, which no longer have their place. It operates through the fascinating or blinding effect of good or of evil, like a flash of lightning that we cannot help but look at but are at the same time blinded by.

We are of course tempted at this point to ask how it is that, in the supposedly total absence of prejudices or pre-formed judgments, certain situations make our contemporary indignant. Might this indignation be made up of judgments unwittingly inherited through culture from another morality? Or is it that we are finally able, for the first time in history, since we have never before gone so far in the elimination of points of reference, to perceive good and evil in their "essential" forms? If the latter is true, subjectivism itself could very well be the instrument through which a human universal is revealed; the most superficial judgment, since it is exclusively reactive and emotional, would then foreshadow a profound truth: it is in the absence of prejudices that nature can spring up in all its force.

In any case, reactive judgment does indeed give rise to a morality, a spasmodic morality perhaps, lacking structure, full of holes and contradictory, but a morality nonetheless. We do not know how judgment works, because our only criterion for approving or disapproving is what pleases or displeases. And this of course cannot help but lead us into innumerable contradictions. For example, our contemporaries would generally advise a pregnant woman who clearly risks having a malformed baby to have an abortion. At the same time, a campaign is underway to allow HIV-infected mothers to carry their unborn babies to term. Here, there is compassion for a mother in a tragic position, a wish to allow her an ultimate joy. In these two analogous situations, the evaluation differs according to the degree of emotion we feel in one direction or the other. In 1995, various well-known personalities were shocked by excesses of a sexual nature on Fun Radio.* An indignant media consensus responded by arguing for the freedom of expression. A month later, Fun Radio happened to make certain ironic remarks about Auschwitz. The same media consensus then revolted: apparently, freedom of expression had found its limits here, but why here and not elsewhere is impossible to say. Hence we see the inconsistency that befalls a society whose morality is based solely on reactive judgment.

It is natural enough that indignation against evil should serve to reveal judgment. Experience teaches us that even when reflective judgment dominates, the moral conscience often remains at the mercy of the way good and evil are presented. Crimes that we see are more repugnant than ones that remain invisible. Moral conscience is easily given over to superficiality, and is dependent at least partially on appearances. Because of this and despite its importance, it is a fragile thing. And, although essential, it makes use of non-essentials—visual representations and what others might think. But it is important to add that the greatness of a civilization lies in its ability to conceptualize good and evil that emotion instinctively

---

* Fun Radio is a popular radio station in France. *Trans.*

identifies. Civilization works towards going beyond emotion, in the same way that it works towards going beyond what Bachelard calls primary knowledge in the area of epistemology. In this sense, our contemporary, as a being beholden to his emotions, is not morally barbaric, but morally uncivilized.

Judgment founded uniquely on complacency or indignation will be unable to bring to society an identifiable or transmissible morality. Although some might believe that this merely constitutes a new form of morality, it is actually more a rambling outpouring of the conscience in a world without ethical structure. One might call it an irrepressible desire to do good and to refrain from doing evil, which has sprung up in the absence of meaning, and expresses itself in a disorderly fashion since there is nothing to organize it. The conscience cannot attach itself to anything other than brute sensibility. All understanding is denied, especially since contradictions are rampant, as we have seen. It is completely unaware of how to prevent evil in the future since it remains ignorant of the causes of evil. The conscience then finds itself relegated to the short term, without any means of escape.

The attitude of our societies towards the Nazi genocide represents perhaps one of the most striking examples of moral judgment dictated by indignation, for it is precisely in those areas where evil is greatest that it is most difficult to apprehend. The obsessive repetition of the facts, which make genocide omnipresent and indefinite, is revealing. Of course, to present the images of the Holocaust is important to avoid having Nazi crimes fade into oblivion. The conscience relies on images in order to preserve its awareness of evil. But here we are dealing with a conscience that is fascinated with evil. If images are constantly repeated, it is because the conscience has nothing else but images at its disposal. That is, it has few real explanations. The conscience has not been able to integrate evil into a global vision in which it would be able to locate evil's roots and the key to its prevention in the future. And so it remains petrified, unable to avert its gaze from horrible visions, like someone who is unable to understand and whose silence testifies to his distress. At the same time, this conscience hopes to prevent the possible return of evil by repeatedly portraying it. Although that strategy might be important, it is hardly sufficient. It is essential to analyze the mechanisms of evil and to demonstrate its deviance and unnatural character through reason. But we will hear nothing of this, because we fear such reasoning might somehow tie us down or commit us to a worldview in which our independence would be compromised.

The absence of a rational foundation or discourse about the truth to ground moral certitude has consequences on the form of the message as well as on the tone used to convey it. Today's moral message is not explanatory, as it was for example in the case of Las Casas in the sixteenth century, who defended the dignity of the American Indians, or of Thomas More, who was indignant about human misery. Our message, on the contrary, is loud and repetitive. It is proclaimed vehemently and always carries a threat against its adversaries. It creeps in through all the cracks of social life because to be convincing it must be constantly repeated. It compensates for its lack of justification by its ubiquity and omnipotence. Its "human rights"-ism is incantatory to the point of inducing nausea. It disguises the lack of a crucial backdrop by hogging the stage, leaving space for no rival. What it is unable to obtain through persuasion or debate, it obtains through the stifling of adverse ways of thought, which are vilified as soon as they dare to show their faces. Evil is not rejected by reason, but hated out of indignation and denounced through invective. At the same time, discourse about the good is set to the tones of panegyric and the smell of incense.

Because the morality of complacency is unaware of its justifications, it attacks its critics not through argument but through ostracism. And because a democratic and liberal society does not like violence, ostracism here takes the form of irony. Religious societies described the deviant as a sinner, and totalitarian societies branded him as insane. There were specific reasons for these definitions. In contemporary society, the deviant is simply regarded as something grotesque, a sure way of moving him out of the way without argument.

It should be noted that making someone look grotesque is a tactic of exclusion. It is a way of excluding that suits a consensual way of thinking devoid of rationally grounded legitimacy. In fact, one would be hard-pressed to show where the dissident has gone wrong, so one simply caricatures his thought, uses insults and ridicule until he is finally silenced. Any critic of complacency in general is thus branded inept. The non-conformist is not contradicted but called names: party-pooper, curmudgeon, or more seriously, inquisitor, extremist, neo-fascist. The consensus, and particularly the media that echo it, gets rid of its deviants by identifying them with the worst adversaries and natural enemies of society. The ethics of complacency would be unable to demonstrate just how its opponents are wrong, for the simple reason that it does not know why it is right, except to assert that which pleases as a value. Thought that is based solely only on that value, however, uses—and abuses—its discretionary exclusion. Opponents of complacency are excluded because they are not accommodating, or because they refuse to please at all costs, or because they judge opinions and behaviors, assigning different places to them in a hierarchy of values.

Dominated by emotion, our era overflows with treacly sentiment. It is almost as if the feelings that were once associated with a certain type of piety have contaminated the whole population. Tear-jerking sensitivity has always been the stock-in-trade of those groups of human beings for whom existence is structured exclusively by morality, to the detriment of knowledge and efficiency. Seeking the good while remaining indifferent to truth gives rise to a morality of sentimentality. Reactive judgment, deprived of thoughtful reflection, engenders fanatical emotion and an absolute priority of feeling over thought. In fact, it is not actually a question of sentiment, since sentiment supposes a historical and rationally consistent background. We are dealing here less with a reaction of the heart than with a gut reaction.

Sentimentality reveals a spirit that is unable to distance itself from the world. There are many ways to step back and gain perspective, through reflective thought, or by invoking a transcendental reality. Whether the subject is Sarajevo under siege or the operations of a sheep slaughterhouse, television reporters use the bleeding-heart tone and vocabulary that everyone has come to recognize. Reflective thought of any depth at all would quickly convince them that the sheep are perhaps not deserving of so much troubled agitation, for what then will one say about human suffering? Even the victims of Sarajevo would blush with shame if they heard themselves described in such deafeningly pathetic terms. Mother Teresa or Abbé Pierre,* to name just two contemporary examples, would never have fallen into this trap. They understood the misery of the world not with their gut, but with a sovereign heart in which the hierarchy of values was clear. The heart echoes sentiments that encompass reflection and maintain a scale of references Emotionality, on the other hand, releases its tide without any thought. It often expresses the irruption of fundamental human aspirations, and may be the expression of a natural morality that lies buried, but since it remains deprived of judgment, it rambles aimlessly.

Max Scheler, in *L'homme du ressentiment*, described "the pathetic modern humanitarianism [that is] obviously the antithesis of the clear, and almost cold, spiritual enthusiasm of Christian love."[1] We seem to have before our eyes today the fully developed and extreme expression of a humanitarianism deprived of transcendence, and consequently lacking any critical distance. It is impossible to acquire critical perspective when faced with tragic destinies or injustices except by pointing to an even more essential Elsewhere—or by knowing via structured thought where to place injustices in a hierarchy. Today, however, the object of emotion is a direct image of the essential, because there is no other representation of it. And anyimage that causes indignation seems worthy of the utmost indignation,because there are no criteria to supply a scale of judgment.

At the same time, the scope of our moral judgment has shifted.

---

* A French priest famous for his work with the poor and homeless in Paris. *Trans.*

We no longer proudly display our ideals, our patriotism, or our spiritual quests. To do so would seem to us to be incongruous or downright dangerous, for we speak highly only of those things that have value or give meaning. And we know too much of those lofty periods in human history when the majesty of high-minded ideals left some human beings shivering in the cold. We know all too well the kind of morality and law before which the heart counted as nothing. We have learned never to exalt collective greatness, while at the same time feelings can never be exalted enough. The individual's feelings alone have importance, not thoughts or glorious deeds. We have, in reality, very prosaic emotions.

Emotion is by nature superficial and temporary. Once emotion is used as the exclusive criterion by which to recognize the good, it condemns contemporary man to superficial moral action. The man of mere emotion is incapable of fervor: he cannot entirely engage himself in a moral act after good and evil have been revealed to him. From this follow the contradictions he is witness to every day and inefficiencies he cannot at all understand. When confronted with absolute evil, he puts up a weak fight, scrimping on the good. The attitude of the West during the Balkan war is revealing in this regard. In report after report, the media described what we considered absolute Evil: ethnic cleansing, the extermination of civilians, race-motivated rape. However, the means we used to combat this evil remained for a long time completely ridiculous, at least in comparison with the tone of the accusatory discourse and the magnitude of our denunciations. It got almost to the point that the official outrage sounded like the kind of armchair indignation that we all despise. In fighting against an evil that spares no effort, we have become used to carefully counting our costs. Admittedly, we do finance humanitarian activities, which is to say, we do sacrifice parts of our existence: time, money, and energy. Yet governments fear having to commit human lives in real combat because they know very well just how unwilling their citizens are, despite their indignant rhetoric about war crimes, to let their own sons risk their lives.

By the same token, our contemporary's indignation over crimes committed by the Nazis and their accomplices and sympathizers loses its force. It almost seems as though we are only capable of preaching to others—most notably to our ancestors, who are unable to answer back—and are hardly able to act for ourselves.

Absolute evil, once it has been clearly identified, needs to be confronted by absolute good: in other words, by what one calls heroism. This term sounds so ridiculous today that one almost hesitates to write it. However, if we discern an objective evil of an unquestionable magnitude, why should the good that opposes it advance timidly? Absolute evil is irrational: it destroys; it does not talk. We oppose it with a good that argues and ties itself up in knots, weighs the pros and cons and takes no risks.

The heroic individual is not the little lamb who runs blindly toward death, nor the pacifist who prefers to stand unarmed under enemy fire rather than deliver a single blow. The heroic individual is someone who runs personal risk, in terms of existence, but also in terms of life, in order to restore a just order. In other words, he dares to violate the norms of rights and security in order to respond to a disorder characterized by an intolerable disrespect for rights and justice. He oversteps these norms not only for himself, but also for others, in the sense that he must step outside of the rational and legalistic world. He must in advance commit to his chaotic adventure, the consequences of which he can only partially predict.

Heroism requires courage, and that is the characteristic we usually associate with it, but above all it requires fervor, which engages one's whole being and makes one capable of anger and revolt. Courage is really no more than a means or a condition, and we have no reason to believe that our contemporary lacks courage, because we often see it exemplified in athletic exploits and various other ventures without high purpose. Or perhaps it would be better to say *external* purpose, since these ventures are largely undertaken in order to prove one's own abilities. In all of these undertakings, however, fervor is lacking, if we understand it to mean a will to commit one's whole being to a battle that is not unreasonable but irrational. Our contemporary is incapable of enthusiasm in the sense of being transported outside of protected existence. He is never outside of himself. He never rises up or gets carried away.

Our contemporary's behavior and state of mind indicate the superficiality and limits of the morality of emotion. Evil cannot be effectively fought without fervor. And this fervor presupposes that we have identified not only the obvious fact, but also the meaning, of the evil to be vanquished and of the good to be defended. It presupposes an ability to expose the roots of emotion and indignation, and to found them on genuine moral reflection.

CHAPTER 8
THE CLANDESTINE IDEOLOGY
OF OUR TIME

The fear of truth and the subjectivity of the good do not keep our societies from paradoxically harboring an ideology of "correct" thinking.

Even though we live in a time when everything is relative, when every point of view has equal value, and when everyone can have his own "morality," it is nonetheless clear that we are taking our common destiny in a particular direction. In fact, a consensus in favor of human rights can be discerned in contemporary Western culture. We are even prepared to eliminate those who oppose this worldview, since we have created laws against ordinary racism, for example. This certitude about the validity of human rights is shared and uncontroversial. It is not subject to dispute. It indicates the common denominator of a multitude of opinions, and is ultimately the mandatory litmus test for all "points of view." As such, it signifies that the range of "points of view," diverse but equally valid, is really not so vast.

The philosophy of rights in itself represents a rather vague vision. It rests on a humanist *a priori* and on the imperative of respect and has been institutionally spelled out in a myriad of declarations and constitutions. But the philosophy of rights lends itself to all kinds of interpretations. Under the guise of human rights and in its name, our era validates and legitimizes a particular interpretation. It claims to represent humanism in its purest, most self-evident form. And yet we really are dealing here with a specific conception of humanism. In other words, we are living under a clandestine, unnamed ideology that maintains its power precisely because it remains hidden.

The particular conception of human rights that is privileged in our societies is expressed and can be seen at work in the "whereas" clauses of the Council of Europe and in European projects in general, in the various recommendations made by committees of ethics, in the speeches and in laws of technocratic governments (which claim to be politically neutral, free from contradictory opinions, and based solely on "science"), and in general in the affirmations of the "politically correct," whether codified into law or not. In other words, within our societies, from the international level right down to the local level, there exists a sphere of acceptability, a catalogue of discourse that cannot be questioned, and a group of "correct thinkers" whose numbers are certainly quite large but who remain only vaguely identified. The ruling technocracies, and most of the media, serve the same specific ideology, even if they pretend to obey nothing more than reason and obvious fact. Most of them are doubtless not consciously aware of this, since they are so soaked in the dominant ideology that they no longer even feel it.

In our societies, there are a certain number of political, moral, and other opinions that the individual contests at the cost of being marginalized. For example, one must join the call for equal representation for both sexes in all spheres of power. One must consider delinquency to be a result of poverty caused by social injustice. Contemporary man must hate all moral order; he must equate the Catholic Church with the Inquisition, but never equate communism with its gulags. He must *a priori* be suspicious of profit and financial institutions; he must be suspicious of the virtuous, who invariably must be disguising hypocritical vices even more dangerous than the vices of the depraved. He must hate colonizers, unless they are former victims themselves. On the other hand, our contemporary must legitimize all behaviors and all ways of life. He must call for equality everywhere, and fight for ever greater freedom for ever younger individuals.

Just from reading this list, the reader will immediately suspect the author of wanting to defend colonial powers or a strict moral order. And it is precisely this suspicion which shows so clearly that a mandatory way of thinking really does exist, and that contemporary man is unable to distance himself from it. Whoever dares to question it, or to even express a doubt about the validity of this sacred discourse, doubtlessly belongs to the camp of the opponent.

The affirmations of "correct thinking" do not represent a written orthodoxy. They impose themselves painlessly upon public opinion. They rest upon certain postulates that express a particular interpretation of the philosophy of rights and thereby represent a specific worldview. In an era in which ambient relativism rejects any vision of what man is, so that all points of view have the right to be, the postulates of "correct thinking" express a precise and well-defined vision of man. Man is considered to be a solitary individual who is and should be devoted to the pursuit of his own happiness, so long as he does not harm his fellow man in a violent or visible fashion. This vision promotes the individual and his happiness not within the context of an extended spatial or temporal framework, but at the present moment and in the personal sphere in which the individual decrees his well-being. The individual is "liberated," or detached from the groups he belongs to, in the sense that his happiness justifies his indifference to any group with which he is supposed to have a relationship. He is respected even in his irresponsibility, if by "responsible" we mean that he must respond to something other than himself, whether it be a commitment, a contract, a membership, a tradition, or a culture.

Stated differently, although we are very much dealing here with a philosophy of human rights, we are doing so within the framework of a particular and specific vision of what man is. This vision claims to be self-evident because it is rooted in what may be the majority view and is in any case virtually the only one expressed in the media. But in fact its purported self-evidence is a subterfuge, for, as we shall see, there are many ways to understand what man is, and other ways to interpret the philosophy of rights.

So just where does this clandestine ideology come from? What are the foundations, or the reasons, for this vision of man that no religion or other ideology supports? Correct-thinking ideology first of all represents a complement or an accompaniment to pervasive relativism, for in spite of the apparent contradiction, relativism does indeed have an ideology. Relativism could not exist if it did not forbid judgment, and above all negative judgment. It must fight against the very idea of deviance, which indicates an objective social evil. Correct thinking therefore tends to level out all judgments about behavior, and eliminate the notions of both deviance and virtue. This is made possible by reducing the distance between the two terms. For example, the negative effects of hashish are minimized while those of tobacco are accentuated. At the same time, there is a campaign to abolish the distinction between legal and illegal drugs.[1] Ultimately, everything is reduced to the same level. There is then no reason to consider the drug addict to be a deviant, nor to judge his behavior. Everyone is on drugs, and so no one is. A further example of this is the focus now placed on hidden crimes committed in the heart of the family—violence against children, incestuous rape—in such a way that we are led to believe that the traditional family is no more virtuous than the broken family. The latter, then, should not be considered deviant, since behind the appearance of virtue lurks hypocritical vice. And so no one is virtuous. Or everyone is.[2] Deviance hence becomes relative, or mundane, while "virtue" undergoes the same treatment but in reverse. Relativist ideology does not claim that "evil" can be equated with "good"; this would be a simplistic caricature. In a much more subtle fashion, it reduces evil and detects evil in the good. The result is a jumbling of previous points of reference, and from that point onward any judgment sounds unfounded and backward.

One might even go so far as to call this an ideology of the apostate, in the sense that contemporary thought is structured around a rejection of the former religious morality. We know that the apostate can be as violent as the convert, but in the opposite direction. The apostate destroys instead of building, but does so with the same zeal as the proselyte. We also know that the apostate is usually someone who has been tricked, or at least feels he has. He has just escaped from a long and deeply rooted certitude. He has become aware that he made a mistake, that he was had, that he was shamelessly duped, that he not only defended but actually covered up iniquities, that he was directly or indirectly responsible for disasters. Naturally, he feels a hatred towards the institutional, spiritual, and moral authorities that led him to this point, authorities that for so long fed him the once-convincing arguments he now considers contemptible. But even more, he now turns against himself. He feels guilty of a horrible crime, and so he must make amends. He initiates a process of compensation for past injustices and of indemnifying former victims. He could be defined as a man with a bad conscience who seeks vengeance and reparation.

The contemporary ideology of the apostate works tirelessly to rehabilitate the victims of the previously dominant morality: the former subjects of the colonial powers, women, and various deviants from the former consensus. It preaches not only equality where inequalities once flourished but reverse inequality, in order to compensate victims or their heirs. We are witness to an immense trial of our ancestors, complete with judges, lawyers, and awarded damages. It is as if the crimes committed over the centuries will never be fully redeemed, that nothing could wash us clean of the follies of our forefathers. From this fear stem the haste and fanaticism of the terrified apostate.

The clandestine ideology of our time aims to equalize the value of all behavior, or stated otherwise, it struggles against the hierarchy of ways of life imposed by the previous morality. It has several facets, however—probably stemming from assorted causes. It resembles a substitute egalitarian ideology, trying to compensate for the patent failure of socialisms to achieve their egalitarian goals. By leveling values, it attempts to erase, or at least to make us forget, invincible inequality. Since we have been unable to offer everyone a balanced existence, let us clear the names of the "deviants" and let us disclose the hidden cracks in the so-called balanced life. Thus, the defense of relativism goes hand-in-hand with the desire for equality. Both have the same objective and give rise to the same consequences.

A collective resentment doubtlessly lies within the clandestine ideology. One indicator of resentment is that, as we have seen, this ideology dwells on the evils committed long ago by authorities who lost power long ago. Its tiresome criticism of the prohibitions imposed by the old moral order is just one example. But another indicator is its acerbic destruction of the inaccessible, if it is true that resentment consists of a bitter devaluation of what one is unable to obtain. The desire for equality, combined with the now-established certainty that not everyone can achieve a basic minimum of happiness, leads to the generalization of mediocrity. "Real socialism" attempted to equalize everyone at the lowest common denominator of economic standing, recognizing the impossibility of fulfilling Babeuf's wish to lead everyone to the summit.* As witness to the failure of this attempt, contemporary man attempts to equalize everyone at the lowest common denominator not of economic standing but of values. It is, however, easy to identify in our contemporary's eyes an obscure admiration for everything he seems determined to denigrate—honoring commitments, shouldering responsibilities, and living with a sense of carrying out one's life-work (*œuvre*). Resentment aims at the destruction of a coveted object that remains out of reach.

* François-Noël Babeuf (b. 1760) advocated a rigorous democratic system of communism during the French Revolution. He was guillotined in 1797. *Trans.*

The desire to equalize the value of different behaviors corresponds at the same time to the imperative of personal dignity, which is the only absolute moral imperative left in our relativistic times. Because the disappearance of objective criteria has made it impossible to judge ways of life, any evaluation of these ways of life becomes an evaluation of persons themselves. A value distinction among patterns of behavior tends to be discriminatory against individuals. Any attempt to establish a hierarchy becomes a denial of the right to be, which is precisely what our whole culture forbids in the name of personal dignity. If no criteria remain on which to judge an act, we can attack only the individual himself; from that point on all judgment becomes personal, and only the suppression of judgment itself can re-establish the dignity of the individual.

This fight against the establishment of a hierarchy of acts fits perfectly with the vengeance of the apostate, since the former religious morality had lost its way to the point of actually nourishing enemies within itself. Christian morality, based on *agape* love and the source of the imperative of respect, in principle did make the distinction between the judgment of acts and respect for individuals. However, it could not resist all sorts of human temptations (the history of this self-abandonment has yet to be written), and thus judged people at the same time it judged their acts, equating the two in the same act of rejection. If one examines the way religious morality treated "deviants" of all kinds, when it should have been pursuing only deviance, one will quickly understand why our contemporary sees all judgment as a major risk. And rightly so. Any structured morality inevitably drifts towards an ideology of discrimination against categories of human beings: this is what our experience has taught us. The apostate is not merely a vengeful turncoat. He is also perhaps a man fraught with nostalgia for a real humanism, regretting the fact that the aging, institutionalized humanism, spoiled by power, should have finally become an ideology—and, in its own way, a murderous one.

In the very rejection of any structure of truth, we are, however, driven unawares by a particular conception of the world. Our contemporary believes he has placed himself in the service of human rights and of a way of thinking founded on reason alone, neutral, beyond discussion and shared by all honest people. In reality, he is in the service of a particular, and therefore debatable, interpretation of the philosophy of rights. But he is unaware of this because the power of this interpretation is so great that, although we are allowed to proclaim it or defend it, analyzing it or even naming it are out of the question. Correct thinking is as oppressive as any other ideology in power, especially since it is clandestine and hard to pin down.

Can a society that claims to be pluralistic tolerate the supremacy of a single way of thinking that seeks to dominate? If not, just how might such thinking be brought down from the heights it now inhabits unless we engage in a debate about its particular interpretation of the philosophy of rights?

PART THREE

THE URGENT NEED FOR
A NEW ANTHROPOLOGY

CHAPTER 9
IS DEMOCRACY UNSURPASSABLE?

Democracy has become the sacred tabernacle of our time, and the discourse that accompanies it its theology. The democratic system tolerates no criticism. It carries in its wake the danger of intellectual subjection, watchful and sure of its legitimacy. It knows no adversaries, only enemies.

Democracy represents the concrete manifestation of everything we believe in, that is, the liberty and well-being of the individual. So far we have not found a better or more efficient way to embody our humanism, which is based on individual autonomy. Modern democracy has without question proven its ability to make society more livable than it ever had been before. It has given to its peoples the three benefits that we assume all peoples dream of: peace, personal freedom, and material comfort. The democratic man is a fulfilled man.

We know that this unprecedented success is due to democracy's fundamental modesty and to its suspicion of utopias. Paradoxically, it is precisely the modesty of its objectives that produces its marvelous results. We also know, however, that this success is the product of an unstable equilibrium that is threatened from all sides. The democratic system could be seen as a sort of a tightrope walk between liberty and authority, between chaos and order, between the private garden and the town square. It seems to us to be a sort of precarious miracle. But because this miracle has provided a heretofore unknown happiness, we also know that it implies a sort of anesthesia. Happiness is natural and calls for no justification or particular attention, unlike unhappiness, which always looks for causes. One of the paradoxes about democracy lies in the fact that, as a sort of equilibrium, it must always be legitimized and defended, while as a source of well-being, it tends to numb and sedate its beneficiaries. This intrinsic fragility makes it all the more endearing, if it is true that we tend to be attentive to and protective of anything or anyone we fear we could lose.

Our democracies have come back from the brink of death and have experienced perils that we still dwell on. We have defended them at great cost against various forms of violence. We have feared for their safety and have several times almost lost them. They are under constant threat: a few red or brown shirts, a shrewd demagogue, fanaticism hidden in a Trojan horse. Although they have overcome numerous setbacks, democracies have turned out to be laborious things to rebuild wherever they have for a time disappeared, and almost impossible to establish where they have no history. Democracy is therefore at once inaccessible to many but prodigious in the eyes of its beneficiaries.

Nevertheless, it is clear today that our prodigy, democracy, is in trouble. It is being undermined by the corruption of those in power, by venomous alliances between powers that should in principle be separate; by the censorship practiced by the press, by the media's self-censorship and lies, where we had hoped that many voices would lead to freedom and truth; by corporatist political parties that eliminate the genuine debate of opinions; by weakness in the face of external conflicts and humanitarian disasters; and by the development of relativism within a system that has an imperious need for certainties. Since we do not know whether we are dealing with circumstantial dysfunctions or with life-threatening congenital defects, we might be tempted to fear stagnation, disability, or, for the most pessimistic among us, a complete breakdown. All of this reminds us of the troubled interwar period, and we know very well what followed.

These dysfunctions no longer induce us to put democracy itself into question, for in an era of weakness, Western societies have attempted before to replace it. Dictatorship has invariably followed. These bitter experiences lead us to think that there can hardly be any middle ground between human rights and human degradation, or between democracy and dictatorship. Democracy is an island beyond whose shores nothing is permitted. And if it is not passionately defended, in spite of its weaknesses, democracy tears itself to pieces. It requires faith, and blind faith at that, since it is the the form of government that is not propped up by force. Its precariousness stems precisely from the fact that its government never uses heavy-handed means. This is why, in order to keep such an enviable and threatened system from sinking, an unflagging belief in the rule of law is necessary.

So it is that contemporary democracy has become the only cornerstone considered to be untouchable. Lacking the inquisitorial methods that it condemns, it practices its own brand of intolerance through verbal ostracism. Whoever dares to criticize, finds himself either scorned for weak or backward reasoning, or accused of barbarity, relegated to the darkness, and placed in the company of our historic enemies. All of which clearly demonstrates the sacralization of democratic thinking: its adversaries are doomed to ruination, diminished by moral condemnation, and deprived of the right to take issue. The sacred is precisely that against which contradiction kills the contradictor.

For our minds, formed by the philosophy of progress, democracy constitutes the final product in the improvement of the world, and is hence unquestionably the best form of government. However, when a sociopolitical model is viewed as untouchable or inviolable, the idea of progress—of endlessly transforming and perfecting— becomes impossible. The philosophy of progress treats every sociopolitical model as imperfect, not absolutely, but with respect to the forms yet to come. At the same time, the sacralization of contemporary democracy consecrates the historical petrification of a model that is considered unsurpassable. It is as if we were no longer able to advance in the process of improvement, both out of fear of change, since democracy can only give way to oppression, and for lack of imagination, since we are unable to come up with a different model that is even better than the present one.

Faced with this mental obstacle, we could conceivably decree the end of history, and understand democracy as the final step of progress, in which the transformation of forms comes to a halt. But this supposition immediately admits its insufficiency, for it supposes an impossible immobility. Experience clearly shows that he who does not move ahead, moves backward. The march of time forbids stagnation. A single clear-minded look at contemporary democracy reveals that it is deteriorating before our eyes, because it cannot be improved upon.

We find ourselves with a model of government that is at once considered perfect, at least with respect to all others in history, and in the process of deteriorating—and thus in need of reform. Democracy is a masterpiece. Can a masterpiece be reformed, if by masterpiece we mean something to which nothing can be added, and from which nothing can be taken away? The only thing to do is to conserve it as well as possible, and restore it, when it becomes damaged. And so this obligation turns us first into conservatives, and ultimately into reactionaries. We start by trying to preserve intact all that we consider glorious. Then, as we helplessly watch the deterioration continue, we try to restore the broken model. For the apostles of progress, these attitudes of conservatism and reaction are strange indeed. We know that. But we have no choice but to act this way, even if we do not really understand what is happening to us.

A possible alternative might be to believe that further progress will be expressed not through the discovery of other models but by improving the sophistication of the present one. And because it is impossible to remain in a steady state—since a static history would be either a history of beasts or of gods—we would have no other choice but to make democracy even more democratic. In other words, to apply its principles everywhere, and to make them more radical. Democracy is thus drawn into an exponential expansion of its principles. The historical process of progressively extending the rights of participation has already led to an ever-wider sphere of governed participants, as illustrated by the advent of women's suffrage and the extension of the vote down to the age of eighteen. Have we not heard, in moments when the sense of citizenship wanes, of lowering the voting age to sixteen, of allowing eighteen-year-olds to run for office, and of giving foreigners the right to vote? Furthermore, there have been recent attempts to extend democracy to other areas of social existence. We have tried to apply, or hoped to apply, the ideas of pluralism, individual sovereignty, and majority decision to groups as diverse as political parties, educational institutions, the family, and the army. In such cases we speak of "democratizing" a sector, and it is as though democracy were destined to expand, in a process at once inescapable and desirable, into every nook and cranny of social existence.

However, by doing this we unwittingly pervert the system we are trying to protect and fine-tune. To apply democracy to an association, a church, the army, or the family in the same way we do to a governmental system is to introduce everywhere the anarchy of individual wills. Social groups are not identical; they all have specific ends towards which they are constituted and they accept as members those who accept these ends, while in civil society the only objective, at least in our culture, is to allow each individual to pursue his own purposes. Social groups, because they are formed on the basis of specific purposes to which members consent upon joining, may apply the principle of subsidiarity, which in no case can be equated with democracy. By attempting to generalize the democratic process to society as a whole, one sacralizes the process itself, which is absurd. The success of democracy comes from its use of mechanisms adapted to civil society as a unique entity. But these mechanisms have no value in themselves: if, for example, we wanted to "democratize" science, we would end up destroying it by transforming it into mere opinion.

The passionate yet legitimate desire to protect democracy gives rise to other consequences that are much more serious than simple errors of orientation. Because modern democracy fundamentally rests on personal liberty, and on respect for all opinions and all behavior patterns, it by definition fears decreed certainties. It allows only for the certitude of tolerance, which is easily seen as the certitude of incertitude. In other words, democracy finds truth awkward, because truth always creates obligations, while democracy prospers in freedom.

Life under liberty is a great gift. He who lives protected by the philosophy of rights is the happiest person in the world—and indeed in all of history. Or at least he is convinced that he is, if only because of the envious glances he receives from the rest of the world. But the emergence of a certainty or truth—which term one uses depends on whether one puts the subjective or the objective aspect to the fore—threatens this hard-fought and enviable happiness. This is why contemporary democratic man does not ask the question, "What is true?" but rather, "How can I live better?" The stifling of the first question means not only that it is secondary, but above all, that it is dangerous. To ask what is true could well spell the end of the good life, since truth creates obligations and therefore limits freedom.

The protection of democracy is thus achieved by a voluntary decision not to reflect about its justification, which is to say that emphasis is placed on the efficiency of its procedures while its foundations are ignored. The rise of the procedural, or means, to the detriment of the essential, or ends, has taken place because the ends are considered to be both self-evident and risky. Politics is founded no longer upon a reflection on its ends, but exclusively upon *how* to reach its undiscussed objectives.[1] What is important is that it functions properly—and as efficiently as possible.

Thus, the ideas of liberty and equality, as they take shape within contemporary democracy, occupy the same functions as has the absolute good in the most obtuse religious and ideological movements in all history. The question of their validity is no longer asked; it simply goes without saying. This sacralization induces a new intolerance, since there can no longer be any discussion with the partisans of contrary ways of thinking. For there are no arguments to be used against them, only pronouncements of radical judgment: thus, John Rawls can characterize the moral hierarchy of St. Ignatius Loyola as demented.[2] He who believes it possible to ignore the question of meaning cannot avoid putting himself in the role of supreme judge, in the process becoming arbitrary and inquisitorial. This is why democracy paradoxically seems so intolerant.

In reality, contemporary democratic thinking does not manifest relativism, for it rests on a profound conviction of its own truth. If we now consider Loyola demented, it is because we cannot understand how he could possibly reject the happiness of liberty in the modern sense. All that can be said is that nothing is objectively true, since the object of desire resists all refutation, and tolerance has no place where desire reigns supreme. This sacralization, however, does not establish a truth in the philosophical sense, but rather the certitude of general and unequivocal well-being.

Democracy is built upon the self-evidence of happiness, not upon the self-evidence of a truth, but this certitude of happiness functions like a truth. In this respect, contemporary democracy is a politics of complacency, which mirrors the ethics of complacency.

Hence, the good of democracy intuitively and by experience knows itself to be a "good for all." It refuses to go looking for the why of its existence for fear of losing itself. It simply is, without knowing from whence it came. It is justified by the avowed well-being of its beneficiaries, and we suppose that this should be sufficient.

Will we long be able to content ourselves with this unexamined happiness? Already democracy is showing signs of wilting and fading. We are finally being forced to recognize this deterioration, but we refuse to look for its causes because we are so sure of democracy's intrinsic value. We remain incapable of changing, unless we count the kind of change that occurs in spite of us. The passage of time inflicts wear, alteration, and damage. Contrary to contemporary belief, we will not be able to get by without reflecting about the foundations of the democratic "good." It is the taboo of reflection that keeps us from reforming, and thereby puts the democratic system itself in peril.

Contemporary democracy finds itself a victim of self-satisfaction and of the fascination it holds for us. However, the role of political thinking is precisely to observe this satisfaction with a critical eye, especially because our historical memory now allows us to make comparisons. Having studied a wide variety of political regimes, the Athenians of the classical era saw no greater political system than their own. Furthermore, they considered their democracy to be an unsurpassable, universal paragon. They never missed an occasion to praise it, to dedicate songs to it, or to reward the descendants of its founders. Their democracy had no defects, only quirks (ridiculed in Aristophanes' comedies), and knew no worthy adversary. Stated otherwise, Athenian democracy was already "the worst form of government, except for all the others."

But other regimes have also been the historical objects of such fascination. Until the revolutionary era, and even beyond, it was impossible to step outside of the idea of monarchy. If one reviews the political thinking of the sixteenth century, which is extraordinarily rich, nothing leads one to imagine anything but a monarchic form of organization: Every single writer worked within that framework, which seems to us today so limited. Monarchy is equally legitimized in Erasmus's moral government, in Bodin's republic, in Althusius's federation, and in Calvin's reformed government. All of these thinkers were imprisoned within the idea of a single form of government, in spite of the various ways in which they conceived of it and criticized its outcomes.

However, in the beginning of the Greek fourth century B.C., certain Athenian speeches began to describe the wayward wanderings of democracy and to re-situate this form of government as part of a cycle in which it would dissolve in order to make way for other forms (Plato). The desire for monarchy appears shortly thereafter (Aristotle, Xenophon, and Isocrates). In the same way, the French monarchic model, which initially withstood the great revolution, finally found itself called into question. History teaches us that European political models have always revealed themselves to be temporary—even more so than elsewhere—because they have always been treated with suspicion. It is a European particularity that its models of government did not so much collapse through the weakness brought on by wear as they were rejected for their inadequacy. European citizens hoped for, and later invented, political forms better suited both to their circumstances and to the fulfillment of their values. The Roman republic was explicitly and deliberately judged to be inefficient in comparison with the imperial ideal. Feudal realms were centralized through a reflection upon power and the state. Absolute monarchy collapsed under bitter criticism of its arbitrary and irresponsible nature.

In other words, if we come to idolize a particular model and seal it off from critical reflection, we should realize that this model will undoubtedly undergo the same destiny as the political forms in all other civilizations: it will end up collapsing in a state of lassitude, petrifaction, misadaptation, and corruption. We cannot cheat history. We know very well that everything must inevitably come to an end. Our tradition in fact advises us to use our faculty of critical thinking with regard to an object of veneration, in order to be a master and not a slave to historical change. Our culture tells us to subdue satisfaction, even when it is justified, in order to gain mastery over the future.

Nothing, in fact, points to the everlasting durability or stability of contemporary pluralistic democracy. Nothing demonstrates that its perfection will remove us from history. When we see in democracy the end of history, we become victims of the same ideological thinking we have only just rejected. Having rejected the contents of ideology, we nevertheless remain prisoners of its form. The end of ideologies reveals that we will no longer wait for Godot, as Havel said.[3] And yet with democracy, we seem to feel that we have actually found Godot. Let us ask ourselves what this means in terms of blindness and suicidal naïveté. That democracy might be irreplaceable does not necessarily mean that it is not transformable, at least if our purpose is not to make of it a relic, forever petrified in its present form. In order to give it a history and a destiny and ensure its survival, we will have to engage in a critical reflection about the contemporary forms it has assumed, and then grasp its meaning anew.

The exercise of critical reflection, though, supposes a frame of reference according to which different models or forms can be judged. It is impossible to engage in critical reflection about democracy if we do not have a clear idea about what "good government" is. And as it is, we have a tendency to equate democracy in advance with "good government," to make of it the measure and the ultimate reference of the political "good." And so we remain incapable of judging it, for what scale of reference should we use when democracy itself constitutes the criterion of any and all judgment?

It is not an exaggeration to say that democracy has today become the new idol, forbidding thought, because it holds within itself alone all truth and all goodness. In this respect it has replaced the dead ideologies, and does so happily, since it does not reign by terror. Nevertheless, it is still no more than an idol, and if we believe we have found in it the absolute, we are fooling ourselves. In an idolized democracy, the intellectual is replaced by the ideologue. And we know by experience that this never bodes well. The vocation of the intellectual should be to step back and gain perspective with regard to the contemporary expressions of our mode of government, in such a way as to understand its weaknesses, and to subsequently correct them.

CHAPTER 10

If, as we have seen, the previous era tried to eliminate politics as a command-obedience relationship, the failure of this attempt has not led us to despise politics any less. However, today we are attempting to eliminate it through other means. Having been unable to equate the governors with the governed, we now seek to equate politics with science, and morality with law, in an effort to free ourselves from a category we consider dangerous. Politics, so we are told now and again, will be made obsolete. Interestingly, the attempt to eliminate politics is taking place within the heart of contemporary democracy, and paradoxically, without our even being aware of it, it deforms this form of government we admire so much. The result is most clearly seen in the rejection and fear of what one might call worldviews.

As a specific activity (that is, as an activity distinct from scientific or artistic activity), politics in principle aims to guarantee both the duration of society and the conditions of its happiness. The question remains as to how to define the happiness of society, and to decide who can define it. Historically, most governments have maintained a conception of social happiness that they inherited from religion, or more generally from culture. For every people, this conception is unique and is not questioned, even though other peoples have different conceptions of it.

In this respect, modern pluralistic democracy inaugurates a new way of looking at things. It presupposes that happiness is subject to controversy, is always defined by a particular belief system, and that it is based on a subjective value system. It postulates that there is no "objective" conception of social happiness, and that because of this, no government can legitimately adopt a particular conception of the "good"—in the sense that tax, education, or immigration policy reflects a particular way of understanding collective or individual happiness. But if modern democracy reflects an ideal of tolerance towards multiple conceptions of future happiness, it automatically engages in a battle, however courteous and regulated by playing rules, amongst these different conceptions. To engage in politics is to endorse a particular vision of the happy society to the detriment of others. And this battle can only be justified by the freedom it expresses: it means that we are free to choose our own way of being happy. Thus, conflict between different conceptions of happiness is the only way to keep the individual from being oppressed by a social conception that claims to be objective.

For example, the problem of impoverished neighborhoods calls for very different responses according to the conception of happiness one adheres to, and consequently, according to the values one holds. Some may think that the unfortunate victims of such living conditions should be given more material aid; others that they should be moved to the countryside; others that the negligent parents should be penalized; and still others that the immigrants that inhabit these areas should be returned to their countries of origin. We are not at all dealing here with a problem of only technical dimensions. This is rather a question of diverse responses, each of which is related to a particular way of defining individual and collective happiness, and therefore, to a particular diagnosis of social illness. Is the problem of poverty due to inequality, to poor urban planning or overpopulation, to educational deficiencies, or to the intermingling of different cultures?

To ask these questions is to see that there is no politics without particular conceptions of society. What this means is that there can be no politics without a particular vision, and that there is no democracy, in the contemporary sense, without a plurality of visions, in two senses of the word: vision as perception of the world (*visio*), and vision as the direction in which one looks (*visere*, the intensive for *videre*). Vision supposes the attentive gaze of intuition and the intended direction of an "aim." It is an attempt to understand the world and at the same time to give a goal to action on the basis of this understanding. Its consideration of social issues presupposes a conception of desirable existence, a coherent idea founded on references that are held to be essential.

To different degrees, the religions and ideologies of previous ages each harbored an image of social happiness to be maintained or put into effect, or even created from scratch. Through experience, we know that these global visions often turned out to be oppressive, whether they belonged to a power-wielding religion or a governing ideology. We have therefore quite naturally developed a real fear of worldviews. We reject conceptions of the good because they have played nasty tricks on us. We are afraid that after a democratic debate, one of these conceptions might actually take over, with all the impracticality and oppression this result would entail. We have, for example, a terrible fear of groups that propose coherent, ordered visions for producing balanced individuals and happiness. But quite apart from the fact that these systems, for the most part Manichean, are sometimes proposed by visionaries and are always subject to takeover by fanatics, there is a second point: we do not know exactly how to define the "good" because our points of reference have vanished. This doubt, which stems from the contempt we hold for worldviews, makes for a technocratic approach to politics and leads us to believe that politics can do without conceptions of social happiness.

The appearance of all kinds of "parties" based not on global visions of social happiness, but on single issues or values or interests, is not coincidental. In France, parties have developed that claim to defend the environment, or to protect hunting and fishing. In Italy there is a party of love, in Poland a beer-drinking party. All of these reflect a belief that every category of interest and every social problem can form the basis of a political movement that, even if it has no ambition to take power, at least hopes to force the government to take interest in the questions and values it feels are being neglected. However, this is no way to keep a pluralistic democracy healthy, or even to keep it alive. In spite of their importance, such limited problems hardly constitute a social vision, either separately or all together. None of these parties promotes the public welfare or attempts to deal with the question of happiness in its entirety. The emergence of special-interest parties stems from the great difficulty we have in forging a desirable conception of existence, of setting an overarching goal for politics. But the degradation of "parties" in democratic political life does not bespeak, as one might expect, a new age in a society at last rid of religious and ideological systems. Rather, it recalls previous types of government, or preceding currents of thought, of precisely the sort from which pluralistic democracy has always sought to differentiate itself. The previous types of government—namely, all the historical autocracies—had as their end an objective "good" that was not subject to debate and allowed controversies to arise only on questions of limited interest. The preceding currents of thought—exemplified by twentieth-century corporatism, well represented by the Maurrasism of Salazar—had as its political motto to "live normally," thus signaling the disappearance of modern "politics" as a conflict of convictions (and the contempt this movement had for parliamentary debate, which it considered to be no more than drunken quarreling, is well known). In this respect, the metamorphosis of parties of ideas into parties of interests testifies much more to a rejection of pluralistic democracy than to its evolution.

If the groups that run for power are not interested in advancing a general vision of society's common destiny, they thereby implicitly acknowledge that the task of defining that destiny lies solely in the hands of the governing authority. This process of abandoning ends is facilitated by the belief that politics is a kind of science, today a widely held belief. Thus, the representation of special interests by parties centered on particular issues quite naturally legitimizes technocratic government. The objective of politics is no longer to reflect a particular image of the good society, an image founded on established references, but rather to propose "solutions" to problems. Politics has taken on the appearance of an activity that is the result of scientific research on how best to respond to problems that arise. Does this then mean that the answers are self-evident? Certainly not. The answers are not easy to find—even though no longer encumbered by the truth derived from references—because human intelligence is inadequate and social reality is complex. If the right solutions do not immediately appear, it is because the problems are difficult, not because the answers are uncertain. Theoretically, a government made up of brilliant minds, assisted by sophisticated machines, and capable of considering all the data on the political problems of the day should be able to come up with the appropriate solutions.

Within this framework, it is not uncommon to think that "good" politics properly consists of disappearing from the picture. The citizen should let the people with the know-how govern. They will solve problems without allowing their difficulties to spill over into the public forum, since these difficulties are after all the business of specialists. Conflicts have no reason to exist, because objective solutions *do* exist, as long as authority is granted to those who are capable of finding them. When the governing authority announces that it has found the unique "solution" to this or that problem, then, it implies that the question is not one of approval or disapproval, but of understanding. We congratulate ourselves today on the courtesy that dominates campaign debates. And of course politeness between adversaries is indeed a sign of democratic health. But when this politeness stems less from personal respect than from a consensus about proposed solutions, it is not a sign of mature democracy but a sign of entrenched technocracy, or rather a sign of a democracy struggling to survive. The citizen is not wrong when he mumbles, "They're all saying the same thing," and his indifference at the polls is not unrelated to this disappointment

Nevertheless, the rejection of worldviews is insufficient to make them disappear entirely. It is natural and legitimate in a country accustomed to critical judgment to propose other models of happiness, and technocracy finds itself opposed by a variety of movements. In spite of their diversity, technocracy tends to classify them all under the heading of "protest movements." It thereby points to their common characteristic, which is to refuse to accept the so-called rational neutrality of technocratic government. By branding them as protest movements it also wishes to send the message that it cares little for their arguments, which are in advance considered unworthy, since they reflect views that the species itself is no longer supposed to need. Having been treated with contempt, rejected in their pretension to think outside the bounds of technocratic rationality, and relegated to the fringes of official reality, these movements, even when they do manage to mobilize large groups of people, find themselves marginalized and consequently easily fall prey to extremism.

However, no political question can boast of giving rise to a single answer. Answers will always be multiple, according to the points of reference to which one wishes to give priority. In reality, there is no such thing as neutral government, and technocracy is not neutral, despite its claims to the contrary. By ignoring or dismissing the different worldviews, technocracy has not done away with them. At least not if we also believe, as we do today, that individuals are diverse and will not adopt the same convictions except under pressure or oppression. By postulating, without debate, answers it considers self-evident, technocracy becomes intolerant, even if it and its citizens are unaware of the fact. Contemporary technocracy is, in reality, the umpteenth expression of the Platonic myth of the unity of minds. The foundation not only of democracy but of "politics" in the Greek and European sense of the word consists of the certitude that in any and every society, diversity is the irreducible reality, and that unity is always artificial; one cannot respect diversity without debate and conflict. This is precisely why democracy gives itself the mission to contain, domesticate, and institutionalize these conflicts instead of artificially attempting to dissolve them.

Thus, technocracy camouflages its true identity, for under the guise of science, it favors one particular worldview over the others, while it considers all worldviews to be obsolete and superfluous. Not that it wants to trick anyone; it is simply a victim of its own ignorance. Every political act is a choice that calls for the concrete manifestation of certain references, even if these references are neither named nor conceptualized. A traditional society, without proclaiming the truth of any worldview, by consensus imposes respect for the community, and is founded on the values of authority and responsibility, to the detriment of the values of personal liberty and equality. Similarly, contemporary technocracy, which claims not to impose any values, to offer a neutral solution, and to act only according to its knowledge of reality, actually offers a specific answer and unwittingly defends a clandestine worldview: that of correct-thinking ideology.

Consequently, techno-politics, which goes hand-in-hand with the politics of special interests, is a politics without tolerance. And this is true in spite of all its contrary pronouncements and appearances. No one can think outside the consensus, unless he wants to find himself on the darkened fringes and accused of being a "protester." How is it that democracy can thus label movements, the existence of which its pluralism is in principle supposed to legitimize? It is worth noting that the "protestor" label is applied, but not defined. Although it has a softer, more polite ring than "hooligan" or "insane," as dissidents were branded by single-party regimes, there is a troubling similarity. The battle between worldviews has not died out, as we believe; it has been forbidden.

Nevertheless, since technocratic government wishes to maintain its democratic spirit, it is forever claiming to act in the name of its "convictions." And indeed, here and there images of social happiness do persist, in general having grown out of the old order. Those images often correspond to particular brands of liberalism or socialism that can be detected behind the veil of consensus. But we are dealing here less with coherent visions than with deficient and partial ideas that have lost touch with their foundations or at least do not dare elucidate them, and certainly do not base themselves on clear points of reference, for fear of calling to mind a worldview that no longer commands assent or that now instills fear. This is the case, for example, with the so-called French preference for unemployment, which would require a whole defense of individual responsibility; with the proposal to reduce the work week without a corresponding wage decrease, which recalls real socialism; and with appeals to protect the family, a favorite theme of the Right, which conceals a defense of social ties and a denigration of contemporary individualism.

The sly substitution of the political representation of opinion for the representation of interests constitutes an evolution that perhaps has not yet run its course. One gets the feeling that, tired of empty and idle plans for social change, our contemporary finds refuge in the handiest group in which he will at least be able to defend his visible interests. He now identifies with the cause of women, naturelovers, or whatever profession happens to be under attack. It offers him a warm shelter and hard-won but clear-cut results. In other words, he retreats to the domestic domain, while the government runs the economy—in the old sense of "managing the domain." In the middle, politics, or more precisely, pluralistic democracy, slowly withers away.

If we have come to this, it is not because contemporary man hopes for nothing and does not long for a better society. In fact, he is neither cynical nor indifferent. But he is no longer able to express this expectation in anything but the most natural, the simplest, and the most elementary image of the good. He does indeed want peace, justice, and liberty, but he no longer knows how to paint a concrete picture of what he wants; he cannot imagine what it would be. He is perfectly capable of painting a picture of evil, and can describe all the forms of society he would not want under any circumstances. But to describe, in advance, an image of the desirable society would instantly commit him to reinventing worldviews—which he knows in advance to be futile and dangerous—to identifying reference points and defending their foundations, and to conferring upon his own action a coherence that would compromise his unfettered liberty.

The flight from worldviews in the political realm corresponds to the general flight from meaning. In this area, as in personal life, "objectives" have taken the place of ends, and aims the place of meanings. Only worldviews hold meaning, in that they reflect the values they point to. Objectives, on the other hand, point to nothing: they respond to short-term necessities, or else must be integrated into a wider vision.

Does this then spell the collapse of the politics of conviction, one of the most brilliant products of our culture? Coupled with the pluralism of images of social happiness, only the politics of conviction can hope to improve society. Today, techno-politics, through its pretensions to certitude, cuts short any debate about the future, and thereby casts aside innumerable answers, many of which might actually prove to be better. This vision-less politics is truncated and lame because it deprives itself of a pluralistic consideration of worldviews, all of which are debatable, and refuses to embark upon the project of inventing a common future under the best of conditions. We cannot refuse to conceive an image of a better future simply in order to escape from the ideologies that once oppressed us. The reference points we cling to forbid us to abandon the desire for progress, the uncertainty of answers, and the political freedom that gives rise to a debate in which a range of answers are confronted. There is no pluralism without concrete plurality.

CHAPTER 11
THE FEAR OF DECISION-MAKING

The decline of worldviews corresponds to a reluctance to make decisions—an even more profound phenomenon, the consequence of which is a difficulty in apprehending situations. Decision-making responds to an aspiration, and it is only made possible by a kind of intellectual navigation. Techno-politics undermines both aspects of decision-making.

Choice requires deliberation; pros and cons must be weighed, because several possibilities hang in the balance. Naturally, this deliberation implies a discussion involving many or even all citizens—when, for example, an issue of national debate arises, such as the Maastricht Treaty. But above all, deliberation entails an internal debate. The general debate in the media about the European question has as its aim the provision of arguments and counter-arguments that will allow each citizen to engage in a real internal, personal deliberation, which will in turn allow him to make a choice and to express it on his ballot. Similarly, the government relies on various sources of information and on its own knowledge of problems in order to deliberate within itself, and finally to make what it then considers the best decision. Its knowledge of the problems it faces, however, is insufficient to ground a decision, nor does it automatically determine how a decision should be made. Another factor inserts itself between knowledge and decision-making, what one might call aspiration. This is precisely the factor our contemporaries have come to forget, with the consequence of imperiling decision-making itself.

The intellect, as the repository of knowledge, deliberates, but it is aspiration that decides. So what is aspiration, exactly? The intellect raises questions and uses memory, experience, and reason to perceive several possible answers, but it is incapable of choosing among them because they cannot be compared in terms of reason, but only in terms of values. And the intellect has nothing to do with that. Should farm land remain under cultivation or be developed? Should prevention or punishment be the favored way of dealing with crime? Should we resist the enemy or collaborate? All these questions relate to values; that is, they draw upon different ideas of the good, and, ultimately, different notions of happiness. And if one looks closely, there are very few decisions concerning the general interest that are unrelated to underlying conceptions of existence. This is why decision-making is a question of aspiration, in the sense that one aspires to create a better society. Here, to choose means to privilege certain references over others. Political decisions are not neutral, or innocuous, with regard to values.

Techno-politics is unique in viewing decision-making as an act involving only the intellect, thus excluding aspiration from the process. There is really nothing surprising about this once conceptions of existence have receded from the scene. Political decision-making, then, is more like setting off a trigger mechanism. It imposes itself without alternative. To speak of actual decision-making becomes difficult, for it is at best a kind of truncated process, from which the essential, aspiration, has disappeared. And this is why the political discourse of technocrats seems so boring. In their disappearance, conceptions of existence took with them all the flame and passion of real debate. In politics, it is no longer a question of "defending" a way of life or of persuading others that a given measure is well-founded. On the contrary, the politician bears more of a resemblance to a professor who is simply saying how things really are.

Techno-politics can be distinguished from genuine politics in that it always favors competence over prudence. Prudence, which is an attitude towards action, naturally includes competence, which no politics can do without. But the more we value competence to the detriment of prudence, the more we push politics towards techno-politics.

If political decision-making corresponds fundamentally to an aspiration, then in the way it operates, it is a sort of navigation. Prudence represents the ability to steer a difficult course through the tortuous world of action. It is an alchemy that combines keen perception, experience in dealing with people, common sense, judgment based on memory, intuition of the unspoken, moral conscience, and knowledge of events. In this sense, politics is the art of wisdom, not a technique supported by reason. The Greeks asked the question of whether, during a storm, it would be better to have as a sea captain a young man fresh out of naval school or an old salt with several decades of experience. No one would hesitate to choose the old captain. Yet we now have a tendency to choose public officials filled with abstract, intellectual knowledge of politics but with little experiential knowledge of society.

With government by competence rather than prudence, we are still talking about government, but not about politics in the Greek sense, which defined politics as the art of governing free men. And we are certainly not talking about contemporary pluralist democracy, because government without prudence lacks the postulate by which all individuals are equal in their ability to decide.

Participatory democracy is being undermined, even if no one openly admits it. Suffrage, especially universal suffrage, can only be justified if political decision-making is based more on prudence than on competence. Everyone is capable of prudence: a poor illiterate does not have to go through any formal training in order to have a reasonable opinion about the future of his country. And his opinion will be no less reliable that that of an intellectual, because in order to make a choice, one must use the kind of common sense, intuition, and experience that every man has—or at least, that are impossible to measure objectively. These are the very qualities of prudence. On the other hand, knowledgeable competence is reserved for a small elite. And because technocracy views specialized competence as practically the only criterion for decision-making, it becomes apparent that the great majority of people will be entirely unable to think politically. Universal suffrage then becomes a ritual in which sovereignty is symbolically given to the people, even while it is understood that they are without the necessary resources to decide. And the concerns expressed by certain contemporary political scientists about the inability of many people to use their right to vote advisedly—even if these scientists point to the increasing complexity of problems—actually rest on the postulate that science is in power. The "incompetence" of citizens is worrisome only to the adherents of techno-politics. Real democracy does not require competent citizens; it requires prudent citizens. Of course, education needs to be widespread if democracy is to survive, not because education allows people to make decisions, but because it is one of the elements of prudence.

One might well ask for what reason the idea of prudence has today been supplanted. The ancients described prudence as a kind of human wisdom. The prudent man is both lucid and modest, lucid even about his own limitations, while the competent man seems more easily sure of himself, which is only normal, since he relies on objective truths. The prudent man knows the mediocrity and uncertainty of the world. He is never entirely sure about anything. He distrusts his own prejudices. And thus his skepticism makes him the author of decisions about which he is nevertheless not entirely certain. While the competent man finds a solution that he imagines as almost tautologically leaping out of the problem itself, the prudent man proposes an answer that is more like a suggestion and imposes itself only because a decision must be made. The prudent man knows he is never fully in possession of the elements required to act. He thereby acquiesces in advance to the possibility of error. He accepts the risk that goes with action. In comparison with the competent man, he enjoys a much wider latitude to act and to decide, but he is much less sure of himself.

It is precisely the uncertainty—the veritable leap into the unknown—of the prudent man that so terrifies our contemporary. And this fear is the principal basis for the more or less conscious refusal to accept politics for what it is. It is a fear of the haphazard, of disorder and the irrational: the modern desire to erase the irrational from the world, an anxious seeking after an assured understanding and a guarantee of action. Haphazardness is that which escapes us, that which we can neither predict nor program. Furthermore, it means that there can still be an uncertain or debatable political decision. After all, prudent decision-making is no guarantee against the vile and terrible aspects of humanity. It can put arms into the hands of visionaries, false prophets, and gurus. The lucidity and experience of the prudent man are not explicit and therefore may be dangerous. The decision to choose the old sea captain has a mysterious alchemy about it: there is no choice but to trust. This kind of decision-making may mask false reasons or personal interests. Competence, on the other hand, expresses itself in the clarity of its reasons, and offers itself to understanding. It knows no murky waters, at least in theory, although complexity encompasses and gives rise to other obscure areas that are simply overlooked. How can the prudent man escape arbitrariness of the most iniquitous sort if he is unable to rely on his noble human qualities? We shy away from this kind of trust—and, in a sense, for good reason. For does our present situation really allow us to rely on moral limitations, which are so rare and so dispersed?

We fear that prudence can easily be led astray because the ethical reference points that alone can suppress its natural excesses are missing, and this absence helps us to understand why we prefer to be governed by competent rather than by prudent men, by recent naval school graduates rather than by old sea captains. From this fear stems, for example, our fear of decentralization: local authorities are less often products of the competent technocracy than are national authorities. Can one run the risk of increasing the number of decision-makers, and consequently increasing the number of decisions and uncertainties, in an era when individual wisdom seems so rare?

Nevertheless, to think that politics can eliminate chance if it is made into a science is a kind of snake oil if there ever was one. Politics, when reduced to a technique, does not address the real political questions; it neglects them without actually eliminating them. It mimics politics, while the real questions spring up outside of it, which other agents are quick to co-opt. The rejection of politics as an uncertain activity does not abolish haphazardness from the world. Technocracy finds itself incapable of handling many questions not because of their complexity, since complexity does not scare its knowledge-based approach, but because they are too human and too singular. Its rationality lets these questions slip through the holes like water through a sieve. And many real political decisions—that is, decisions made with the public interest in mind—end up being made completely outside the political arena. Techno-government complains of being undermined by the unprecedented development of non-governmental, sub-governmental, or para-governmental structures, which make decisions in its stead. Real "politics" develops on the black market, in all the informal and narrow spaces where technocracy's starchiness cannot go. Techno-politics casts envious, suspicious, and worried glances at these agents (NGOs, private associations, private schools, etc.): envious, because they sometimes succeed where it has failed; suspicious, simply because they do not "toe the line"; and worried, because intellectual honesty would seem to require a re-opening of the question of the adequacy of techno-politics.

But above all, the illusion of a decision rooted in competency alone gives rise to catastrophic errors. The past few years offer two excellent examples: the contaminated blood scandal and the Furiani Stadium affair.* The blame game yields disappointing results, and there is a widespread impression that scapegoats are being punished to appease public anger. In reality, no one is responsible for this kind of decision because, in these cases, no real decisions were made. It is not that the decision-makers were more lax or cowardly or fearful than others, but that they were trained to follow an administrative logic in which knowledge of regulations trumps all else and "governing" is the monopoly of laws and regulations.

Let us, for example, consider the case in which public school teachers manage to breathe life back into a poor slum area by organizing activities there in their spare time. When time comes around for them to be promoted, they are sent to another city, despite the successes they achieved and the sums they invested, and the area then falls back into despair. Those who transferred them are surprised by the general indignation, for they cannot even imagine that someone might question the administrative logic that decides promotions. The habit we have of believing in government by abstract rationality in fact gives rise to problems everywhere, because the best response does not necessarily lie in the application of a regulation—far from it. Not that regulations should be disobeyed. But they should be applied less narrowly. The best answer can usually be found by feeling things out, comparing situations, identifying negative effects, and analyzing them—in short, through deliberation. Regulations are of course necessary preventives to chaos and arbitrariness, but they are meant to serve decision-making rather than take its place. Reality is richer than any administrative logic; there is no comparison, and if one attempts to enclose it within the narrow networks of this logic, it ultimately takes its revenge. This is especially true since the

---

* In 1992, a section of one of the upper levels of the Furiani stadium in Corsica collapsed, causing fifteen deaths and thousands of injuries. The causes of this catastrophe have never been clearly determined. *Trans.*

reigning rationality, through its inflexibility and, especially, the passage of time, ends up creating a separate world, dominated by habit, in which no account is taken of new circumstances or changing needs. Life goes on as if volunteer work in the slums were a sort of civil service work capable of being done by interchangeable individuals, while in reality, given the great complexity of the social problems in these high-risk areas, this type of work has become more of a role, which certain people are able to play because of their particular talents. Life goes on as if it were advantageous to collect blood from prisoners because, before the epidemic, this measure contributed to the socialization of these outcasts. In the case of slum volunteers, the damage done by administrative rationality is not evident, because it cannot be measured in casualty figures; it perniciously takes its toll on the mind. The damage done in the contaminated blood case, on the other hand, is visibly apparent.

The governing official, if he has any pretensions to this name at all, assumes responsibility for the common interest, and not merely for the correct functioning of the administrative machine, since these two are not necessarily identical. Only the governing official who accepts the role of prudent decision-maker is capable of taking the risks required to bring about improvement and of responding to a changing reality. Putting meaning back into politics requires a farsightedness that openly takes on an irrational world and welcomes its challenges. Politics, then, requires humble men who know in advance that they will never possess all the elements truly needed to be sure of any decision, and who therefore accept the risks of error and failure. It also presupposes moral reference points that cannot be definitively integrated into the framework of rules and regulations, but constantly remain a source of inspiration for all decision-making.

CHAPTER 12
THE SACRALIZATION OF RIGHTS

We suffer from the illusion that democracy's destiny will be fulfilled if we apply its mechanisms on the widest scale possible. We also cling to the illusion that this will happen if we expand its founding principles to the utmost. Thus, we develop rights with no exceptions and no limitations, convinced that any expansion of rights corresponds to progress, as if democracy became ever more perfect as it coasted along its pre-set path. Is it not true that every presidential candidate includes the expansion of rights in his platform, whether they be freedoms or entitlements, whether they be rights to do or rights to have?

And so, in conjunction with the sacralization of democracy we see also the sacralization of rights. Eclipsing all other values, they have come to represent a kind of absolute. No one would dare contest an existing right or a newly acquired right, for against which standard could this materialized holiness possibly be measured?

This contemporary phenomenon can be understood by considering the new conception of personal dignity. While in the past, man spoke of his *honor*, contemporary man invokes his *dignity*, which apparently means the same thing: belief in his own grandeur. But one can see that the criteria that define this grandeur have varied over time. It is easier to see the differences by looking at cases in which man's grandeur has been deprived him. When one spoke of a man without honor in former times, it was to describe a man unaware of his own grandeur—which is intrinsic—and consequently incapable of demonstrating it, or someone too cowardly or lazy to display the required level of grandeur. Honor in previous societies was earned, so to speak, individually. Each man had to existentially demonstrate and in a sense achieve his status as a human being. Honor, therefore, relied on effort—sometimes, paradoxically, on superhuman effort—since one could lose both one's strength and one's personal advantages in the process. An individual felt compelled to strive to achieve an image of himself that he believed was enviable. This image generally derived from the worldview shared by his social group, and became manifest in a "code of honor."

The objective criteria by which grandeur was previously defined—for example, honesty, being true to oneself, or honoring one's commitments—disappeared with the worldviews that legitimized them. This does not mean that contemporary man is without grandeur, or that he is unaware of the idea of his intrinsic grandeur. What remains of the old notion of honor is an awareness of his dignity—in other words, the root but not the flower. And the concrete image of grandeur, that is, of dignity achieved, has changed. Man formerly achieved his dignity and earned his honor in an exhausting attempt to live up to an externally defined image; he now finds both dignity and respect by claiming his rights. His tangible grandeur is expressed when he secures the minimum wage as a right, free schooling, and all sorts of other entitlements, which he is willing to defend with any and every argument. He is hurt to the core if he is deprived of them. This is the reason for the 1994 revolt against the CIP,* a desperate revolt, because individual honor has become located in, among other things, the minimum wage, and to deprive man of it is as bad as calling the man of the past disloyal.

---

* In 1994, the French government under Balladur proposed a change in the minimum wage that would have allowed employers to pay young people entering the workforce less than the official minimum wage. This initiative provoked a massive revolt. *Trans.*

By means of a gradual historical process, the concrete way in which human dignity is to be expressed has gravitated from living an ethical life in conformity with an external standard, to being provided with all the rights that can be expected from society. It is clear, of course, that the Christian era's notion of dignity was ontological and thus not earned; it represented a grandeur given at birth and given once and for all, whatever life should bring. Thus, the contemporary demand for rights constitutes a continuity, for it still involves a demand that requires no justification except that of being human.

Nevertheless, in spite of the continuity of meaning, there is an enormous gap between ontological dignity—as grandeur of being, an inalienable grandeur, no matter how imperfect human beings may be—and the acquisition of rights, which are "created" grandeurs and therefore subject to the vagaries of material and temporal circumstance. He who situates his own grandeur in ontological dignity knows that in spite of any contempt directed towards him his worth remains untouched. Of course, being the object of contempt will not hurt him any less, but the value of his self-image is sheltered from sociohistorical circumstance. On the other hand, the kind of dignity based exclusively on rights is constantly in mortal danger, since it is identified with, and tied to, that which is contingent. Contemporary man therefore fights with desperate passion for his entitlements and his freedoms. And who could fault him? In a way, his liberties and rights are the only things he has to certify his grandeur. From this perspective, it is easy to understand why contemporary man views rights as sacred, is eager to expand them, and is troubled when they are not respected.

Copied from the previous model of ontological dignity, and functioning more or less in the same way, rights are applied without limitation (the respect due to man, because of his status, is unlimited), and aim for the most perfect equality possible (ontological equality is total, and takes no account of existential differences). Thus, we find ourselves, and not for the first time, in a situation where the secular and the spiritual have been confused, and wrongly so, because the ontological grandeur of man is unfathomable, but concrete rights cannot be expanded infinitely. Ontological equality is absolute, but there can never be complete existential equality.

Two consequences grow out of these considerations. First, contemporary man finds himself no longer in the position of one who acts, but rather in the position of one who receives, since his grandeur is expressed less by his demonstrated qualities than by the rights granted to him. Second, there is no end to the demanding of rights because they *themselves* are the ultimate criteria, having taken the place of ontological dignity, which was also unlimited.

Today, rights are the pretext of every claim of complacency. Anything contemporary man needs or envies, anything that seems desirable to him without reflection, becomes the object of a demanded right. Human rights are invoked as a reason for refusing to show identification, for becoming indignant against the deportation of delinquent foreigners, for forcing the state to take illegal aliens under its wing, for justifying squatting by homeless people, for questioning the active hunt for terrorists. It is not only desire or whim that leads to rights claims, but instinctive sentimentality and superficial indignation as well. It would therefore be wrong to assume that such claims are selfish—not all of them are. What they have in common is that they are rooted in emotion, be it selfish or generous.

Like the proliferation of rights in the spirit of complacency, the immortalization of acquired rights is another distortion of the philosophy of rights. It consists of legitimizing rights, not because they reflect a desire for something either for oneself or for others, but out of custom, with custom now viewed as a virtue in and of itself. Here, a right becomes irrevocable by the very fact that it has once existed. So it goes for the right to a cost-free university education, for the right to a minimum wage, for the right to have civil servant status within certain professions, and for a wide variety of other rights with which our society overflows. The attempt to immortalize acquired rights stems, of course, from complacency. For who would not defend a pleasant advantage? It stems also from the ideology of progress, according to which human happiness can only come from an accumulation of freedoms, entitlements, enrichments, and leisure. Complacency, whim, and custom have few critics when they hide under the mantle of rights, and it feels inhuman to challenge a right.

The exponential accumulation of rights comes partially from the way in which we confuse non-prohibition with legitimization—in other words, the way in which we suppose that anything that is tolerated should be facilitated or even encouraged. A type of behavior, however, can very well be permitted—in the name of individual liberty—without actually being legitimized or facilitated by law or material aid, for the reason that it has negative consequences that can be objectively identified. But our contemporary believes that any tolerated behavior should be legitimized, and consequently supported by the provision of the means necessary for its practice. This way of thought comes from thinking in terms of rights and entitlements. There is an obvious hypocrisy about abstractly conceding the right to an education for all without making education free; similarly, there is a hypocrisy about disapproving of a behavior pattern that society tolerates. This way of seeing things also results from the disappearance of an objective "good" and the general refusal to establish a hierarchy of acts. And in conjunction with all this is the movement from essential tolerance, based on the idea of the equal dignity of persons, towards procedural tolerance or relativism, based on the idea that all lifestyles are of equal value.

Inspired by the former ideal of tolerance, it is conceivable that we should indeed become indignant to see homosexuals considered pariahs, while at the same time thinking that if we legitimize homosexual behavior by considering it of equal value to heterosexual behavior, we ruin our society's future, and we must therefore refuse to legalize gay marriages and the adoption of children by homosexuals. But our contemporary revolts against this type of proposition because his tolerance is based on the idea that all behavior is equal, rather than on respect for the individual, irrespective of the value of his behavior. In any case, if one expects to challenge the Cornellian conflict* between moral absolutism and relativism, which forbids any hierarchy of values, then only the distinction between what is *tolerated* and what is *legitimized* can take into account the harmful consequences of certain lifestyles without having to prohibit them. What is tolerated or allowed does not then automatically become a right. An employee may be allowed to miss x number of days of work during a given period for family reasons. But if everyone considers this extension of tolerance a right, one can expect anemic economic results, which would someday make tolerance itself an unaffordable luxury. We might tolerate passive euthanasia, but if it became a right, we could be sure that horrifying abuses would soon occur. It might be said that whatever is permitted or tolerated is part of the law in the sense that it is legal, but it is not a right in the sense that it is something we are entitled to.†

The contemporary individual has the right to be protected from natural disasters, and this is why he claims compensation in the case of drought or flood. He has the right to a successful medical operation, and in the case of failure, he sues the doctor. Can the right to normality be far off, when in the United States, one sees a handicapped man sue his mother for not having had an abortion? The concept of rights has infiltrated every space, is both atmosphere and prism, wiping out every other value.

We believe we have invented an absolute "good" here, one that is appropriate for all times and circumstances. Yet the present situation tends to prove the contrary: concrete rights, whether they are rights to do as one wishes or rights to make claims, can actually stand in the way of necessary change, neutralizing the remedies of social ills, stifling the essential processes of survival, and becoming themselves the source of perversions. In principle, we admit that anindividual right ends where someone else's freedom begins, or that it

---

* This expression refers to the tragedies of Pierre Corneille, who in his plays frequently dramatized moral conflict. *Trans.*

† The point the author wishes to make here arises from the fact that in French the word *droit* can mean either "law" or "right." *Trans.*

ends when it harms others. In their contemporary form, however, certain rights are destructive in ways we do not admit. When the right to privacy permits the transmission of a deadly disease with impunity, that right is nothing but an excuse for a barbarity, and the fact that the perpetrator was first a victim himself makes him no less a criminal. The case is analogous to the way different family patterns are now being considered. We think that everyone has the right to organize his relationships the way he pleases, that this is the very least we should expect in a modern democracy. Legal and economic regulations confirm the right to the most diverse family forms, while at the same time facilitating the concrete manifestation of this right. Yet thousands of scientific studies have demonstrated the negative impact of broken families: the immense majority of delinquent, suicidal, depressive, and violent children come from broken families, for the most part families without a father. Thus, certain lifestyles, justified by the right of adults to do as they wish with themselves, deprive children of *their* most elementary rights. One feels tempted to say that a child has the right to a father much more than the single mother has a right to a child. Our contemporary will of course ask on what basis one is allowed to affirm this hierarchy. The answer is by taking into account "goods" and the hierarchy of "goods." These "goods" are not based on any moral code, since today we can no longer invoke absolute moral norms, but on their contributions to happiness. No one could de-legitimize the behavior of a single mother in the name of traditional morality, but the well-established statistical probability that her child will experience grave distress can allow us to question the legitimacy of her behavior. Or at least basic honesty should. In contemporary pluralistic democracy, no one can any longer decree what constitutes "the good life," but experience can teach us something about what contributes to "the bad life."

In some cases, rights end up hurting the very individuals they were meant to protect. For several years now, the right to university entrance based solely on successful secondary school graduation (*le bac*) has multiplied the number of student failures. We are educating bitter and jaded generations, ripe for personal distress and rejecting, understandably, the society that has betrayed them. And we are doing it consciously: everyone knows it and everyone talks about it as if it could not be avoided. However, no government would dare question the right to university access,* because to do so would give rise to protests and violence, as we all know. If it is extremely difficult to explain to students that they are in possession of a false right the existence of which is paradoxically harmful to their own future, it is because rights have become sacred. Similarly, we should be asking ourselves if the payments given to the unemployed do not actually discourage some of them from seeking or accepting work. We should be asking if the rights of organized labor groups, which initially corresponded to their legitimate desire for security, do not actually create two distinct social classes: those who are vulnerable (of which there are more and more) and those who are protected. We should be asking if the link established by experts between the unrestricted sale of violent images and the emergence of child assassins does not argue in favor of a limit to the freedom of expression. All of this comes down to the question of what the real benefits of rights really are. But this question is itself a politically incorrect one.

On some occasions, a right can cost far too much to the collectivity, which, being unable to challenge it, finally sees the right become an empty and false one. We know in what conditionsEastern Europeans were housed when the state provided everyone with housing. The material situation of our universities reveals the same logic at work. That the right to higher education has turned out to be bloodless does not, however, motivate us to reconsider the whole idea. It is as if what were important is that the right be stated as a fact, and whether it is empty because we do not have sufficient resources to implement it properly is immaterial. This situation is a triumph of incantation and propaganda over lucidity; it should help us see the extent to which we remain captive within the ideological mentality.

* University education is free in France. *Trans.*

A society of false rights reveals a lack of realism, that is, a misunderstanding of reality or a refusal to take it into account. Our society lives on two separate levels: that of our discourse about rights, and that of our actual existence, levels that do not coincide. Where false rights exist, "black markets" naturally develop as an alternative to them. While we go about proclaiming equal opportunity, private and very costly educational institutions allow wealthy children to avoid failure. If employers are hesitant to hire because of the cost of state-mandated benefits, it means that the multitude of rights these benefits correspond to are false rights, that they destroy the system and at the same time give rise to black-market work, which is without any rights. The refusal to introduce advanced placement classes in high school in order to preserve equality is undermined when those parents who are informed (especially teachers) register their children in rare languages to escape leveling; school boards, created to avoid disparities, are being diverted in the same way. The black market indicates the absence of a desirable reality that claims to exist, but does not, or at least no longer exists. The black market compensates for this non-existence with a reality that does not have the right to be, that hides itself and lives under prohibition. Since, in theory, it does not exist, it escapes all supervision and is therefore prone to arbitrariness and injustice. It would be better for individuals to have a less ideal but recognized, legitimate reality structured by laws than to live a double life between an increasingly arbitrary official fiction and a clandestine reality. If this hypocritical system were allowed to continue unchecked, it would lead to the Soviet model, with its bright beacon that shone for no one and its unknown shadows full of real people. It also expresses the refusal to live within human fragility. It reflects a pretension to be what we are not.

By closely observing our society we can see just how tenaciously we cling to this pretension, even if we know it to be excessively idealistic, to the point that we put up with an uncomfortable reality just to maintain the fiction. This discrepancy between the official and the real can only widen with time, in various ways, because society changes while rights remain fixed or develop only in an ever-widening circle. This dualistic existence is, however, unhealthy. It glorifies the lie. It would have us believe that everything is legitimate, as long as the door is closed. Yet it is not healthy for citizens to resort to illegality in order to live normally; such is the implicit belief, for instance, of those who claim residence in a different area to gain access to a better school. They know they are getting around the law, but the act seems legitimate since the law seems to ignore reality and basic needs.

Yet how is one to reform or contain rights without judging them? And how is one to judge them if they represent the only point of reference? We believe that a policy is necessarily better if it confers more rights: we measure the good of things against the standard of rights. But shouldn't it be the reverse? For if we realize that a right has negative consequences—if we at least have the courage to recognize them—it is because we have an idea of a "good" that goes beyond rights. But how can we grasp and define this idea if at the same time we reject in advance its possible objectivity?

The only way to get out of this impasse is through anthropological reflection. We must not forget that rights are primarily a means of guaranteeing respect for man. Because we have increasing trouble knowing what man is, we have raised rights to the status of supreme points of reference. Rights remain, nonetheless, the means, fragile and contingent ones at that, by which the need for respect is fulfilled. But the content we give to rights must vary with time. In addition, rights cannot continue to be extended exponentially, because they find their limits in human realities. In other words, if rights are really means that have as their ultimate purpose individual happiness, we can only judge rights in the light of an anthropology.

Until now we have tended to consider rights as powers or services related to a certain phase in the humanist conscience and irrevocable once acquired. From now on we will have to consider them as signs of an uncertain recognition of human dignity, which alone is sacred; signs of recognition linked in their instantiation to human capabilities, to historical possibilities, and unceasingly to be re-adapted not in their principle, but in their actual content.

If rights language has given rise to excesses, it is because even though we know man must be respected, we no longer know who this man to be respected is. Furthermore, it is because we have answered wrongly Kant's third question, "What am I allowed to hope for?" In fact, we have taken the question out of context, and because of this it has become impossible for us to answer it with the least chance of success. For this question cannot be separated from another question, "Who am I?" He who does not know who man is can have no real hope for man, only empty illusions. Because he does not know who the beneficiary of rights is, rights become guarantees without users, analogous to sumptuous but ill-fitting clothes.

Naturally, such affirmations suppose the existence of human specificity, something resembling a "nature," to which rights must be tailored if they are to serve their purpose of ensuring respect and happiness. But modern thinking is built precisely on the principle that man is a soft wax capable of being infinitely reshaped by the will—an idea that was born already in the fifteenth century in the mind of Pico della Mirandola. No theory, be it religious, moral, or otherwise, can challenge modern thinking on this point. But what finally does call it into question are the observed excesses and disasters caused by its concrete manifestations. It is in the light of these disasters that we find ourselves forced to reflect upon our anthropology. For if our intellect whispers to us that certain rights are harmful, it is because we still cling to a particular image of man—if not, the adjective "harmful" would itself mean nothing.

Our culture forces us to consider man himself sacred, regardless of his race, class, or religion. But this universality of status is insufficient. We must still determine what it is in man that is worthy of being protected, respected, and safeguarded. We do not protect criminal impulses, which are nonetheless very human. In fact, everything boils down to defining what is and what is not criminal. Female "circumcision" under French law is considered a crime of mutilation, while under Muslim law it does not contradict a humanism that calls for gentleness and understanding towards women. The way in which we define what must be respected in man depends on the way we understand individual and collective happiness. And this in turn depends on the understanding we have of the human phenomenon. The issue comes through clearly in the social debates of the second half of the twentieth century: should we protect the child from a father's slap, or should we protect the rights of the father? Should we protect the child from scandal, or should we protect the freedom of expression of pornographers? Should we protect private property at any cost, or should we nationalize indispensable or rare goods? The answer to all these questions depends on our image of man: Does the child have such a great need for a father that an overly harsh father is preferable to an absent one, and if so, to what extent is this true? Is man generally capable of taking care of collective property as well as he takes care of his own? And inversely, is he able to make his own wealth prosper without undermining the common good?

The problems of society rest upon two distinct questions: "Who is man?" and, "How is he the happiest?" To respect man is to protect both what he is and what he hopes for. The problem is that the answers to these questions remain rather subjective, and vary considerably with time and place. Excesses tell us, sometimes with great clarity, that an answer is wrong. The right answer, however, remains difficult to see and is yet to be discovered.

Our present negligence in defining this man to be protected has set us adrift in a sea of rights, which represent a temporally circumscribed form of morality. The anthropological question we must answer in order to know how to turn the philosophy of rights into concrete reality concerns the relationship between what makes the individual happy and what duties he is able to take on without negatively affecting the very happiness for which he hopes. For example, a man needs freedom to live well, but what kind of freedom can he have without alienating others and himself? A man has a need for security, but just where is the limit beyond which security leads him to be negligent and lazy; in other words, what kind of security will not end up harming the collectivity or the individual, either directly or indirectly?

The question becomes even more complicated when the parameters of circumstance are introduced. Because man, even if he does always retain certain characteristics, is a metamorphic rather than a static species, an adequate anthropology will also have to ask which kind of liberty and which kind of security the man of this time and place is capable of. When in the *Politics* Aristotle criticized the communism of Plato, he clearly grasped that the man denied the right to private property would find himself unable to put his heart into the care of collective property. And he was probably describing a perpetual characteristic of man: collectivization of property in certain countries in the twentieth century has shown us, via its consequences, that Aristotle was right. And yet, if it is true that certain human traits change very little over time and space, the limits to what the individual is capable of, to what he can assume without risk, and to what he needs, vary across human history and human geography. Thus, we must ask questions like the following: to what extent can the citizen of Eastern Europe, after fifty years of collectivization, immediately bear the weight of individual risk and autonomy? Or analogically, if in France we chose to give more responsibility to those who are directly involved in social action, what level of individual autonomy could we impose on the French citizen, who has become accustomed to state providence, without his falling victim to despair and helplessness like a prematurely weaned infant?

Ideological systems claim either to reject all anthropologies or false anthropologies, which amounts to basically the same thing, because once again, to reject any and all conceptions of man is to conceive of man in a certain way. But the contemporary era tells the story of humanity's revenge, because ideological attempts at human transformation were calamitous.

The re-examination of rights, then, will have to be based on a conception of man as he is to be respected, which implies an anthropology, and further along, an ontology. The first question is: Who is man? Scientific discoveries have dramatically raised anew the question of what criteria define humanity. Who is man when evolutionary theories cast doubt on the biological limit between the last of the apes and the first humanoids, when the development of the embryo is entirely gradual, when we can create clones and monsters? The decline of religion contributes to the fading of the founding ontology: How can man be described when he is no longer the product of any creative will, or any structuring history? This man who does not understand himself either as a creature or as a well-defined species becomes a sort of phantom, a silhouette with imprecise contours. We no longer know very well, know perhaps less and less, who man is, or what it is in him that must be respected. And this comes at a time when, perhaps more than ever, the necessity of this respect is is most urgent.

A movement such as deep ecology, which stems from feelings that are more widespread than one might think, bears witness to the excessive uncertainty of our times. In deep ecology, the norm of respect is applied to an equally demanding degree to all of nature. In doing so, it becomes diluted and weakened, since if everything has an equal claim to dignity, nothing is really dignified. What we are dealing with here is a right without a beneficiary or subject, since it is clear that not all beings in nature are subjects. As far as that goes, if everything is a subject, then nothing is a subject, and the status of subject vanishes. In this confusion, the hierarchies established by affections or emotions reappear. If the norm of respect applies to everything, the lack of differentiation signals the triumph of discretionary preferences. Often borne by a latent misanthropy, deep ecology ends up turning the old order of things completely on its head, ultimately permitting one to prefer the bird to the hunter, the baby lion to the human infant.

The question of knowing who a human being is takes on crucial importance when the progress of science forces us to define the status of the fetus, the severely handicapped, and the profoundly comatose.

But the question of what a human being is also escapes our analysis. However, our problem today is not only to determine whether we are under an obligation to respect the fetus and if so from what point in its development (who is a human being?), but also to determine whether offering to someone on a silver platter, and without any effort on his part, everything he needs to survive, or to deprive him of a father, or to crown his individual liberty with no other limit than that of the liberty of his neighbor, really constitutes respect (what is a human being?).

The disasters of the twentieth century have allowed a new idea to take shape in our minds, that of a "decline" of the self. This is an anti-modern idea. After all, if man has no status, what status could he decline from? In other words, if there is no paradigm of man, what heights could he fall from? A troublesome and unexpected question indeed, which points to the expectation of and need for a conception of man precisely when he had given up on all points of reference, and when he had become the creator of his own points of reference. The end of the century has brought forth the question "What should man be?" because of its cruel certitude of what he should not be. And the intuition of this normative status also reveals the necessity of an anthropology.

Our obsessive investigations into the psyche of the human butcher have exploded the claim that the human status is undetermined.* The torturer torments his victim precisely because he does not respect the latter's status as a human being. But at the same time, he gravely offends his own self-image and distorts his own nature. Barbarity is a disowning, but of what exactly? Of a model, of an unstated paradigm. About the death camps, a Jewish poet cries out, "Because it is so, may the Ever-lasting take the name of man away from me; if this is how men behave, I no longer belong to them, I am leaving this company, I disassociate myself from this

---

* The French word *bourreau* "butcher" calls to mind figures like Eichmann and those who worked in the Nazi death camps. *Trans.*

infamous companionship." In other words, it is impossible that man should be thus. And if it must be so, I would just as soon abandon my membership in the race.

To speak in such terms (and who among us could not?) supposes that behind the described perversions lies a model of humanity that must have served as a criterion for this impulse to reject what one sees as inhumanity. What kind of species would I want to belong to if I could leave this infamous band of companions? What is man, if he must not be that?

The modern desire to strip man of any normative status banished all saints and heroes from our universe, but this desire eventually ran afoul of our most basic needs. Thus, we still crown the heroes who exemplify what humanity can be, who serve as models. The various winners of the Nobel Peace Prize provide an image of this need to set apart those who exemplify a desirable humanity beyond what the common mortal is capable of achieving. No idea of "superior man" finds its way into this feeling, because we know all too well what horrors result from a claim to superiority. But the hero— Martin Luther King or Lech Walesa—proves by his very existence that humanity can be more than what it is in ordinary common existence. The designation of these heroes does not call upon religious points of reference. But it does reveal an implicit acceptance of a human model, a model that forces itself upon the individual from without and undermines his pretensions to be no more than a blank page. If man's status remains extremely difficult to define, in the context of a biology in the process of complete transformation, and in the face of an empty ontology, on the other hand, a human model still appears here and there in the guise of a desirable model. This model calls upon no theology or structured morality. It stands tall in the mind and speaks to the conscience like the statue of a commander, that is, from atop an invisible pedestal.

We are not, however, in any particular hurry to reflect on anthropology, to seek an image of man that might be used as a criterion for rights. We are not indifferent or intellectually lazy but rather fear the consequences of what we might discover and affirm. Any positive anthropology that is not a mere description of this modern man who is capable of becoming anything would ruin our age-old hopes. It would entail that we recognize that man is partially determined or conditioned, which we refuse to accept. It would signify the end of the ideal of the new man. At the same time, a rediscovered image of man would resemble the previous idea of "nature," which modernity has attempted to get rid of forever. And we know very well from experience that an anthropology can easily harden into a closed system; the description of irreducible human characteristics can become an essentialism in whose name any improvement or change is rejected. An essentialism of this type can be found in several contemporary Christian movements. Under the pretext of a respect for man, these essentialisms imprison him in a "human nature" that definitively destroys his hopes. Thus our contemporaries have no intention of subjecting the law of respect, and the rights that make it concrete, to a philosophy of human nature, which can so easily be used as an alibi and a façade for inaction.

And so we find ourselves in the midst of a contradiction. We have learned just how far the law of respect can deteriorate if it is a slave to happiness, for man cannot do with himself what he wishes: or rather he can try to do so, but risks demeaning himself. Yet we fear anthropological reflection, which alone would help us to see clearly, for we fear that any truth about the human condition carries the seed of the temptation to establish a moral order. The only way out of the dilemma is to formulate an anthropology that would both integrate the metamorphic character of humanity and, from the outset, subject its own postulates to the criterion of tolerance.

CHAPTER 13
UTOPIAN EQUALITY

The consecration of rights corresponds to both the ethic of complacency and the entrenchment of the ideal of intrinsic equality,
which we inherited from the Enlightenment and its avatars. If
ideologies were unable to bring about real equality, the dream is
nevertheless still pursued through the way in which we organize our
societies. We unceasingly attempt to equalize individuals by the way
in which we regard individual action.

Over the course of two centuries, we have gone from a society of
roles to a society of functions. A role is conferred in advance, often
inscribed in the destiny of the individual, and inalienable. A function is chosen by the individual, is exterior to him, and he appears
interchangeable in that function. A society of roles is hierarchical
and differentiated. A society of functions tends towards equality
and homogeneity.

The first and at the same time most visible metamorphosis, probably symbolizing and leading to all the others, was when political
authority ceased to be a role and became a function. The monarch,
king by filiation, and therefore by birth, had to assume—for better
or for worse, and for as long as he lived—the role of ruler, which his
education prepared him for, but in which his will played no part. In

a way, he was thrust into the world for just that purpose. By governing, he carried out his personal destiny, the content of which had nothing to do with his abilities, moods, or dispositions, or even his desires. Perhaps Louis XVI would really have liked to have been a locksmith. But two centuries later, the seat of power, once a king's throne, is now symbolized by a vacant chair to be occupied by an elected official. Today's ruler has a function as opposed to a role. Nothing illustrates this better than the profiles painted on the walls of the National Assembly subway station in Paris: black silhouettes of unidentifiable, anonymous men, indicating that the places of the representatives are seats to be filled or shadows to be personalized, and for which an individual is chosen, at least in principle, because of his specific abilities. Furthermore, he may lose his seat and leave the place he occupied to another person considered to be better suited.

At the same time that the nature of political activity changed, almost the entirety of social activities and even personal relationships gradually moved from role to function. The hereditary professions, in which a certain skill was transmitted from father to son, whether he was a shoemaker or an entrepreneur, were replaced by merit-based professional jobs. Family roles, distributed by nature and by birth order, also disappeared. With the advent of the career woman and reconstituted families, the educative roles have, in part at least, been replaced by functions.

In this metamorphosis, a fixed society, in which each person found his place practically from birth, gave way to a fluid society in which, theoretically, anyone can occupy any place. This change springs from our desire for equality, but more profoundly, it corresponds to the ideal that everyone should fulfill his own potential as best he can by finding the function for which he is best suited, instead of slipping into a role, which might be well- or ill-fitting, but to which in any case he is destined.

In pursuing and achieving this social transformation—the benefits of which no one would contest—we postulated that the roles of the previous society were rooted only in circumstance; in other words, we wagered on the purely historic nature of the notion of "role." We have done so to such an extent that this notion now no longer exists in our usage except in its derived meanings—in the sense of a character in a play, or of the personal charisma of an individual in a group. In fact, we know practically nothing but functions. Yet it is far from sure that social life can do without roles. And the complete eclipsing of the notion of role in its former sense has given rise to harmful consequences.

We speak of the "function" of an element in an ensemble, or of a part in a machine, which helps to ensure the correct functioning of the whole. We speak of "carrying out" a function, but of "playing" a role. We think of the role of a character in a play, in which the role remains associated with the mask (persona), from which the idea of person is derived, the person being an irreducible substance in its specificity or particularity. The act of playing a role carries the implicit idea of a play, since each character (personage) remains unique. To "hold" a function, in contrast, implies the possibility of substitution, since in the idea of occupation there is inevitably an element of precariousness. One can play a great role, but one holds a high office (function); the latter connotes a place within a measurable hierarchy, while the former suggests no measure beyond the self.

One fulfills a function, which suggests a substance somehow filling an empty container. The collective structure consists of a row of containers awaiting their contents. Functional activities are generally learned and require competency. Since they are well-defined, they can be placed within an ordered hierarchy. They can be counted and more or less catalogued. On the other hand, to play a role in a group or a society is to be less predictable. The character, a person in the theater of the world, is totally involved in his role. He relies on his intimate intuitions and feelings much more than he would in fulfilling a function. He counts neither his time nor his effort. He mobilizes all his faculties. The function brings to mind the kind of work that produces a reliable result, is measurable and verifiable. But the role suggests a vigilant presence, aiming for an end described in terms of well-being or happiness, which is to say that it cannot be measured. Naturally, the two can be combined, but they can never be reduced to one and the same thing. To say that a CEO has played a major role in the company is to say that he went beyond the framework of his function, not quantitatively, but qualitatively; or that he brought to the company an extra dose of efficiency and well-being beyond that required by his function.

Functions require interchangeable actors with equal levels of required competency. A typical example is the army, in which by definition the players must be instantly replaceable; they must therefore become indistinguishable from their functions, whence the anonymity of uniforms and the use of rank for identification. In similar but less obvious ways, a hospital requires a radiologist, a university requires a medieval specialist, and a business needs a sales manager.

Roles, on the other hand, remain personalized, whether they are obscure or highly visible: the mother in any particular family cannot be replaced by any other, nor could we find a substitute for the Czech hero Vaclav Havel. While functions depend on competency, roles depend sometimes on nature, as in the mother's role in the life of her children, and sometimes on irreplaceable experience, as in the case of Havel, whose personal history conferred a role upon him in the reawakening of his country. But each of us finds himself in a role with respect to those close to him. For example, as everyone might agree, it is more natural to drive one's mother to the hospital oneself rather than to call a taxi, even if one prepays the fare. In a number of cases, the necessary action cannot be reduced to a series of technical gestures leading to a specified result, but rather calls for an emotional investment on the part of a given person. One would never think of sending someone else to console a loved one in mourning. Often, a role supposes a set of qualities that are necessary in order to act in a given situation. This is why an unusual situation might require that a role be "played," even if it is not necessarily an extreme situation in the sense of being exceptionally tragic. We often recognize that in certain diplomatic situations, or in difficult social or family circumstances, only such-and-such a person can "play" this or that "role." These situations go beyond the realm of daily life in which functions hold sway. Whether it is a question of dealing with a particularly irritable and unpredictable warlord, a committee of defiant laborers on strike, or an adolescent in danger, we are often forced to cast aside the person whose "function" it is to convince, and call upon one we know has the necessary charisma, skill, and experience to be successful.

In a practical sense, roles remain determined. Not that playing them is compulsory—a mother may abandon her child, and Havel could have refused to lead. But to take on a role is very often a response to a felt moral obligation. In a sense, the person inherits the role because of the position he is in, the responsibility he has accepted, or the irreplaceable experience he alone can draw upon. Because he is irreplaceable, and because action is necessary, he simply cannot turn away without failing to live up to his duty.

The very idea of obligation, in combination with the inegalitarianism inherent in the notion of role, has led contemporary society to reject roles in favor of functions. Functions have no obligations because they can always be carried out by someone else. They leave open the freedom to abandon one's post, which is not considered a desertion. And because of their neutral and anonymous character, they presuppose that virtually every and any individual can fulfill them. Functions serve both liberty and equality. And so our contemporaries reject roles, which create both obligations and distinctions.

Just as functions have replaced roles in modern society, the individual has come to replace the person, the latter phenomenon being the corollary of the former. The person is unique, the individual interchangeable. The more functions there are, the more human beings define themselves by their competencies and repertories of technical abilities. This is the price of equality. With the disappearance of roles, the individual is left to himself and is henceforth able to choose anything. A society cannot make absolute equality a reality. In our society, however, we have managed to at least make it a virtual reality: anyone can, in theory, take the place of anyone else.

Thus, the modern individual no longer expects at all to be "indispensable." Everywhere replaceable, he has become free and indistinct. He has gained liberty at the expense of his uniqueness, and even further, at the expense of his identity. For we identify with what makes us distinct from others more than with what makes us the same: we prefer to present ourselves to others by talking about our athletic accomplishments, the volunteer work we do for such-and-such a cause, or a hobby in which we have suddenly found interest, rather than by referring to our professional titles, which we share with a hundred thousand others. It is obvious that personal identity is attached to roles rather than functions.

The society of roles saw inequality everywhere, even where it did not exist. The society of functions sees equality everywhere, even where it does not exist. The previous society favored roles to the detriment of functions, often to the point that it chained individuals to tasks supposedly ordained by fate and identified them with their assigned activities. The emphasis placed on roles guaranteed social stability and solidified the offices of power: the aristocrat, the father, the husband. The almost ontological foundation of the role justified a spiritual way of viewing tasks, turning them into missions, and thereby engaged the individual quite apart from his will and conferred upon him more duties than rights. Each individual found himself bound to a particular place and to a particular task. Modern society, on the other hand, considers every task a function, to the point of denying the very idea of the role. The excesses of the previous society without doubt spawned other excesses, as is often the case, for there is nothing more arduous than moderation. The society of roles used the pretext of fate to justify assigned roles and cited nature as its reason for limiting the abilities that individuals could develop. It excluded women from all sorts of activities for which they have clearly revealed themselves to be as gifted as men.

The opening up of such a petrified society could in fact only have come through the notion of function.

It would be wrong to become nostalgic about the society of roles, in which some people imagine that every task was approached as a vocation, that is, with a sort of sacred fervor. Nor would it be appropriate to challenge the society of functions on the grounds that it dehumanizes tasks by making the individuals that perform them interchangeable. For this anonymity and neutrality are the corollaries of personal liberty, and especially of the the idea that personal abilities can be developed, which the society of roles denied to almost everyone. It would, however, be worthwhile to ask ourselves whether all social activity can be accomplished in a functional way. One of the shortcomings of our societies, which can be suffocating and paralyzing, lies in our inability to conceive of the reality of the role. It does indeed exist, even if our desire for freedom and equality has tended to abolish memory of it. There are situations in which functions are insufficient. What today is commonly called "the couple in crisis" is actually caused by a huge confusion between roles and functions, and is often due to an ignorance of the very existence of roles. In the "bourgeois" mentality, which was born in the nineteenth century and spread throughout society in the postwar period, the father of the family considered his role to be that of material provider and social representative. He thus tended to leave child-rearing entirely to the mother. But it turns out—as experience has taught us—that women can indeed support a family and also have a personal social life. It also turns out that the father's place in child-rearing is not at all a function for which a replacement can be found, even if the replacement is the mother; it is precisely a role in which the father is irreplaceable.

The absent father confuses roles with functions, or, to put it differently even though the result is the same, the absent father does not understand that his role must always take precedence over his function: If I am not responsible for my role, no one else will be. There will always be other individuals capable of taking up the multitude of professional projects into which I have put my heart and soul, but if I am a father, I am the only one who can enable my son to detach himself from his fascination with his mother, and thus to become a full-fledged adult. And women, as they are beginning to be allowed to take on all of which they are capable, are attempting to transform their own role as mother into a function—without success, of course, for it is impossible to turn the most obvious of roles into a function. When one speaks of task-sharing between two parents, it can only be a sharing of functions, since roles cannot be shared. And if most women carry a full workload in their jobs and spontaneously shoulder their responsibilities at home, effectively doubling their workload, it is because they know very well that their role as mother cannot be delegated with any kind of adequacy. The totalitarian societies that tried, for egalitarian purposes, to transfer child-rearing to educators, inevitably failed. The same failure often awaits the single mother who thinks she can be both mother and father at the same time. There is no need to bring morality or religion into the issue, since the educative results are quite sufficient to make one realize that the role of father and the role of mother are both indispensable to the child.

Contemporary society, in its desire to extend personal freedom and equality to everyone to the utmost degree in all areas of life, has come to functionalize most social tasks, including sometimes the most personal ones. If we pay municipal employees to take our grandmothers for walks, it is of course because more women now work, and because of the inverse age pyramid, which leaves fewer descendants in charge of an ever greater number of elderly (the opposite used to be the case). These two factors force us to partly functionalize tasks once considered roles. But have we not fallen into excess when we allow ourselves to forget that we have a personal role to play in the lives of the other members of our natural community? This state of affairs does in fact appear to worry us, because we do our best to "personalize" the functions that pick up where the forgotten roles left off: neighborhood social workers, hotline volunteers at help organizations, for example, are praised for their exceptional ability to listen, and they attempt to replace—but can they really?—the parent, brother, or close friend that the functional society has allowed to disappear.

Contemporary society is organized in such a way that only official and measurable guarantees, such as the diploma, status, and career, open the door to many different kinds of activities. Thus the ability to play a role, which requires charisma and a wide variety of other unmeasurable qualities, remains ignored, or is even held in contempt. And this causes all kinds of dysfunction. For as soon as a task involves human relationships in difficult situations, success depends more on personal charisma than on academic achievement. And so it is that many of our teachers, in spite of their impressive academic pedigrees, are completely lacking in pedagogical skills, because it is never on the basis of such skills that they are hired. Students who wish to take care of young children can only become early childhood educators if they pass mathematics and English tests. The very idea of vocation, linked to a role, has become foreign to us.

While some may bemoan the loss of a sense of calling in these professions, which work so closely with moldable human minds, they need not do so. Vocations are still born; they are simply no longer used as criteria in the hiring of personnel. Naturally, the development of a mandarin-style society, with its hierarchy based on diplomas attesting to measurable knowledge, has served the cause of equal opportunity very well, and has, at least until recently, eliminated the acquisition of position through nepotism. But the successful performance of many jobs does not depend on the measurable criteria of the academic establishment. The troubling issues of the housing projects, education, and child-rearing are made more difficult because of our desire to turn everything into functions to be carried out by interchangeable agents. Our social failures largely stem from this calamitous idea: the development of the functionalized society gives rise to human disasters, which cannot be remedied, unless the importance of roles is recognized. The adolescent who steals car radios to pay for his dope because his father has never taken the time to even look at him is in dire need, at the very least, of teachers hired for their pedagogical skills. But the same reason— a misunderstanding of roles—explains the absence of the father and the replacement of an educator with an intellectual.

We are condemned to find inadequate solutions to our problems as long as we cannot find the courage to look at their source. That no individual can any longer simply be assigned to a position constitutes a significant advance in civilization. But must we then conclude that each individual is made for everything? That he no longer possesses his own unique vocation, not in the sense of an external calling, but in the sense of an intimate and unspoken appropriateness to a task? The notion of individual interchangeability, on which our whole social edifice rests, is an ideological certitude that bears little resemblance to social reality. We will have to rediscover the place of roles within our society of functions.

CHAPTER 14
PRODUCTION AND CARE-GIVING

In the overall transition from role to function, the crucial question of unemployment forces us to profoundly transform the way we consider human activity. If we are no longer able to provide a paid job to everyone, and if personal dignity depends on useful social action, we must then promote unpaid activities—either for some, or for everyone on a part-time basis—in the event that job sharing becomes a reality.* Since the individual identifies himself with what he does, and through it acquires his social persona, his self-image, and the recognition of others, it would make sense to accord value to every activity, even unpaid activity, that finds meaning in society—in other words, ensure that all social activity is recognized.

This new challenge calls for imagination. But not just that. The answers are first to be found in an understanding of history, for we have just spent an entire century conscientiously depreciating unpaid activities, and we have done so for very precise reasons. We

---

* In several European countries, the idea of job sharing has been considered as a possible solution to the unemployment problem. For example, five people working at 80 percent could share four full-time jobs. *Trans.*

must now move in the opposite direction—without, however, going back to the previous situation. We must understand what it is that we have lost if we want to invent new ways of existing.

Two types of social activity can be distinguished: activities of production and activities of care-giving, each of which responds to different needs. Production activity includes manufacturing things, cultivating the land, generating wealth through commerce and finance, creating works of art or of the intellect, conceiving and attempting to achieve a better society through social action. Care-giving activity involves the keeping and safekeeping of other beings. It consists of raising children, of simply being thoughtful by expressing affection or friendship, of vigilantly standing by the sick and frail, or of being attentive to the needs of any fragile or destitute individual. Of course it might seem strange to consider care-giving as a full-fledged activity. However, if one thinks about all the human needs that must be satisfied from birth to death, one quickly realizes the magnitude of the care that we crave, expect, and must receive. We are nourished with material goods, culture and artistic appreciation, power and reputation. But the amount of vigilance, care, friendship, and patience that must be given any person, if he is not to be driven insane or to despair, is almost literally incredible. It is tempting to say that care-giving is not an activity per se, and that all this does not count, or that it happens automatically. But this is precisely what is at issue. Our present problems stem in part from the fact that we have progressively devalued care-giving activities.

In the previous society, the activities of production were reserved for men, and were remunerated. The activities of care-giving were generally reserved for women and clerics, and were voluntary and unpaid. Women raised the children and ensured that loved ones were taken care of; the clerics took care of basic education and of the ill, and ensured that the destitute were provided with at least the minimum necessities. Once educative or medical care developed into an activity of the intellect, it immediately changed hands and status: doctors and professors were men and, generally speaking, laymen who were paid for their work. Attending to the basic needs of human beings indeed demands no special competency, nor any official knowledge. But the status of those engaged in each of these areas of activity—that is, the difference in recognition through remuneration or non-remuneration—clearly showed the extent to which there were two essentially different and, properly speaking, incomparable types of activity. This radical distinction must be grasped if we are to understand how one of these two types of activity eventually came to be rejected, and how our present situation is worsened by this rejection.

The activity of production allows one to acquire visible success, reputation, power, money, and social standing. Through this activity, one invents, manufactures, buys and sells, organizes, and then plays games as a sort of diversion from productive acts, in which one exorcises his seriousness by mimicking it. In the previous society, women were not seen playing cards or other games; women did not "play"; they could be idle, but not playful. The world of production pursues concrete results that, if often immaterial, are in any case visible and measurable. Relationships in the world of production favor the exchange of goods, gains (in the sense of the successful wager), and appropriation. The story of the individual is told in his ostensible tribulations, in the glory of changing or enriching the world, or in the triumph of his appearance.

The activity of care-giving, on the other hand, is more difficult to describe. It is not itemized in catalogues. It concerns the person, no longer in the context of the success he achieves in his active outward life, but rather in the basic relationships he has with his fellow beings. It requires of him a heightened vigilance. Every individual gives of himself not only in productive tasks that can be counted in terms of time and effort and correspond to an expected result, but also in a multitude of acts that have no other aim than to maintain and enrich the lives of those around him. In general, these acts concern his relationships with others in the most mundane and trivial sense. These acts do not measure time, nor are they calculated in terms of their profitability. They do not seek to produce, but to per-petuate a simple kind of happiness. And for this reason they seem useless, vain, and even to be dictated by a sort of folly, at least if they are measured according to the standard of production. They gener-ally do not require any certified competency, even if they do require specific abilities and qualities (for there is such a thing as the emo-tionally handicapped, and geniuses of indifference). In the realm of care-giving, all values are inverted: justice consists of giving propor-tionally according to need and not according to merit; the law of giving triumphs to the detriment of that of exchange. Finally, the goods that are offered, such as friendship, confidence, or affection, are multiplied rather than progressively exhausted as they are dis-tributed. Our cultural history symbolizes this truth in the biblical account of the multiplication of the loaves. In that story, what is essential is not so much the miracle, which the mind of the reader generally has difficulty accepting, but the transformation, for there is no miracle in the infinite renewal of giving: in care-giving activity, this sort of miracle happens quite naturally on a daily basis. To the extent that the loaves symbolize the specific values of care-giving, there really is no miracle at work at all.

The activity of production keeps a ledger of solid and verifiable values. The activity of care-giving, which corresponds to invisible values, watches over mysteries. The former, for example, takes shape in the pursuit of a career; the latter, in child-rearing. Naturally, and fortunately for us all, the two worlds are not mutually exclusive: in these two characteristic examples, the pursuit of a career can be car-ried out without neglecting the care-giving values of attentiveness and faithfulness, and child-rearing is not entirely devoid of visible and result-seeking actions. But if we observe these two examples more closely, we find ourselves face-to-face with two character types: the ambitious man, and the woman devoted to her children. The first throws himself into a project and fills his thoughts with hopes for its success. He may at the same time earn a living to feed his family, but his eyes are much more set upon personal achievement.

In the eyes of others he is the actor and author of successes and failures. He identifies himself with his acts and their consequences: profits, relationships, awards. He tells the story of his travels and his encounters. He projects himself outward, and wherever he goes, he is preceded by his good or bad reputation. To witness his undertakings is often to see his entire being: a serious failure instantly ruins his exterior image and the opinion others have of him.

The devoted mother, on the other hand, knows only thankless tasks, and her life is not punctuated by dramatic milestones. She devotes her life to a kind of solicitude, the generosity of which lies hidden in an infinite number of simple and repetitive gestures. In the eyes of others, she is known only by her personal qualities: patience, clear judgment, a spirit oriented to justice rather than to results (since the results these qualities could boast of cannot be evaluated). Her existence, which lacks major events or identifiable projects, disappears behind the inward being, for she has no story to tell, being content to simply be what she is. Her "boring and easy" work goes unpaid because it is priceless, having in itself intrinsic value. She lives in the sphere of giving, in which one provides without exchange, and works without expecting either a wage or consideration. Her invisible work leaves no trace in history; it is useless work, at least when measured against the values of social existence. Considered from an outside point of view, child-rearing is a monotonous and harrying activity carried out in uncertainty, devoid of any model, yielding the worst remorse if it results in failure, and in the case of success, the kind of indifference that accompanies normalcy: it is the work of the "useless servant," lacking any grand plan. If traditional women went to church more often than did their husbands, it was not, as is often thought, because they sought consolation from their fate, having been consigned to ignorance and imprisoned in superstition, like Marx's proletariat, but because their educative task gave them an understanding of, and kept them in natural proximity to, the spiritual world. Between child-rearing and prayer there is but a step; between selling and prayer, there is an abyss. It is through a multitude of insignificant tasks that child-rearing paradoxically carries out very lofty aims. Thus, the women of yesterday knew no middle ground—and this was apparent in their conversations—between the banalities of daily life and the most profound wisdom.

For different reasons—the disappearance of mystery and the desire to hastily resolve everything rationally, the development of economism, the prestige of appearance, and the predominance of functions over roles—the contemporary era is a flight from the world of care-giving. Our contemporary gives himself almost exclusively over to the enterprises of production. This can clearly be seen in his permanent need for outside recognition. Even his charitable actions require the presence of cameras. He will hear nothing of being appreciated for his basic humanity. He needs his projects to be visible.

This evolution is epitomized clearly in the phenomenon of women's entry into the world of success, recognized action, and the career, in short, into the world of production. Our contemporaries here justifiably hail this change as another expression of a culture that has always favored the development of all human faculties. The access women have gained to social success is part of the long history of the spread of knowledge to everyone, and of the substitution of status based on merit for status based on birth. But this sort of revolution, the consequences of which we have yet to see play out, is also a response to the depreciation of care-giving activities. The women of yesterday were the guardians of immeasurable values and, as a rule, found in these values their essential reason for being. But if they were able to work without wages or social recognition, it was because the society of the time gave so much importance to their activities. The "useless servant" of the Bible, who took on an almost angelic and yet perfectly serious status, expressed a density of being, a certain loftiness of conscience, even if he could not have pretensions to competency and social honors. Today, on the other hand, the rise of a society in which nothing is valued that cannot be counted or weighed has reduced the value of care-giving to nothing. Thus, through a shift in interpretation, the "useless servant" has now become a "superfluous man," to use a term from nineteenth-century Russia. An entire population given over to activities of care-giving, and especially child-rearing mothers, suddenly found themselves de-valued. And so this population, in order to avoid contempt, was eager to enter the world of production. The values of care-giving quickly disintegrated and seemed to lose their intrinsic importance. Naturally, the converse was immediately observed: The care-giving world was abandoned as its defenders left it. We see here a case of social transformation that intermingles causes and effects, and the metamorphoses, as is often the case, are mutually sustaining. It is easy to see to what extent we hold this disappeared world in low esteem by the way we describe it: it was the poor and simplistic world of the three K's, *Küche, Kinder, Kirche*—kitchen, children, church—reduced to repetitive rituals, meals, and child-rearing formulae. Expressed in the words of production, the world of care-giving sounds hollow; it expresses a silent and miserable world, an ersatz life.

For the past century, our desire to detach ourselves from religion's constraints, and our concomitant depreciation of spiritual values, have led us to transfer more and more care-giving activities to salaried employees. And so we have witnessed the widespread proliferation of nurses, social workers, daycare workers, teachers, playground supervisors, and so on. Remuneration has indeed helped to give a certain social recognition to activities that have too often been looked upon with disdain. Or at any rate, remuneration partially compensates for the derisory nature that the prevailing economism attributes to them. Nothing today, however, is more depreciated than the care-giving activities that still go unremunerated, which are simply considered the occupations of the idle. This is why the dream of our contemporary is to have a society in which all care-giving activities are exercised by wage-earners: as social assistant, I keep your bored grandmother entertained, while as daycare assistant, you raise my children, whom I can no longer take care of. But if I raise my own children and you take care of your own grandmother then these activities are considered derisory, wasted time—the activities of a wasted life.

This evolution, which no one, and especially not women, could deny the advantages of, has today, however, overrun its limits; it has reached the point of producing perverse effects. The contempt for care-giving activities has at length left out in the cold more and more individuals who cannot be traded for merchandise that can be counted and weighed, but who remain deprived of vigilant care, including delinquent children, the lonely elderly, and so on down the list of all the socially disinherited. Never before has society been in so great a need of solicitude towards human beings, and yet never before has it held this solicitude in such contempt, especially when it goes unremunerated.

Perhaps, then, it is today less a question of revaluing non-salaried activities as it is a question of revaluing the activities of care-giving. Concerning the idea of "work-sharing," the agent of production would most probably agree to work less if he were not ashamed to spend three days a week taking care of his family or performing a social service of some kind. The kind of feverish activity that holds our contemporary in its grips so tightly that he would blush to leave the office early, or to sacrifice evening meetings, comes from a frenzy of production, and not from a frenzy of action as such. By making production his priority, he is escaping from a number of equally important activities, but which he considers more or less unworthy of his time.

The aimless wandering, helplessness, and marginalization that characterize our societies stem above all from the waning of solicitude. The revaluing of care-giving activities would in the long term therefore contribute to the reestablishment of a lost equilibrium. And it would suppose that we had a clear-sighted understanding, without preconceived notions, of human needs. But the reconstitution of our understanding of the human, or of anthropology—

the necessary prelude to an answer to our political and social problems—requires that we take a fresh look at history and time.

PART FOUR

MASTERING THE WORLD
IN A DIFFERENT WAY

CHAPTER 15
FALLEN FROM THE HEIGHTS

In *The Revolt of the Masses*, Ortega y Gasset wrote of our obligation to be equal to our times—that is, out of a sort of *noblesse oblige*, to live up to the level of culture and civilization we have attained as a result of human striving throughout history. Each one of us feels this moral-historical obligation, together with the nagging worry that we are falling further and further behind, in spite of our good will. Are we still worthy of the height of our time, when there is ethnic cleansing in the heart of Europe, agony in Africa, and fourth-world misery in our own streets? It is as if fate had caught up with us, and as if contemporary thinking had come to doubt Progress.

Ortega y Gasset's time saw itself as decadent. But here it will not be a question of decadence. We wish only to try to show that the idea of Progress is due for revision. If we sometimes have the feeling that we have fallen from the height of time, we need not despair, for this is a fall from a misapprehension that might actually turn out to give us reason to hope.

A recent successful movie involved the meeting of two eras. While the characters from the Middle Ages were easily able to adapt and live happily in our time, the reverse scenario of a contemporary man plunged into the Middle Ages was horrifying to the film audience.

There are roads we would rather not travel back up again in reverse. Cicero, for example, wrote, and justly so, that a people could move from despotism to a republic, but would not willingly move in the opposite direction.[1] And this is what worries us: it is clear that through the sophisticated development of freedom and well-being we have achieved, we have today attained a certain "height of time," and yet certain of our conquests seem now to be in question, which makes us feel as if we are moving backward: in other areas, it seems to us impossible to move ahead any further, and since there can be no standing still, we seem destined to regress; furthermore, progress often does not bring the happiness we had hoped for.

The first two observations put into question the inevitability, and also the permanence, of progress. Is the Western achievement of peace, well-being, and material security now to be challenged? Is it really a failure, and in what way, to now fall to such a low from the height of time? Furthermore, our feeling of satisfaction leads us into an insurmountable contradiction. Certain of our achievements—and democracy probably constitutes the best example—seem so perfect that no change could possibly improve them: we simply cannot imagine anything better. In theory, if no improvements can be made, perfection has been attained. But this is far from the case. The third observation, that progress has not brought the happiness for which we had hoped, reveals a doubt about the postulate that progress and happiness are identical. The observation can therefore go so far as to question the validity of progress itself. At the very least it calls for a renewed reflection about what constitutes happiness.

These disappointments should not be understood solely as an admission of powerlessness (i.e., that we are no longer capable of achieving improvement); they are also, and even more so, the reflection of a sense that a promise has been broken, as if history has not kept its word.

The ideology of Progress describes man as being a creditor of time. The constant improvement of societies resembles the attainment of adulthood—one speaks of societies still "in their infancy."

Maturity is not merely an appropriation, but a claim to be redeemed from time. Human societies, like children, hold hidden potentialities within them, which time must reveal. Man has a claim to greatness, a claim not earned, but given because it lies hidden in History. Thus, the man of progress becomes a conqueror of the inevitable. Everything he undertakes leads him to his goal; after all, "one cannot stop progress." Time thus presents itself as a theater for the expected arrival of greatness.

Henceforth, to fall from the height of time indicates not only a historical fall, but an ontological fall as well. Has Western man not defined himself as a being of progress? In fact what worries us today is less the troubles we suffer than the shattered ontology that these troubles signify. What worries us about the war in the Balkans is not so much the bitter hatred that has shown its face as what this war has revealed: a catastrophic deviation from the historic order of improvement. Had we not come to believe that war would soon seem to be nothing but provincial quarreling, like an issue from another era? In his *Three Conversations*, written in 1899, Soloviev has a politician who represents the intelligentsia of his time say, "The military period of history has come to an end. . . . I am perfectly convinced that neither we nor our children will know great wars, real wars. . . . Does war have meaning? It depends. Yesterday it may have had a meaning everywhere, today it has none outside of certain regions in Africa or Central Asia, where there are still savages; but tomorrow it will have no meaning anywhere."[2] Today, the man on the street shakes his head and mumbles, "A war in Europe, at the end of the twentieth century . . . !" In other words, we have come all this way for nothing! How can such an incredible setback be understood? For lack of a historical or philosophical explanation, a sociological one is found by designating a scapegoat: the ex-Yugoslavian combatants were drawn from "primitive" or "medieval" tribes characterized by prehistoric customs. Thus the ideology of Progress is saved by blaming the war on the lost savages still found in the midst of modern men. This argument, however, rings false.

The peoples of the West know very well that this war reveals a failure of their theories.

For a long time we have believed that to live in times of satisfaction was our due. So when war, misery in the heart of our cities, the unstoppable epidemic of AIDS, and the trampling of human rights in Africa and elsewhere persist, they seem like acts of provocation. These events represent irrationality exploding within the rational, ancient evils irrupting in the heart of a highly perfected universe. Nothing led us to expect them. Everything led us to believe that such problems would be progressively but definitively overcome. Whence the dumbfoundedness of contemporary man, who looks for culprits to explain the wayward straying of history, and who tries to find things to blame for the broken mechanism: the state, Europe, immigrants, national or international neo-Fascists. When at the peak of his distress he is faced with a world that seems to be crumbling before his eyes, he sometimes, ashamed of his own species, gives in to misanthropy. At the end of the century, after so many disappointed hopes, man finally seems to be nothing more than a barbarian. Why then value him more than trees or animals, which are innocent? It seems as if humanity had become unworthy of the standing that Western culture has conferred upon it since the advent of Christianity. If deep ecology is an anti-humanism, and the first anti-humanism to flourish since Nazism, it stems from the disappointment caused by failed utopias. What is man worth after all, if he cannot preserve his achievements or answer for his legitimate hopes?

Over the past fifty years, we found ourselves in a situation that was in some respects unreal, almost ahistorical, a period that seemed to corroborate completely the ideology of progress. Our circumstances were such that we could believe that a "height of time" had been attained. The relative paradise of the postwar period, the exponential development of medicine, the unbelievable rebirth of democracies, appeared to signify the birth of the kind of "satisfied times" spoken of in the nineteenth century, in the sense that men could finally be self-sufficient, or could have a sufficiency of everything they had hoped for. The Cold War decades also placed us in an unreal situation. We lived without war, we had relegated conflicts to the shadows, repressed and impossible. And yet we lived with the anxiety of facing the possibility of a war that would be the last, if it came, destroying any possibility of future wars. In other words, war was conceived as being outside of history, because it was both impossible and final. The Cold War in a sense ensured peace, but its silence also bespoke the preparation of the apocalypse. Neither this peace nor this war was normal, human, or historical. The first was like shortened breaths in preparation for the second, which would put an end to our history.

We have, then, just emerged from a long interlude. The abundance of the postwar era, as well as the Cold War, were digressions. Misery and conflict were largely absent except as abstractions. We have now returned to time, to normality. We are faced with the frightening rediscovery of a fragile society, of exposed man. And we are also faced with the intuition that our certitude of an inevitable historical victory was mistaken.

Apart from our inability to preserve certain achievements, there is something perhaps even more disquieting: our achievements themselves have generated new and unexpected misfortunes. Our comfortable societies have given rise to disorders of the soul. Prolonged life expectancy has given us a population of lonely and despair-stricken seniors. The universalization of education has not eliminated illiteracy, which remains surprisingly high, nearly 20 percent in France at the end of the twentieth century. The consumers of abundance still seek to understand the meaning of their lives. It would be easy to draw up a full catalogue of the ills caused by our happiness.

Whence this self-evident conclusion: we may be able to do a lot, but we cannot do everything without impunity. The limit we perceive in the march of progress does not reside in what can be identified as impossible, or in the limits of action. It resides rather in the finitude of the good. Progress is probably infinite in its realization, but the resulting good has shown itself to be finite. We can provide everyone with a mass of benefits, not only material, but cultural and spiritual as well, but we cannot guarantee their happiness. On the contrary, most of the advantages we can provide create other, unanticipated ills.

Furthermore, even if progress is infinite in its concrete manifestations, these manifestations always remain fragile and uncertain. It is precisely this fragility that we are now discovering. Our conquests tell the story of a tremendous effort to master not only physical nature, but human nature as well. But our efforts have not, however, transformed the human fabric. Behind the glorious façade lurks everything we thought we had rid ourselves of. All of our acquisitions are temporary, and in order to maintain them we have no choice but to prolong our efforts. Exhaustion threatens every acquisition, and thus there must be a comparison between each acquisition's advantages and the sacrifices that have to be made for it. The age of democracy, technology, and international law is ultimately an age of constraint. And every generation must reassume this exhausting effort of self-domination. For our achievements are accompanied by self-doubt, and this doubt begins with a questioning of the universal value of our successes and of the necessity to export or impose them elsewhere. And while we go about this questioning, our societies search for a new definition of happiness, since it no longer seems to be so securely tied to knowledge, exponential increases in comfort, or unlimited freedom.

We have perhaps made the mistake of too quickly equating human happiness with its circumstantial and partial expressions, as well as the mistake of believing that the indefinite extension of happiness comes from an indefinite extension of its temporary expressions. The concrete manifestations of freedom and security in the modern era are naturally understood as representing an immense improvement in our well-being. However, liberty, when exercised without limits, distorts and disorients the personality. And the individual, when excessively protected, is stunted in his growth; having avoided all risks, he becomes anxious when faced with even the smallest challenge, and thus lives a petty existence. Growing with no other limit than the financial capacities of the nation, and in general even beyond them, rights viewed as entitlements ultimately make a society impotent; paradoxically, some gifts eventually impoverish.

It is as though the definition of happiness has been literally confiscated by a few ideals deemed sufficient in and of themselves: liberty, security, material well-being, and the diffusion of culture. We act as if it were sufficient to take these ideals to their extremes in order to achieve social contentment. Liberty and security, to name two characteristic examples, are rendered sacred by being thought of as definitive and complete expressions of happiness. But their excessive realization actually undermines the very happiness they were supposed to generate.

Our disappointment in discovering the insufficiency and the vicissitudes of progress tells us that happiness should really be defined as a balance of opposites: liberty and responsibility, security and risk. Such conflicting ideals are necessarily difficult to attain and maintain. Their equilibrium is, in every era, the fruit of patient labor and always remains precarious. Each era must carry out the troubling task of discovering a workable solution. And each government must walk a tightrope, summoned by circumstances to develop freedom where it is lacking, and to arouse responsibility where it falls short. If such is the case—if the happiness of men and of peoples consists of this ill-assured equilibrium—then it goes without saying that our collective ends must be thoroughly reexamined. It is not a matter of promising or guaranteeing, as politicians are wont to do, ever-greater protection, because protection ultimately deadens the sense of personal responsibility, and destroys humans' ability to achieve personal autonomy. Nor is it a matter of ever-greater peace, for if peace comes at any price, peoples lose their dignity. Instead, we must vigilantly consider where the limits to security lie, beyond which protection actually destroys individuals—a question we do not now ask, of course, convinced as we are of the absolute value of personal security. We must also constantly ask ourselves at what point peace becomes undesirable, the point beyond which the protection of human lives deprives a people of what was once called honor—again a question we do not now ask, convinced as we are that human life has absolute value above any other consideration.

We are learning from our uncertain and as yet unconceptualized experience that we have yet to form an adequate image of happiness. Condorcet and his epigones left us with an image of human happiness defined by certain gains: liberty, comfort, equality, and victories over illness and death. Happiness does in a way involve all these things, but it still remains a mysterious alchemy. This is why redefining the idea of progress has become a necessity. If progress is understood as an irresistible and beneficent advance towards ever more equality, liberty, comfort, security, and peace, it is ultimately brought into question by precisely the advantages it procures. For in many areas, we have pursued these gains to the point where they now work to our detriment. And if progress is understood as a constant expansion of happiness, as the enhancement of the most diverse of human abilities, it must take other avenues than the ones to which we are accustomed. We will have to reflect upon our humanity with each step we take in order to discover which recipes for equilibrium are appropriate. In this sense, progress must be thought of as a discovery of humanity as much as an improvement of the human condition. As things stand now, every discovery—social, medical—reveals to us the face of a humanity we do not know, or that we have forgotten, or that we have been pretending to forget.

Progress, no longer equated with the exponential development of certain gains, must rather be defined as the continuing perfection of humanity as it continues to reveal itself, and the continuing perfection of humanity as revealed through a constant inquiry into what constitutes happiness. Heretofore, the notion that progress merely consisted of the acquisitions of liberty, security, etc., made any questioning of perfection useless and superfluous, while at the same time it deprived us of the criteria needed to guide such questioning. It seemed pointless to ask whether such-and-such an advance in liberty or security made man happier. Of course it did. The definition of happiness was closed. Consequently, modern progress could be achieved simply through the competence and imagination of technicians.

The feeling of a discouraging fall that haunts us today does not, in fact, reveal that our points of reference were mistaken. For liberty and peace do indeed contribute to the growth of human happiness, and in this respect they have not led us astray. But our discouragement does reveal our error of conferring absolute status upon these points of reference, the error of completely and utterly equating them with happiness, of which they are essential but partial and imprecise conditions.

Our times, therefore, require not a reversal of values, but rather a repositioning of values according to the criterion of a happiness that is less theoretical or ideological than it is experimental. This constant refining of the definition of happiness, grounded in a better anthropology, will furthermore allow us to escape the deepest disappointments that now confront us. Convinced as we have been that progress would eventually cure all our ills, and believing that human nature could be reshaped, we have until now viewed our condition as the sum of various illnesses. And in this respect, our disappointment stems not from poorly directed action, nor from a decline in what we thought was a promising dynamic, but from an erroneous understanding of human reality. This is why only an unceasing anthropological quest can give us a better chance to discover just which avenue progress should take.

CHAPTER 16
FRAGMENTED EXISTENCE

Each era expresses its spirit through its specific vision of measureless time. This vision may be expressed by the idea of eternity, as representing new and unlimited life beyond death, or the idea of immortality, as representing the very negation of death. Man may imagine himself as personally surviving death, or on the contrary, he may imagine himself becoming incorporated into the cosmos, or he may seek to perpetuate himself symbolically through historical works. Because man invariably finds the idea of his precariousness repulsive, in one way or another every culture attempts to carefully work out an expression of permanence.

We have emerged from two successive eras, each with its own concept of how the individual would perpetuate himself. The man of the religious era expected an eternity in which a never-ending life awaited him after death, even if the form of this life was unknowable. The man of the ideological age chose to survive himself through the values he defended within his lifetime, and through his political and social legacies. He believed that every fully free and brotherly man of the future would, in a way, exist in his name and in his place. He thought that the radiant future, built by his hard work and determination, would forever maintain the ideal that gave meaning to his life.

Very broadly, the previous man learned, from childhood on, to prolong his precarious life in the service of institutions he typically had not created himself, but to the perpetuation of which he was devoted. He defended established beliefs or certitudes within the context of a movement, lineage, or nation, and sometimes out of simple loyalty—his biological or cultural ancestors had fought for them. He committed himself to institutions in order to guarantee their stability and duration. He transmitted to his children a way of life that he himself had inherited, thereby pointing to values worthy of immortality and identifying himself as a participant in their immortality. He sought to eternalize the concrete achievements of his forefathers, whether business enterprises or other projects. Finally, he took pains to maintain and safeguard the material things to which he was attached beyond their utilitarian value, whether they were trinkets, furniture, or buildings, because they had a value based on memory. He also deliberately located himself within a set of relationships and meanings the durability of which he in turn had to ensure. And so he felt that he was participating, as a mortal, in something immortal, at least with respect to himself. He knew that his own image, even after he had died, would survive through the material or immaterial works of which he had acted as guarantor.

The man of today does not seek immortality any more than he seeks eternity. He has discarded religions and hopes of eternity. He has dismissed both ideology and millenarian hopes of social immortality. But what is more, as a sovereign and independent individual, he has severed his existence from all human works that go beyond himself. It would seem then, and this would be for the first time in history, that contemporary man is absolutely deprived of the concept of measureless time.

One might well ask why it is that we have refused all identification with anything that would allow us, even symbolically, to survive. We have not lost the idea of our precariousness, nor the inner revolt that makes us hate this precariousness. We still hope against hope to last, even while we know that we will not.

But we have seen how man's hope for measureless time has ultimately held the present hostage. The temptation of Christianity was to sacrifice time to eternity, which had as its consequence the relativization and devaluing of individual existence. The ideologies of the modern age substituted immortality for eternity by temporalizing the human hope for durability. But the same temptation pushed them to sacrifice time to immortality, present society to future society. Indeed, they obliterated the present, a process that totalitarianism displays to us in all its abuses.

The religious sacrifice of time to eternity confined human existence to a lesser state of being, which men not only had to content themselves with, but which they also had to go beyond, in a quest for perfection, in order to gain access to eternity. The ideological sacrifice of time to immortality made existence blatantly inhuman. For it was no longer a question of assuming and going beyond human mediocrity, but of actually eradicating it—and to reach this end, the mediocre man had to be crushed.

In a similar way, the man of previous ages, having achieved symbolic immortality through his identification with a family, a business, or a work, had to sacrifice all or part of his individual existence for the protection of this immortality. In a sense, he had to earn his symbolic immortality by forever valuing his lifework over his own inclinations and personal projects. He could only last by identifying with a work capable of lasting. He defined himself as a trustee, in self-effacing service to and responsible for his charge, these works of existence which promised him the endless time of immortality.

Today, we acutely feel the futility of all these sacrifices. So many individual existences have been given over to projects that in the end did not last. It was with the laudable aim of giving all value to immanence that modern ideologies denied religious eternity and made heaven come down to earth. For is it really necessary to give up what one has today, however precarious, in order to attain eternal benefits, of which no one can guarantee the reality? The immortality offered by ideologies, however, turned out to be an even more tangible fraud, because in its name entire peoples were massacred, deported, dispossessed, and left utterly without the ability to hope. As for the kind of symbolic immortality conferred upon the individual through his participation in collective works, this also demands self-sacrifice. We are all aware of the coercive way generations of sons found themselves bound to common traditions, to family businesses, to certain skills, and to their fathers' convictions.

Must we believe, then, that eternity and immortality can be nourished only by devouring the present? That such visions of measureless time are imprisoning? That the idea of immortality kills life? That the individual must be diminished in order to gain the means for survival beyond his own lifetime? We believe we have made a cost-free renouncement: eternity is a hypothetical notion, and social immortality entails the acceptance of dangerous utopian ideals. Thus, contemporary man no longer seeks any joy he cannot have in the present. If he dismisses eternity and immortality, it is because he is tired of seeing the present sacrificed for an uncertain future. Too often duped, like someone whose hovel has been expropriated on the promise of a palace that never materializes, he now only wishes to take advantage of his brief but sure duration on this earth.

Our contemporary considers it normal that the individual of each generation should question the certainties of his forefathers. He suspects, and often rightly so, that institutions transmit ideas that lead nowhere, that they are but empty suits of armor. He questions the upbringing he received. He will hear nothing of sacrificing his own inclinations in order to perpetuate a family business or preserve material things, especially since the economic and demographic circumstances in which he lives often reduce inheritance to a mere memory. He has seen so many inherited certainties, institutions, and behavior patterns turn out to be indefensible that it is without regret that he abandons all of these obligations.

Over the course of previous ages, the present was devalued because of its precariousness: it was better to put ephemeral reality to work for a durable reality. Today, it is this very precariousness that makes the present so precious: life is too short, says the advertiser, to dress so poorly. . . . In other words, the individual prefers to live a life without any restraint whatsoever rather than to limit the richness of his present in order to prepare for a possible afterlife, either real or symbolic. He prefers a liberated existence reduced to biological time to an existence that hopes to survive itself, but which is more or less sacrificed to whatever it hopes for. In fact, very few of us would contest this way of seeing things. There is only one existence of which we can be sure, and that is our biological existence. We cannot bear the thought of sacrificing ourselves to a theoretical God, an imaginary radiant future, or institutions that the future will prove futile.

The question remains, however, of just how our temporal existence is then to be organized. Is the duration of our biological life sufficient unto itself?

An observation forces itself upon us: not only has the existence of our contemporary been liberated from the vision of measureless time (in the form of religious aspirations, institutional legacies, community symbols of that which endures), it has also been divested of its own continuity. In fact, the two are probably related. As soon as the categories of eternity and immortality disappear, individual existence becomes fragmented. Stated otherwise, individuals have abandoned the very idea of a life-work (*œuvre*). What is left of time is not simply a shortened duration; it is time shattered into many fragments.

This fragmentation can be seen today in all areas of individual and social existence. It represents the structure of, and the backdrop to, our societies. The individual's life, no longer the account of an *œuvre*, consists only of moments or scattered slices of life without connections to each other. We see a fragmentation of social and political existence because we do not know what kind of society we want to build, and we are content to simply deal with the crucial problems of the day. We see a fragmentation of history into "memoirs," each shedding light on an event called forth by emotion and separated from the whole where alone meaning can survive. We see a fragmentation of ethical norms, the constraining force of which is determined by indignation or sentimentality instead of any guiding principle.

Why does existence stripped of the concept of measureless time fragment in this way?

First of all, it is very difficult to accept the idea of death if one has deliberately accepted that the duration of the person, taken symbolically, ends at the limit of biological life, or if one has decreed that no one can survive death, either as oneself in eternity, or by identifying with immortal ideas or works.

Both the religious man and the ideological man had come to terms with their own death. Both voluntarily sacrificed aspects of their biological existence for the promise of eternal or immortal duration. Religious man believed that each moment of this life shaped the life he would have after death. Ideological man thought that his combat for a radiant future symbolically inscribed his acts in capital letters in an immortal future society. Both, in different ways, were able to face their own death and, in living out their lives, to rob death of its power. In the same way, the man living in a stable, traditional society made sacrifices every day in order to maintain certain immortal undertakings—the nation or the tribe or any valued institution—and thereby rose above his own biological death by making it relative. All of these men were able to accept their own death in the name of spiritual hope, social hope, or the survival of a work or institution. In other words, their life had meaning; it signified or stood for something, and could therefore quietly disappear behind its points of reference. And so death did not mean an absolute end; it was subordinated to something greater and therefore devoid of any sense of catastrophe.

Contemporary man no longer has at his disposal anything more than his own limited existence, of which death constitutes the absolute end, no longer only biologically, but also spiritually, socially, and symbolically. He no longer hopes for any beyond. He no longer considers that his existence can stand for anything his biological life will never know. He is thereby entirely given over to his own finitude, understood as a prison from which there is no escape. Because this situation is unbearable, he escapes by fleeing from time itself, by fragmenting the duration of his existence.

The man of fragmented existence may be unaware of, or pretend to be unaware of, his own finitude. For he floats through events and ventures one after another without tying them together, each one forming a whole that is interrupted only by a subsequent event or enterprise. We are not dealing here, however, with Pascal's man of distraction. The fragmented man does not necessarily seek to distract his mind from the weight of necessities, nor to find pleasure in the moment through hedonism. He knows very well that he must die, but its necessity never presents itself to him because his fragmented acts do not demand the integration of this idea into a complete whole. Contemporary man lives through successive deaths, for each of his projects is fleeting. Yet at the same time, he lives as if death did not exist. One might say more precisely that he lives in the moment, or as if he were not the creature who has been known to wonder about the enigma of death.

Death, however, is the fundamental question of existence, primarily since existence is only meaningful because of its precariousness. If we take away the certitude of its ending, it loses its essential structure. Even our greatest joys, which we recognize as being moments of eternity, draw their grandeur from their comparison with the precariousness of everything. There is another reason that death is the fundamental question of existence: it is that man's existence is always more limited than his thoughts, which very naturally strain against their limits, as they forever look beyond for an invisible horizon. Thought resembles a wild horse penned up in a corral, never staying in the middle, but always running up against the fence, forlornly contemplating the forbidden spaces beyond. We must admit that we simply do not know if something exists beyond death. This ignorance indefinitely leaves the question open. And no one will ever be able to keep us from wondering if this existence is the only reality, to be ended one day by death, or if some other reality beyond death will relegate our present existence to a sort of second rank. Stated otherwise, we naturally walk the tightrope between the conviction of contemporary man, for whom reality is summed up in life and for whom death is a catastrophe, and the intuition of Socrates, who, when speaking about his debt to Asclepius, intimated that life is an illness death cures us from by delivering us into immortality. The sort of questioning that this alternative stimulates, and which individual minds, peoples, and epochs have formulated in their own ways, is part of what is intrinsically human. Man is unique in that he does not find life sufficient.

Our contemporary looks upon death with contempt. Not that he is ecstatic about his situation, attached firmly as he is to this world, a little bit like the village idiot. He is not unaware of the precariousness of his existence, and yet he obstinately refuses to consider this precariousness as a question. It is as if he uses his properly human abilities not to remain in the uncomfortable position at the edge of a precipice, looking out into the unknown, but rather to relentlessly suppress the questions that seem to spring up everywhere. He does not even allow questions about death to formulate themselves, and balks in disgust when such questions are presented to him. He has simply decided to live as if present existence is all there is, and as if death were nothing but its catastrophic end. Perhaps he is right and Socrates was wrong. The problem, however, really lies elsewhere. For man is the anomalous being who asks such questions, and if he supposes that they have been answered even before they have been asked, then he can be sure that an essential dimension to his life is missing.

This is undoubtedly why the appearance of AIDS, a sort of death that lurks about pervasively, generates such a feeling of terror and revolt. Of course, it is quite natural that we should feel revolted and terrified when confronted with death, but in our fear of AIDS, something else is going on. For here we are witness to the brutal and unexpected irruption of death into a world where it had virtually been forgotten. By the undoing of time, and by its fragmentation into discontinuous moments, death had been removed and, in a way, had become impossible. But its plausible proximity, its ghost, has now become present in every corner, and has given rise to a panic of which every image of our time bears the trace.

If existence, when deprived of the concept of measureless time, ultimately fragments, it is because the internal structure of the self must maintain certain relationships with the future. By what process can existence in general ensure its continuity? What is the cement that keeps existence from breaking up into chaotic and incomplete undertakings? An examination of the individual whose life is ordered, a character not seen very frequently in contemporary society, gives us the key to the answer. Such a man is someone who follows through on what he says and does, for example, by keeping his word right to the end, or by respecting the commitments he has made. His life forms a whole, or rather, a plurality of wholes, which do not contradict each other but are rather in harmony. In other words, he takes others into consideration in all his commitments. He attempts as best he can to not speak unless his actions can back up what he says. He repairs any damage he has caused. In short, he is responsible. He answers for himself and for the impact he has in the world, which is to say that he accepts responsibility for his own desires and opinions in the same way a father accepts responsibility for his son: he assumes responsibility for their effects and attempts to ensure their consistency.

Of course, assuming responsibility is an exhausting business. Intentions, full of youthful zeal when first conceived, quickly tire out. Commitments, undertaken in full enthusiasm, quickly become heavy burdens. The urge to balk or to back out comes easily. But actual accomplishment remains difficult. It is always tempting to give up at the first sign of difficulty. How then can responsibility exist? What force can motivate an individual to assume responsibility for his actions and their consequences to the detriment of his momentary desires? The answer is nothing, apart from the idea of the œuvre, that intimate desire to be able to look back upon one's life as a life-work, and the fear of having to look back upon nothing more than a succession of scattered, disjointed periods and actions. Every man fears leaving behind nothing but a series of random acts representing the failure to satisfy this desire. He vaguely fears this failure because he feels that a human being worthy of the name can do more than live a fragmented existence, that it is possible for man to unify and give structure to his life, and furthermore, that life is worth more in the end if lived as a whole.

We can clearly see this desire at work in the expressions of everyday speech, which always have great significance. If one regrets having "spoiled one's life," or "wasted one's life," or "made nothing of one's life," it is because one feels that one's life has been insufficient. We are not talking here about sheer emptiness, because no existence is devoid of actions, encounters, and enterprises of all kinds, but rather about an existence that seems full of things that ultimately amount to nothing, because when considered as a whole, they simply make no sense.

Existence is our only inheritance. It is a gift of time, the span of which we do not know. Man is not identified with his existence, which is exactly what "ex-istence" means. He stands back from it to get a better look at it. He plans for, dreams about, and shapes it, at least as long as melancholy or despair do not paralyze him. His dearest desire is to be the master of his existence and to not become a plaything of destiny, as the Greeks used to say. He hopes to not become like the man who lets events dictate his direction. It is as if each of us is given a single blank page and a single pen filled with indelible ink. The page cannot be replaced and the pen strokes cannot be erased, much to the chagrin of our contemporary, who loves all things temporary, "starts his life over" again and again, and easily believes that he can be born again, thereby contradicting the old adage that "you've only got one life to live." His chagrin at not being able to wipe the slate clean, however, also expresses his hope for a life-work. We cannot edit things out, but we can fine-tune things, honing them to perfection if time permits. But there has to be a dream or a plan to start with. One cannot fine-tune chaos. Furthermore, the original blank page fills itself in if we do not willfully fill it in ourselves. Many people fret over the fact that the page is already so full, in spite of their not having purposely decided to put anything there. This undoubtedly indicates a desire to name and characterize one's own existence. To have a life-work means to have a name. The fragmented life has no name; it leaves no recognizable traces.

To pursue a life-work is to create order amidst the overall disorder of the world. It is a flower in the tumult, meaning in the midst of meaninglessness. Even if the work does not express anything great, it mysteriously bears witness to what man is. It is a sign of the depth of humanity and as such establishes a sure link with symbolic immortality. Through it, man defines himself as a being who can escape from the chaos of contingency to dominate the passing of time, a being who resists the absurd by trying to shape scattered bits and pieces into a meaningful whole. In other words, he is a being who challenges the necessity of death, both hopelessly and with confidence. Since one day he must shuffle off the stage, he hopes to leave behind a sign of his presence, a minute yet significant trace: an existence with a name. The life-work is a reflection of its author and remains after him, as if the image lingered in the mirror after the person himself had left.

Existence lived out as the fashioning of a work of art tells the tale of a battle against chaos. The infant experiences no more than a series of scattered sensations and feelings, the adolescent, a series of scattered meanings, while the adult is one who names and gives structure to existence. But this structure always remains uncertain and precarious. At every instant some elements are being added while others are being lost. We spend our lives sifting the known from the unknown, trying to gather bits and pieces into a cohesive whole. One's feelings, fears, abilities, and failures all must be named. We unceasingly re-establish hierarchies and points of reference. New elements of experience must be recognized and judged. We must exercise discernment in order to detect elements we judge to be unacceptable. Our plans, ventures, loves—the monuments of our lives—must be constantly rebuilt or they will fall from neglect. We have two adversaries: the labyrinth, where meaning is hidden, and disorder, where chance reigns.

The life-work shapes its author at the same time that he shapes it. Each of us becomes what he can be by gathering his life around him, and by building himself around a mobile but unbroken axis. The reality of the concrete person, of the being having become, requires a continuity that is sought, if not always found. The life-work expresses a destiny, not in the sense of a fate, but in the sense of a meaningful history. The man without a life-work has no destiny. Those who suffer from the illnesses of destiny of which Lipot Szondi spoke are men with fragmented existences.[1]

The man of fragmented existence consumes his life instead of shaping it. One can indeed consume what is given. Life, however, is not given, but lent: it must be given back. Given back perhaps, but to whom, one might ask, since God the creator has disappeared from the realm of certitudes? And yet the disappearance of God leaves this self-evident truth intact: the man at the edge of death cannot help but want to answer for himself by asking, what have I accomplished?

Man is as much an author as he is an actor. Through his actions he can leave behind an architecture of being that survives him. The reality of the life-work represents the author's being and makes him unique. Thus, the life-work lifts man into existence by conferring upon him the status of author. An individual cannot be defined by his hidden abilities or potential. But neither are his acts sufficient to define him, because one can after all act chaotically. No, he is defined through his life-work and if he does not take up this task, he will never know who he is. And no one can accept death before he knows who he is.

Nevertheless, man as creator of a life-work is exposed to tremendous risks: His work can come undone, leaving him naked and exhausted. For that reason, contemporary man takes no risks. It is not that he disdains the idea of a life-work, for he admires and even openly envies the artists of existence, and yet he fears being taken in or making mistakes. In short, he is afraid to invest in projects that may turn out to be worthless. And so he chooses the certitude of the present. He therefore resolves to live exclusively through his actions, and so he busies himself, running away from emptiness. It often happens that he lets entire swaths of his life slip away, out of neglect. Meanings pile up without hierarchy, thrown one on top of the other. Man seems to come undone, scattered about himself in pieces. His universe is a forest of contradictions. He allows the unanswered questions and the uncertainties to accumulate. Sometimes, when he becomes troubled by all this inconsistency, he tries to create a space where meaning can thrive. But he grows weary. The entropy of it all overwhelms him and drives him to despair. More often than not he goes to great lengths to point at what he finds unacceptable, without managing to identify it by any means other than his own indignation.

The morality of complacency generally undermines the creation of a life-work, since the author of a life-work has to sacrifice many of his immediate desires for the sake of his creation, not because he is an unreasonable masochist but in order to protect a continuity. Everyone knows how difficult it is to pursue a life-work, whether it be a professional, intellectual, artistic, educative, or sentimental one. It often involves negotiating contradictions, making the potential actual, undertaking the unthinkable, and daring to do things others find reprehensible. A life-work is fragile to the point of being discouraging. It requires the very qualities that the morality of complacency rejects: patience, responsibility, commitment to one's word, and faithfulness to oneself.

How can a life-work find its purpose exclusively within itself? The cohesiveness and the structure it implies makes sense only if, in one way or another, the result is intended to be worthy of immortality. The image of shaped and ordered destiny, on which its author can look back in satisfaction, acquires worth only insofar as it has the quality of a human model. If the author wanted this for himself, and for his own happiness, it is because his happiness required a higher sort of existence than the kind that gets lost in a chaos of incoherent meanings and actions. He wanted to show what could be done. And in so doing, albeit unwittingly, he often locates points of reference for the rest of humanity. He leaves behind him an order that bears meaning; he does "useful work." He registers his name in the future. Thus, the structure-building will that is able to ensure cohesiveness in the finite time of a biological life finds its roots in measureless time.

Is a lifetime sufficient? This is one of the questions that should trouble the minds of the present age. Without a desire for eternity nor a desire for symbolic immortality, time simply breaks up and takes the form of a pile of sand or a shapeless mass of atoms set adrift. Our contemporary's fragmented and fleeting existence, so often described in sociological accounts, results directly from the inability of biological time to be sufficient when the idea of a personal future beyond death is absent. It is as if it were impossible for us to live within the short horizon afforded by biological existence. We must either prolong it or fragment it.

We observe today that, while the individual rejects responsibility for the institutions of the past or of the future, there remains a single area in which the individual accepts to consider things in the terms of a future that lies beyond him: the environment. In environmental issues, contemporary man has a rekindled sense of the notion of responsibility. He refuses to act as a steward of the institutions, projects, or traditions of his predecessors. He does not assume responsibility for the continuity of the human undertakings that represent his cultural environment. Yet he readily acts as a steward of the natural environment. He would protect any forest before he would defend any institution.

What are we to make of this exception? Why forests rather than institutions? For contemporary man, who now chooses his values and his lifestyles, the only thing left to preserve for the future are the conditions that make individual choices possible. What is important is to ensure the continued duration of an open world in which everything will be possible, both at the cultural level and at the level of values. This explains why he worries so much about keeping the natural and biological milieu intact and so little about prolonging the works of culture, which cast a shadow over his inventiveness and his autonomy. The environment represents the empty theater without which nothing is possible, but above all, in which everything is possible. It is the faceless and nameless milieu in which the future man with no ties and no obligations will find himself. To be ecologically responsible is to maintain the minimal natural conditions that will allow man seen as lacking immortality, to perpetuate himself as such.

On the other hand, with deep ecology a radically different relationship to time is established. Deep ecology obscurely reflects the resurgence of the disquieting desire that we all feel to survive ourselves. This phenomenon in itself reveals to what extent we are destined to desire the concept of measureless time. It is one of the signs indicating that we truly feel biological time to be radically insufficient, even if we claim to accept it. Deep ecology expresses the rebirth of a desire for immortality after the waning of religious conceptions of eternity and ideology's concept of social immortality. In deep ecology, nature is what survives us, and thus man becomes secondary in comparison with the immortal natural world with which he will one day be fused: clearly, this is a contemporary variant of pantheism. But this unique vision of immortality today represents the only door open to a possible afterlife, and the only struggle for which contemporary man agrees to make sacrifices. For he indeed feels responsible for the preservation of nature, and is proud of the vigilance he shows in exercising this responsibility. Our contemporary, who considers Christian fasting on Fridays or Muslim fasting during Ramadan to be absurd, may, however, become a vegetarian out of personal conviction. He has here discovered something more important than himself, and above all, something more durable; and his stubbornly perennial disappointment at being mortal latches onto this discovery. Ecology has here become a worldview in its own right. It has its gurus, its priests, its fashions and patterns of behavior. Containing all the elements of a religion of the pre-Christian era, it testifies to the inability of man throughout the ages to live within the narrow and too-soon fractured span of his biological existence.

CHAPTER 17
GOD IN EXILE

At the dawn of the third millennium, the peoples of the West find themselves voluntarily devoid of religion, while at the same time, a large number of people on the planet have nothing but religion. A strange situation, to be sure. Neither of these two circumstances seems "normal," in the sense that it is doubtful that societies can maintain themselves in either case. Furthermore, the proximity of these two worlds makes for an extremely explosive situation.

If man asks the religious question, it is because he must necessarily die, even while he harbors within himself the desire for immortality. Yet the thought and the certitude of death do not sum up what life is. A happy man must be able to act as if he would live forever, building projects with as much passion and interest as if nothing could destroy them. And he must also live as if he were going to die tomorrow, seizing precarious joys for what they are— moments when existence seems blessed with the kind of fullness which finitude specifically lacks.

Those peoples who possess nothing but religion appear to be devoid of precisely these worldly projects and undertakings that constitute the primary prerequisites of happiness. Because, for a variety of historical reasons, they have failed to resolve their economic, political, educational, or other problems, they find refuge in religions where the importance of this failure can be minimized. But men are not angels. An ascetic or a saint, through perseverant personal effort, may achieve a certain level of detachment from earthly tasks and may discard personal comfort, success, and feelings in order to live in closer proximity to the absolute, or at least to what he recognizes as being the absolute. But an entire people is incapable of doing so. For to live on religion alone requires a fervent personal will, and quite probably, constant meditation and sacrifice. In other words, those who are unable to obtain worldly joys are not therefore necessarily condemned to content themselves with joys of a purely spiritual nature. If religion becomes a refuge for a nostalgic or bitter spirit, and if it represents the only structure of existence for an entire people, it quickly becomes a secular undertaking itself, and a potentially harmful one. Religion must not be made anything other than the recourse of the man who seeks meaning beyond daily life and this finite world. It cannot replace daily life. And if it tries to replace it or to compensate for its failures, religion immediately deteriorates into extremism and madness. When it attempts to rule the finite using the categories of the infinite, religion invariably terrorizes. Thus, those peoples with nothing but religion, far from appearing to be composed of present or future saints, are instead rather frightening.

The Western part of the world, on the other hand, finds happiness entirely in the enterprises and successes of finite existence, to the point that it generally claims to be able to do entirely without questions about its finitude. But with this claim, the West forgets its own precariousness and lives with a false image of itself, which forces it into inconsistencies, if not into the natural excesses of the demiurge. These two worlds—the world of the a-religious, affluent West and the world inhabited by poor, thoroughly religious nations—cannot be brought together. They are potentially in a war situation, and are destined to hate each other. This hate feeds here on contempt, there on envy, even if these two sentiments are only hesitantly proclaimed in broad daylight, and are usually hidden behind compassion and pride. The problem of the rift between the rich world and the poor world involves an immense split between the rejection of religion on the one hand and the triumph of unbridled religion on the other. Those who have nothing but religion would very much like to possess something else—well-being, freedom, education—but are unable to do so. Those who have no religion would love to have one, and yet do not want it, as paradoxical as that may seem. Between the two a bitter rivalry develops. The former world may, out of spite, attempt to destroy the calm secular happiness of their neighbors, a happiness they were unable to produce in a similar way for themselves, and in so doing they may feel that the absolute has definitively triumphed. The latter world may, out of fear and disdain, try to force the foreign world of mystical dynamism into submission, thereby spreading its own prosaic happiness across the face of the globe.

The abandonment of religion on this side of the planet does not constitute a forward step for the conscience, as our contemporary generally believes, but is rather most likely a temporary phase in our history. A historical acquisition signifies its definitive success by the obvious well-being it procures to peoples who henceforth cannot and will not do without it. So one can say that the system of political freedom, even if it remains forever precarious and threatened, and always imperfect, represents a historical acquisition, an objective step forward: this is self-evident from the esteem it has enjoyed over the long term. But such is not at all the case for religion: for the peoples deprived of religion experience this deprivation as an absence, even if, for reasons which will be given later, they do not wish to call back the gods they have left behind. The confrontation between the feeling of deprivation and the refusal to restore what has been abandoned is one of the defining characteristics—and not the least of them—of the contemporary spirit.

The successor to the kind of militant atheism we once knew, then, is indifference, which harbors only contempt for God. Militant atheism no longer holds meaning because the faces of God and the institutions safeguarding transcendence are themselves no longer meaningful. In this respect, modernity's ultimate battle seems to be over, since modernity, among its many hopes, aimed precisely to deliver men from the illusions of transcendence that alienated them from their world. Ultimately, it was not the communist revolution but rather the Western world that accomplished the task put to the fore by the ideology of progress: the stamping out of religions.

Yet if we have abandoned our trust in the faces of God and in the institutions that relayed their presence, the desire for the absolute has not thereby disappeared from our mental universe. This contradiction plays a part in our contemporary distress. The advent of the first society in history to be deprived of religion does not spare us from having to deal with the meaning of life and death. If modernity has indeed liberated man from a variety of forms of subjection, it has not fundamentally transformed him. Man remains a being who wonders about the enigmas of death, about his own finitude, torn as he is between the desire for the absolute and his own limitations, between the desire for perfection and his own imperfection. Because the answers to these questions escape his knowledge, it can be said that man finds the world of knowledge to be lacking. He is an explorer of mysteries. The desire for the absolute, and the expression of the desire to escape death and finitude, no doubt constitutes one of those human categories that is grounded in our very being, and thus any attempt to root it out must fail.

Nevertheless, the permanence of desire, which reveals a lack of something not known, still stuns us like a slap in the face. Two centuries of effort have managed to delegitimize religions by making of them purely historical and psychological phenomena. Now we must attempt to historicize the desire for the absolute itself, which has suddenly reappeared, seemingly out of nowhere. This is precisely what Richard Rorty tries to do when he states that the need to escape finitude is a Platonic need.[1] For if human existence were to be revealed as being intrinsically insufficient, then what could it be relative to? The question, let alone any answer, opens up a fatal abyss. Thus, we seek to present our dissatisfaction as historically contingent uneasiness, or as the anguish of an ill person.

It is as if, after having relativized all of its expressions, we were now at the point where we must relativize the foundation of religion itself if we are to definitively rid ourselves of religion as the expression of that foundation. But here we are up against a wall. Religious hope, in spite of all our attempts, has not been able to find a sufficient substitute in any of our secular hopes. The desire for the absolute as foundation has survived the failure and the destruction of its historical expressions. Furthermore, if in the nineteenth century religion was seen as a compensation for earthly insufficiencies—as the opium of the people—this conception no longer holds with regard to the desire for the absolute. It is obvious today that that desire is not a response to social or historical insufficiency in the form of injustice, misery, war, and so on. Rather, it expresses an ontological hollowness. For it is stamped on the forehead even of those who are well-fed, healthy, and happy. It strikes happiness itself. Unhappy peoples maintain religions that might still be considered compensations for their unhappiness, but happy peoples have not abandoned the desire for the absolute because they are happy. To anyone of good faith, all of this reveals two truths: that the desire for the absolute is not linked to unhappiness, and that it is very much this desire, rather than unhappiness, that gives rise to religion.

After abolishing religious expressions, we find that we can advance no further in the process of negation. An unnegatable core is left: the question of death and finitude. An unavoidable question, to be sure. Not in the sense that there is no answer—for that is for each of us to decide—but in the sense that we can neither ignore the question—for example, by historicizing it—nor can we find an answer in indifference—by avoiding it through escapism. Even a society as given over as ours is to entertainment cannot avoid this question. We are confronted here with enigmas that simply refuse to be suppressed and forgotten.

Progress may be able to offer us every comfort, suppress pain, and gratify us with the longevity of Methuselah, but it will never deliver us from our feeling of insufficiency. In principle, limitation is always relative. If I consider myself ignorant or cowardly, it is necessarily because I know others who are more knowledgeable or braver than I. But in the case of our religious desire, no such comparison is operative. The astonishing thing is that we know our existence is limited, but do not know relative to what. To claim to be limited means to imagine something beyond our limits. And when we do so, we give meaning to the obscure reality that lies outside of those limits.

Jan Patocka wrote that every one of us resembles a passenger on a boat that is inevitably headed for shipwreck.[2] It is inconceivable that this passenger will not have the desire to sound the waters. He may claim that the question of death does not interest him, that it is a futile and ultimately pointless question. Yet he will not be able to keep himself from thinking that he is not a mere animal, for he finds himself haunted by the idea of limitation and death. The rejection of limits means nothing other than the desire for the absolute, or the desire for that which has no limits or confines. And the absolute is one of the names of God.

A culture can only with great difficulty do without God: this becomes clear when we observe the monstrous products that cultures immediately invent to replace gods, once they are deprived of them. Either the desire for the absolute or infinite attaches itself to something limited or finite (resulting in the idolization of a leader or a system to the point of fanaticism, for example), or else the desire for the absolute, ridiculed by "correct" thinking and stripped of religious expression, invents black market religions.

As far as the absolute itself is concerned, our ignorance is complete and only theologians make claims to possess knowledge of it. What is important here is less to know than to question. Patocka's man sounds the depths of the sea. We are watchmen of enigmas. What we call the soul represents the faculty of attention to mysteries. The soul is the part of man that unceasingly stays on the fringes of existence, ever on the lookout for what it intuits but neither knows nor sees. Animals are unaware of enigmas: this is precisely why we have so much trouble today distinguishing what really separates us from them, for we now are also unaware of enigmas, at least for the time being.

We say metaphorically that a house has a soul, in the sense that it evokes events from the distant or recent past, a past that has become mysterious to us. A house has a soul in the sense that its dwellers do not treat it as a mere place to pass through, but leave behind in its objects and atmosphere a part of themselves. The soul is a house that lives with its mysteries, sheltering them, taking charge of them as such, and constantly blending them into the events of the present. The soul is the part of us that *recognizes* the enigmas of existence, without actually *knowing* them. It recognizes that these enigmas convey meaning, but does not know what that meaning is. It is that part of us that accepts the awkward presence of unanswerable questions. In other words, it represents the conscious limit of the mind, the eye that remains open to the void.

At the Rencontres Internationales of Geneva in 1947, the French author and playwright Georges Bernanos made the observation that when civilization is in decline, man begins once again to look for an empty lot or street corner, where he can discard his immortal soul, in the hope that no one will bring it back to him.[3] Bernanos was trying here to describe the temptation to avoid the question of finitude and the desire for the infinite. For it is a discomforting question indeed, one that throws us into the abyss. And we have a tendency to close our eyes to the questions that make us ill at ease, to push them aside, especially if our day-to-day existence manages to satisfy most of our desires, which is often the case today. There are ways to relegate mysteries to the subterranean labyrinths of consciousness. It is a natural temptation, in which the soul allows itself to be forgotten as soon as we cease to watch over it. It does not actually destroy itself, since finitude, in all its forms—the certainty of death, the inadequacy of everything we attempt to do—is an irreducible reality, even if it is a conveyor of questions. The soul does, however, disappear from the surface. It does not imperatively reassert itself like the body or the mind. It reappears only when the eye is willing to contemplate the darkness, to peer into the nocturnal depths at the edge of existence.

A certain humility is necessary in order to confront unanswered questions, because when we stand before enigmas, the idea of our own smallness overwhelms us. The hope of modernity was to secure the triumph of man over enigmas. We know today that this hope was an immensely pretentious one. But now this pretentiousness has abated. We are beginning to understand that progress is incapable of eliminating the mysteries of existence or of making us the masters of them. And the fact that we are again being forced to turn our attention to these mysteries, to take them into account as such, constitutes a rupture with the previous order of things—the founding event of a new era.

Nevertheless, we have still not been convinced to take the step toward the search for the absolute. Or, to again take the example of the Czech philosopher, to sound the depths of the darkened seas upon which we are floating. We remain, rather, in an empty and uncertain space, where the premonition of mysteries runs up against the refusal to question them. During the course of the previous era, the quest for the absolute was denied legitimacy by the arrogance of man, who claimed to be the creator of his own condition. Today, the quest for the absolute is blocked by the fear of the triumphant absolute.

The Enlightenment had hoped to vanquish God by default: to so perfectly fulfill man's expectations that he would no longer turn to an Other. This is not how things have worked out. God has not been abandoned because of his uselessness, but out of our listlessness and fear of the excesses that religion encourages. The rejection of God, like a slammed door or a chair pulled away from the table, reveals our fear of the consequences we associate with religious faith. It does not express the satisfaction of liberated mankind, as the Enlightenment promised. The question of God has not become a senseless question. But any answer seems perilous.

The atmosphere of contemporary thought everywhere expresses the brutal denial of what we no longer wish to see. Our time, traumatized by the abuses of belief, has decided to reject without explanation anything that might give rise to similar miseries of thought. The fanaticism of certitude, no matter where it comes from, has rightly been stigmatized as a cause of misfortune. In this respect, ideologies and religions are equally guilty. Modern forms of totalitarianism are troublingly similar to the system of the Inquisition. Thus, it is a burdened memory that has engendered our unconditional rejection of any final certitudes. The experience we have of their consequences forces us to uproot faith from our minds. For it seems that as soon as we leave the solid ground of knowledge, we go mad.

The resurgence of the desire for the absolute will probably not give rise to a "return of religion" in the sense of a return to what once was. Peoples who have experienced religious fanaticism and who have suffered because of it, or who have analyzed and rejected it, will never be able to propose the same answers to the same questions. We will not repeat history, for bitter experience has worn us down. Every religion must institutionalize itself in order to ensure that its certainties endure. In the process, it arms itself and becomes a conqueror. European societies, to escape from these excesses without actually rejecting religion, distinguished the political sphere from the religious sphere. Yet religions deprived of the sword can still be oppressive. They ostracize by anathema and cast shame over the credulous. They impose reductionist moral codes on their followers. As soon as institutional Catholicism re-emerged in Poland, recovering its legitimacy after decades of communism, it hastily attempted to restore a moral order that obviously only reinforced the intuition of our contemporary concerning the danger of any religion at any point in history. Polish intellectuals, finding themselves between Scylla and Charybdis, now fear the tyranny of the clergy: "Black is worse than red," it is said in the streets of Warsaw.

And yet . . . is wanting to discard religions because of their excess not unlike throwing the baby out with the bathwater? If the religious category is indeed an integral part of the human condition, can we exclude this category with impunity under the pretext that if we do not, excesses will occur? We can see here just how subject we still are to ideological ways of thinking, which consist of wanting to suppress the economy, politics, and the family because they give rise to excesses. One might as well blow up a whole town to rid it of poverty. And so contemporary man rejects commitments in order to avoid the pitfall of promiscuity: let us have pure love or nothing! The ideologue destroys life in order to rid it of imperfection. But reality persists. And because man is fundamentally a religious being, the desire for the absolute persists, if only in soft and fragmented forms. Our a-religious time finds itself riddled with ersatz absolutes of the most fantastic variety. Our gurus and apocalyptic prophets give expression to a latent pantheism through which religious desire survives without being identified as such and without becoming institutionalized. Our contemporary converses with the dead, revives long lost gnoses, and pays all kinds of charlatans to interpret his dreams. These scattered and fluid bits of religion dance merrily about in the spirit of our times with neither form nor structure: thus, our anxiety about the absolute finds an outlet without our having to fear the excesses of official truths.

Contemporary man internalizes his questioning. For it is not answers as such that mutate into orthodoxy and then into constraint, but social answers borne by a community. Our man prefers to meditate upon the great mysteries of life alone, aided by obscure passing prophets, because he is well aware of the danger of shared certitudes. This is why we no longer publicly ask questions about death and finitude, even if some people do so individually. The public arena does not express anxiety about the enigmas of existence, but rather leads us to believe in a liberated innocence. It does everything to repress, in the Freudian sense, our anxiety about the human condition. In general, however, a culture responds to the sense of abandonment that mankind feels in the face of the mysteries of life. We are then dealing here with an incomplete culture that camouflages the essential and therefore is a sort of diversion. The wager is that everyone will keep fundamental questions to themselves, entering the public arena simply to unwind. What really happens, however, is the following: a large number of individuals, either because they are too young or too indifferent to lift the veil off what the diversion tries to mask, mistake the public arena for life itself. And so we find in our societies a very sophisticated intellectual culture and a very poor spiritual culture. For anything concerned with the soul is considered not incommunicable, but *dangerous* to communicate. Our contemporaries may respect and even admire a religious spirit, but they will fight fiercely against it as soon as this spirit makes any attempt to win them over. Ultimately, the attention paid to life's mysteries is diluted because they are kept out of sight.

What is more, the fear of an unveiled religiousness leads to an outright rejection of any quest beyond the rational and conventional limits of daily life. Some questions could be answers in themselves. One must not imagine that the men of previous eras actually "found" God. But they did come to know him by having sought him for so long. Thus contemporary man distrusts doors that are ajar. He deliberately shuts the door to anything that might give meaning to his desire for the absolute. When confronted with the slightest sign of mystery rising to the surface, he stiffens. In other words, he refuses to let himself ask the questions that, because of his human condition, very naturally come into his head. It is as though the questions contained their own taboo. If a question about transcendence comes up, he stifles it as if it were a bad dream or a guilty temptation. So he sees without really looking, if he does not engage in outright camouflage—for this profound concern cannot really be forgotten, even if it can be temporarily avoided through all kinds of subterfuge.

Using different means from those employed by ideologies, our contemporary is still attempting to quash a dynamic force that is woven into his very being. His reasons for doing so are not ideological, because it is the fear of excess that drives him and no longer the pride of the demiurge. His means are different in that he no longer seeks to make man self-sufficient, since he now knows that is impossible. Instead, he forcefully postulates that this world is all there is and that nothing is to be found beyond it. Except self-delusion. As Jorge Luis Borges said, "Metaphysics is nothing more than a chapter of fantasy literature." Nevertheless, if it is obvious that while no one can demonstrate the existence of an absolute, neither can one demonstrate its non-existence. And that is why the certitude of non-existence hammers away at us in the absence of any proof. It falls upon the undecided with the same violence as it does upon its opposite, the religious believer. And if one faults the certitude of non-existence for doing so, it responds by saying that at least it is not dangerous, that on the contrary it cries out in order to help us avoid the dangers of belief, for its mission as a negative certitude is precisely to wipe out the positive certitudes that are always ready to impose their authority. However, it thereby imposes its own authority, forcing easily influenced minds to live in a truncated world. For it is a truncated world indeed that must be content with finitude without being able to name it as such, that is, without even questioning it.

The rejection of the religious as an irruption of the absolute into the realm of the finite, or of the irrational into the realm of the rational, is an extension of the modern spirit. Modern man first postulated that reason would resolve all questions, thereby supplanting the transcendent, which would then become useless and imaginary. It has spent two centuries trying to come up with rational systems that would resolve all the enigmas of existence. It has failed in this task. It therefore concludes that the great enigmas are finally vain questions, since reason cannot deal with them. It would be better to admit the insufficiency of reason. But to admit that the enigmas were neither resolved nor suppressed would be to admit failure.

Such seems to be our predicament. Previous societies lived in the heart of a structure of meaning, in which even though not every question had an answer, the most impenetrable mysteries at least had a home within a reassuring whole. Our own societies live in the helter-skelter atmosphere of meaningless questions and contradictory answers. They scarcely complain. They prefer this chaos to structures of meaning that exclude some and punish the recalcitrant.

Still it would be more appropriate today to try to imagine the conditions for a non-oppressive religion instead of merely rejecting what seems to be both necessary and dangerous.

If we agree that as a form of the human condition, the desire for the absolute must have the right to be, and not remain, as it does today, relegated to the realm of the forbidden, this desire must express itself in new ways. For the old religions were shaped in ancient times and seem to be incapable of offering what we expect from them. The dialogue between any of the organized religions and the man of our time, if it still exists at all, has become pathetic. Religions that rest on their traditions and faith find themselves confronted with a man who senses the fanaticism behind faith and for whom traditions no longer have meaning. They take pride in having survived history while our contemporary finds in history only the echo of his disappointments. They base their hope on transcendence while he has been raised in the consecration of immanence. They are proud of their durability; he lives in a precarious world. They speak of truth; he does not know what truth means. In fact, the two are so far apart from each other that it is a pitiful sight indeed to see the efforts religions make to convince him.

Does this mean that we are radically different from the people for whom these religions were instituted? We are naturally identical insofar as the human condition marks us in a similar fashion. This is precisely why we express the same religious desire. Yet we differ from our ancestors on two points that ultimately converge: first, the weight of historical disappointments, if it does not entirely dishearten us, has conferred on us a pioneer spirit, the desire to start all over from scratch; second, we have won for ourselves a freedom to judge that we will not let go of easily, after having lived under the folly of all the purveyors of absolutes. It has therefore become very difficult to make us obey the way we once did, and, in the name of religion, to impose upon us a regulated way of thinking and behaving.

Religions do not seem to have understood either of these two radically new aspects. Contemporary man, disillusioned and weary of everything, expresses his desire for the absolute with all the innocence and candor of the first man. And only the essential can take on meaning for him. Thus the details of religious truth or morality, refined over twenty centuries of history, seem to him to be no more than petty wrangling. Institutional religions, however, because they are so ancient and deeply rooted, have ultimately given the greatest importance to forms that obscure the essential and hide it from view. And so now if our contemporary wishes to sincerely meditate upon the enigmas of existence, he is instead presented with dogmas and traditions that, having taken on a sacred status themselves, appear perfectly superfluous to him, at least in comparison with the questions he asks. For example, the existence of a triune God seems superfluous to a man who is only at the point of wondering what makes him different from the other animals. This sincere individual who seeks God in his own way, cannot help thinking he is being made fun of when he is answered in such a way. He would like to hear about the absolute, and he encounters byzantine quarrels about the color of lace. The new seeker, who looks for truth like Thales at the dawn of history, feels as though he has traveled back in time. Curious and often hungry for the primordial questions, he finds himself faced with religions that rest on thousand-year-old doctrines and awkwardly attempt to enlighten him by beginning with the end. If permanent reference points are necessary, they should only have to do with the essential, that is, with the disquieting quest that has no words to express itself. But religious institutions seem weary because they are encumbered with history in the midst of a new world. The Catholic Church, for one, seems to our contemporary to be petrified in ancient and seemingly meaningless moral, doctrinal, and hierarchical structures.

This resistance to change leaves religion on the sidelines and increases the gap between the enormous masses of those who consider it to be a miraculously preserved yet innocuous dinosaur and the tiny number of faithful who, because they are increasingly marginalized and the object of ridicule, are tempted to fall into extremism. The Catholic hierarchy, more present in a country like France, now finds itself so distant from contemporary man that it lacks the resources to be able to understand him, and the misunderstood cannot be persuaded. The Church sees nothing more than a degeneration of thought and behavior in present reality. This is why it has invested its hope in the Third World in a bid to survive. It is as if the Church aspired to replace one group of faithful with another, like the ruler of old who wanted to change peoples. All of this belies a profound contradiction: if this religion suits only premodern peoples, then it its only justification is historical and thereby contradicts its universal vocation. Its universality, although achieved in a physical sense, has not kept pace with time, to which it admits defeat.

Religion tends to consider contemporary man as simply an heir to Sodom and Gomorrah, when he is really an anxious individual who must be accepted with all his disappointments and wayward wandering. This does not mean that he is right on every point, only that a distinction must be drawn between his essential errors and the metamorphoses he has undergone because of his historical circumstances. This distinction, however, would lead to a profound reform of religious institutions, in which only the essence of dogmas would be retained. No religion will be able to re-conquer consciences except by proposing beliefs and works adapted to the times—no one, not even an institution tied to transcendence, can claim to be the master of time. And it is because they have shown themselves to be incapable of this task that religions as they stand have not managed to fill the contemporary spiritual void. Common sense willingly believes that intellectual fashions swing back and forth like a pendulum and that religions will naturally reappear on the scene. And it is indeed doubtful that Western culture will be able to survive for long without setting out on new spiritual journeys. Yet these journeys will undoubtedly be different from those of previous eras, for the break with the preceding age is deep, and we resemble the man who strikes out into new territory after having burned his vessels behind him. The present multiplicity of pseudo-religious initiatives, strange communities, and visionary preachers certainly expresses a desire for the absolute to which the official religious structures no longer know how to respond. But at the same time it represents the hesitant quest for religious structures adapted to the present. A dangerous groping about, to be sure, because in the darkness charlatans are easily mistaken for sages. Nevertheless, this perilous proliferation is better than the total disappearance of the soul. It is even sometimes tempting to think that this proliferation is what might prevent a religious pretension to having a monopoly on meaning. But what is essential is that the unfathomable questions are once again daring to rise to the surface.

CHAPTER 18
THE RETURN OF AN
UNCERTAIN WORLD

A varied literature has amply shown the voracity of contemporary man—his desire to possess everything, right away, and in ever-greater quantities. Consumerism expresses a gluttony without limit. Yet this feverish desire to possess is evidenced in other modes of being as well, including the desire to solve all problems instantaneously. Our contemporary is essentially an impatient man, and not only impatient to acquire, but also impatient to find solutions.

No life is without its difficulties, which were once called troubles (*soucis*) and which today we call problems (*problèmes*).* This change in terms is not entirely innocent. A trouble is something that gives rise to worry, something that torments. A problem, since Greek times, designates a question of geometry or logic. The first term

---

* The word "troubles" is not entirely satisfactory here since to North American readers it usually conveys the notions of worry, angst, and concern. However, it can also be given a more profound meaning, as in the so-called "troubles" in Ireland, which used to refer to the insoluble, ongoing conflicts there, and the use of the word in the classic spiritual, "Nobody knows the trouble I seen." Thus I believe it is the most appropriate rendering of *souci*. The author's original title for this book, *Le souci contemporain*, might therefore be rendered faithfully, if somewhat awkwardly, as "Contemporary Troubles." *Trans.*

puts emphasis on a disposition of mind or heart that is characterized by preoccupation and anxiety, while the second emphasizes the need to find a solution. One *bears* a trouble and *solves* a problem.

That each one of us should wish to be rid of our torments as quickly as possible is only natural. Any difficulty tolls the death-knell of the dream of perfect happiness. And when things become desperate, nothing can stop us from seeing the difficulty as somehow insane. But the present age is unique in the way it views obstacles. Contemporary man considers any problem to be a wrench in the wheels of a machine that in theory should perform without a hitch, or else he sees it as an anomaly, even an injustice. One of the particularities of our time resides in this certitude that happiness is everyone's due, such that a normal state of existence is considered to be defined by the absence of worries.

The man of the previous era knew that his life ultimately required navigation around more or less fearsome obstacles. He accepted this state of affairs in advance, which he understood as being character-istic of his condition. His outlook could be summed up in this aphorism of African wisdom: "Life is both trial and proof, for it is in trial that a man proves he is a man." But our contemporary con-siders any obstacle in his path to be an insult or provocation.

Many of life's difficulties either admit of no complete solution at all, or work themselves out only over long periods of time. When no way of getting around them can be found, they often just become part of life, like grumpy companions of whom one eventu-ally grows almost fond. An incurable illness, a repulsive physical trait, or a child always in trouble do not keep one from enjoying real happiness. But contemporary man does not see things this way. For him, real happiness comes from a leveling of all obstacles, which generally spring up in our path like so many weeds. And so he is always looking for remedies. He takes his child to the psychiatrist at the first sign of possible failure in school. If he is afflicted with a Durante-like nose, he insists it be changed and wonders why his medical insurance refuses to reimburse him for the operation. He

demands that his doctor put an immediate end to his minor physical afflictions. He is unaware that many of life's difficulties require
more nurture and patience than they do any technical solution. And
patience is precisely the quality he lacks the most.

The rise of the impatient man—etymologically, "he who refuses
to suffer"—can be explained naturally by the incredible progress
that has occurred in the development of conveniences of all sorts.
And we cannot see why we should deprive ourselves of anything that
would make life easier. That many of our problems are now solvable
does not necessarily mean that life should henceforth be exempt of
difficulties. But the considerable improvement in our well-being
legitimizes the philosophy of progress and leads us to extend its
internal logic: we are convinced, whether we are aware of it or not,
that in time solutions to all of our difficulties will be found.

The way we deal with insurance and risk is revealing. In order to
at least attenuate the consequences of certain inevitable misfortunes,
we have managed to insure a large number of risks. Life obviously
becomes much less dramatic when accidents, illnesses, and pre-
mature deaths are subject to contracts that compensate their victims
or their victims' families. But as the twentieth century advanced, the
idea of "zero risk" developed, according to which all misfortune calls
for reparation. In a mechanized and bureaucratized universe, it is
imperative to immediately identify the perpetrator of each malfunc-
tion or catastrophe: here the manufacturer of a machine, there the
official who granted the building permit. Even those misfortunes
clearly due to natural causes have a passive culprit: for instance, not
having invested enough in research, the government becomes the
object of accusations from the victims of incurable illnesses.

The attempt to insure all risks is equivalent to a refusal to assume
them, and deep down, to the certainty that these risks should really
not exist. This insistence upon generalized insurance means that, as a
cause of misfortune, we accept nothing but those responsible for the
functioning of the social machine. Evil then comes only from human
or technical errors—medical errors, legal errors, bureaucratic errors,

or building errors—none of which really exist, because in principle contemporary man should reign as master over everything that concerns him. It is as if we had eliminated evil from the world, and as if whatever evil did remain was the result of an occasional misfire that could be eliminated by improving the performance of the machine.

This means that we reject at once two very different factors: chance and personal responsibility.

Personal responsibility finds itself diluted if not outright eliminated in a regulated society in which the individual, as a cog of the social machine, can ultimately take very few initiatives. No one can be responsible for what he has not chosen. Accustomed to being blameless and to attributing any mistakes or faults to those who would restrict him, the individual tends to reject all accountability. He can scarcely imagine how he might be the origin of something bad, his existence has been made so antiseptic. If a child gets hurt, it is not because of poor supervision, but because the toy was dangerous.

The rejection of chance is no less interesting. The objective of Enlightenment thinking consisted precisely of getting rid of it: "The human species," wrote Condorcet, "once rid of all its chains, freed from the tyranny of chance, as from that of the enemies of progress, and marching with firm and confident strides upon the road to truth, virtue and happiness . . ."[1] Chance here refers to unexpected events. Chance means that we do not possess mastery over everything that happens to us. But progress tends to "free us from the power of chance" by making risk so minimal that it approaches zero, whether in the field of medicine or transportation or some other area. As the masters of nature, we fear the obscure, the shadows, the incertitude in which our omnipotence is compromised. We do not accept the idea of the world's contingency, except to the extent that we regard this contingency as constituting what remains of human impotence, soon to be subjugated by the exponential development of science and technology.

And so we willingly imagine our personal and social existence as a long-distance race, difficult of course, but during which every obstacle will in time be removed. It is a little bit like those games that call upon players to advance through a series of clues in order to find an answer that they know in advance. Our ultimate aim is to find as safe a shelter as possible. Yet there are still two things that unsettle us: invincible evil and unresolved questions. The present age could almost be summed up in this refusal to be tormented, a refusal that grounds itself in the promise made to us two centuries ago: the promise of man reconciled with himself, with others, with society, and with the world. The refusal to be tormented finds expression in the way in which we find tragic and crisis situations to be incomprehensible.

The tragic places on the stage a kind of unhappiness that is without a culprit. Here the individual finds himself torn between two equally honorable but mutually exclusive values. Either that, or, because tragedy always concerns a decision to be made, he finds himself torn between two equally fearsome futures, but without a possible third way out, or between equally compelling yet contradictory prospects. In other words, the choice is both necessary and impossible. Sartre gave the example of the young man torn between staying with his aging mother and going off to war. This terrible alternative between two duties seems oddly out of place today. For an equivalent appropriate to today, a different example would have to be found: for example, what should I do if I have to choose between love and a successful career, if the two are mutually exclusive? The predicament is insoluble. And a villain is nowhere to be found. The difficulty is just inherent in the circumstances.

Our contemporary objects to having to choose between tighter college entrance requirements and the diminished value of a college degree, between responsible sexual behavior and the risk of AIDS, or between such measures as a lower minimum wage for young people and growing unemployment. Of course, we can in these last two instances eventually hope to get around such dilemmas. But meanwhile, we are forced to choose what seems to us to be the lesser of two evils, or the less displeasing alternative. But is it really necessary to cast matters in such a light? That is what seems unacceptable to most people, so much so that those in government do not even dare to present these unpopular dilemmas as dilemmas. Has a politician ever been known to explain that, unless the circle can somehow be squared, top-notch degrees can never be bestowed without imposing certain selection criteria? All the speeches we hear, without exception, propose both dreams at the same time, leading us to believe that they are somehow not contradictory. In so doing, they reinforce a lack of realism on the part of citizens.

By viewing policymaking as a science and policymakers as technocrats, we clearly demonstrate our inability to understand or accept the tragic dimension of existence—in this case, collective existence. The technocrat does not perceive the conflicts that pervade reality, for his decision, which is not really a decision at all in the truly political sense, lies in the superficial realm of the problem, and he must find his solution by grasping causes and effects. Because he does not integrate worldviews or conflicting values in his approach, he unwittingly remains mired in the contradictions between them. In foreign affairs, a government misses the essential if it is unaware of or refuses to see the tragic aspect of history, which, for example, is reflected in the unhappy paradox that peace cannot always be defended by peaceful means.

When the tragic aspect of existence is denied because mutually exclusive alternatives cannot be faced, the individual becomes the plaything of circumstance. Events decide things in his stead. He ultimately falls victim to the less avoidable of the two evils. This leads him to blame the whole world. He simply cannot imagine an evil without a perpetrator. Contemporary thinking always tends to situate evil externally, to look for it elsewhere, which amounts to finding a culprit to be punished and gotten rid of. But tragedy teaches us that evil is woven into the fabric of being, a teaching that we reject. Tragedy also reveals to us what might be called the solution-less situation, that intermediate state in which one remains unsatisfied—in other words, tormented, a state of mind we reject as outmoded and demeaning.

In the same way, we have immense difficulty admitting the reality of the limit-situation, that is, the limits imposed by what is fundamental or essential. Here, life encounters the categories that go beyond it and mark its boundaries, such as death or evil. And at the same time, such encounters invariably bring all of existence into play: When I look death in the face, it reduces my existence to a cloud of dust, in which everything loses its value.

If catastrophe is considered unthinkable, it is not only because of its shamefulness when measured against the quasi-perfection of the technical universe. Above all, catastrophe forces us to look squarely at the essential, which we find frightening. Our contemporary knows full well that he must die one day, but he does not want any event to remind him of that fact. Any event that results in loss of life gives rise to general indignation—and not just the kind of legitimate compassion that naturally causes us to revolt against suffering. No, we are dealing here with indignation about the very possibility of catastrophe. We are convinced that this kind of thing simply should not happen. As soon as it does, a whole system is called into question, whether it be an administrative system, a transportation system, or whatever else. Much to our credit, this rejection of imperfection signifies that we will not give in to fatalism. Yet by the same token it expresses an unrealistic vision of existence.

The limit-situation brutally uproots us from the warm and closed world in which everything is in order. Contemporary man has come to believe that he is completely at home in this world, entirely acclimatized to its atmosphere. Our society, in the image that it gives of itself, portrays existence as both instantaneous and immortal, which ultimately amounts to the same thing. And this description is false. Everything that is said, done, and sung, expresses the freshness, the light-hearted gaiety of the individual who lives cut off from reality. Everyone finds himself confronted with extreme situations here and there. But since we cannot understand them, we ignore and forget them, which does not amount to actually eradicating them, since that is in no one's power.

The limit-situation is an objective reality in two ways. First, we cannot personally decide that such a situation does not engage our entire being. We may consider it from an esthetic or ironic angle, like the theatrical buffoon who dies laughing at himself, either out of defiance or in a final attempt at high theater. But this can only be artifice, behind which lies the reality: I am here irremediably subjected to suffering evil and death, which bring my entire existence into play and relegate everything else to the level of idle occupation. Second, the limit-situation is historically objective, and it is so in spite of all the modern attempts to suppress it. We remain creatures whose destiny it is to break away from our world. The limit-situation forces itself upon us, both personally and historically. It belongs to our condition like a "beyond" that is ever-present in our rationality and our strengths. It represents the critical margin of daily life, at the same time both its edge and its source of light. For it is when crises arise that the ordinary world reveals itself for what it is.

The limit-situation reveals truths that would remain hidden without it. It first of all reveals the truth about oneself. One has but to observe those who have never encountered any serious difficulty or personal misfortune. Their lives are as light as soap bubbles. They can allow themselves, if such is their character, to settle into a kind of permanent artificiality. And then suddenly a grave difficulty arises. At last we find out who they really are, for better or for worse. Whether it arises on the personal or the collective level, the limit-situation unveils the points of reference that lie behind it. When one is faced with danger, one learns why one lives. In the same vein, entire peoples come to be known for their heroic deeds as well as for their acts of cowardice. Not that ordinary life does not mean anything. But it does not lay bare the reality of men's capabilities and characters, especially if it is easy. Being reveals itself not only when confronted with physical danger or death, but also when it faces long-lasting and painful difficulty, which can threaten long-term existence. And so the easy life we now enjoy maintains many illusions. Our society is filled with good intentions that we content ourselves with because they can be expressed publicly. These intentions may indeed be sincere, but they are not true, for their truth would be revealed through acts that show that they really exist.

The limit-situation thus separates what is essential from what is peripheral. This sorting out can only happen when the essential is called into play, which is not the case in ordinary life. When security and comfort are such that the essential practically never comes to the fore, life finds itself confined to the peripheral, but to peripheral realities that are soon considered to be essential. An easy life does not exempt one from problems: it simply places the problems at a lower level. Closed and protected communities, where no one has to struggle to survive, find themselves engaged in Lilliputian quarrels in which enormous amounts of energy are invested. Certain people in our happy societies apparently undergo expensive psychotherapies to rid themselves of their fear of spiders. It is a pretty safe bet that in war-torn Sarajevo or Grozny, no one was particularly concerned with arachnophobia.

A society like our own, not having directly known war or rationing or political oppression for decades, has finally come to forget the reality of the limit-situation. It is understandable, then, why we as individuals have lost the notion of what is basic. And it is also understandable why, as in the case of arachnophobia, insignificant stakes—the only stakes there seem to be—are now written in capital letters. These phenomena, which might seem laughable to anyone not entirely humorless, nonetheless reveal some rather disturbing prospects. For a society of this sort develops laws and habits that increasingly ignore the fundamental aspects of life, and ultimately lives in a world of illusion. Our society has almost forgotten that its world can break apart, since for so long it has devoted itself exclusively to cultivating its own comfort. Thus, when an unexpected and explosive breakdown suddenly occurs—poverty, epidemics, etc.—our contemporary is totally helpless, naked before the plague, paralyzed by incomprehension. Ill-adapted as he is to dealing with profound questions, he falls prostrate in despair, looking everywhere for culprits—who are in any case only scapegoats—and imagining that he is a victim of some persecution.

It can also happen that the limit-situation exists but escapes attention. A whole society can then be thrown off course. In A.D. 256, when the Persian army took Antioch from the Roman Empire, the inhabitants found themselves at the theater, oblivious to the enemy archers who had climbed up behind them in the stands, while the actors desperately tried to warn the spectators with hand signals. An interesting symbol of a fortunate society, so deeply engrossed in its own amusement that it does not see the dangers whose very names it has forgotten. We live in an analogous situation. The profound ruptures that today affect our societies are signs of limit-situations to come. But the very nature of this type of situation is beyond the grasp of our culture and its categories. We have become used to considering the defense of the most minimal interests to be essential, and so we cannot accept the breakup caused by global changes. We have become conservative out of sheer blindness.

In spite of what we may wish to believe, we live in a terribly conformist and over-simplifying time. Contemporary man does not want to take risks, not for lack of courage, but because he fears the uncertain, fears encountering unanswerable questions. He not only needs material security, but peace of mind as well. In this respect, our age is a kind of high-security zone, in which technology and the state allow us to avoid risk. It is as if the considerable progress accomplished in order to further our well-being and peace of mind had proportionally reduced our ability to expose existence to risk. So just how is the "risk of existence" here to be understood? In fact, we are dealing here with a situation in which the individual is confronted with questions to which no manual has the answers, a precarious time because of the novelty of the difficulties we face, making for a necessarily uncertain future. A typical example is afforded by the evolution of the family. In times past, the number of children a family had was often due to chance, and parents, without really having made the choice, frequently found themselves immersed in the high-risk venture that raising a large family entails. Births are now under our control, which is no small gain. Large families have become extremely rare because few people decide to undertake such an effort. At the same time, raising a very small number of children also seems to cause insurmountable problems, because now nothing must be left to chance. We are inundated with books about how to be good mothers and how to take care of our children. Child-rearing is always a hazardous and unpredictable business for which there is no model, in which decisions must continuously be made without certainty or guarantees. And contemporary man, however autonomous and sovereign he claims to have become, is in constant need of guidelines for every situation. Naturally, this need stems primarily from the fact that the complete transformation of life over the past fifty years has made the advice of the previous generation obsolete. But it also comes from his refusal to accept the unexpected, the uncertain, the potential danger lurking in any situation he cannot control.

The example of high-altitude mountain climbing, mentioned in the introduction, offers a metaphorical explanation of how this evolution in mentality has come about. A climber who has managed to attach his rope to a solid rock can advance without fear of anything more than a harmless fall. He can make bold and audacious moves. The well-anchored spike does not protect him entirely, since he can still slip sixty feet, hang in thin air, and possibly get injured. But free fall is impossible. By contrast, our contemporary finds himself entirely without any certainties that might give meaning to his life. His temporary wishes, and a natural desire to simply extend his biological life, represent the only certainties he has. Two consequences ensue: first, he can scarcely make anything but transparent, mundane, rational decisions, and he is overwhelmed by extreme situations that require reliance on reference points; second, with every decision he risks everything he possesses, finding himself in exactly the same position as the mountain climber who is unsure of his footing and for whom any minor slip means a fall into the abyss. If contemporary man does choose to take existential risks, he risks losing his material stability, his leisure activities, or his professional interests. And because this is all he possesses, if he loses them, he loses everything. In reality, he finds himself in a limit-situation much more often than did men of previous ages, since crisis lies just beneath the surface: if he loses his job, it is a catastrophe, since he has nothing more than that left. At the same time, he no longer has the ability to react to such extreme situations, which is why he both dramatizes everything and has no understanding of tragedy. Little wonder that we find him so scared and circumspect, so little inclined to adventure.

It is tempting to say that together with a bourgeois society goes bourgeois thinking. The bourgeois demands that his life be lived always within and under the rule of the norm. Any excess seems to him to be an illness in need of a cure. Léon Bloy laconically described him by his inability to contemplate the absolute. The bourgeois mind is constantly calculating and searching for security, both physical and mental. He sees evil in anything that strays from the beaten path. He prefers to live in mediocrity in order to avoid tragedy, a prospect that terrorizes him. He detests grandeur in all its forms because it is invariably the expression of some form of incoherence and imbalance. More than anything, he fears the kinds of situations in which life takes a sudden turn, strays off the beaten path, beyond the tranquil world of the known and familiar. He seeks a predictable, ready-to-wear kind of happiness at a bargain price. He reveres convention because he finds it reassuring and because it carries no risks.

Sociological and institutional reasons could probably be added to the "spiritual" reasons we have given here to explain this process of normalization. The growth of the bourgeoisie and the rise of bourgeois thinking are interrelated and mutually sustaining phenomena. Society has become a vast middle class, and in France in any case, bureaucratization has done much to foster the security-seeking mentality and the desire for a life both mediocre and risk-free. But above all, the almost complete disappearance of existential adventure stems from the recession of meaning and its correlative points of reference. One might say that our contemporary no longer takes risks because he is all alone on Earth: by ridding the world of God, Nietzsche helped to entrench precisely the kind of petit bourgeois he hated.

But another circumstance, an intellectual one, has also contributed to this phenomenon. The defunct ideologies exalted enterprise and risk-taking. One recalls how fascism dreamed of bringing an entire people to life in the enthusiasm and feeling of the extraordinary. Ideological epics, still present in our memory, resembled fits of pure folly. We are now convinced of the advantages of a well-understood mediocrity. We no longer wish to live in the exceptional. Those risks we do accept—like extreme sports—seem to lack a purpose other than to demonstrate limited courage, unless they are the manifestation of disorders caused by boredom.

Because any change in social existence is risky, we are becoming incapable of innovation. The security we enjoy is such that any venture at all would call it into question, even if only partially. We are no longer able to react to new problems because any real attempt to seek original answers would threaten our quietude and lead us into unknown waters. And so presidential candidates are left with no choice but to reassure voters that the safety net will be maintained or promise the impossible. They either swear to protect bourgeois thinking with its petty advantages or propose to make unemployment illegal. No one can really be certain whether political candidates are being demagogic or simply naïve. But it is highly certain that a different approach would cost them votes, since citizens will not hear of risking the things they have acquired, nor will they consent to be told about the impossibility of having one's cake and eating it too. Our situation shows clearly to what extent our contemporary is unable to understand political language regarding objectives that would seek to cautiously renew society while realizing that knowledge is fallible and the results uncertain.

Obsessed as he is by comprehensive risk insurance, contemporary man does not know what it means to have confidence in the future, which calls not so much for a predilection for spine-tingling and playful adventure as for an openness in which the unexpected is, paradoxically, expected. Confidence in the future confronts more than just fear; it confronts anguish, for it is an acceptance of the possibility of finding oneself face-to-face with the unknown without trembling. It accepts in advance the weight of a nameless future. It does not need to know the outlines of what lies in store. It requires a mind that is mysteriously ready to encounter what it has neither prepared nor predicted. The man of confidence keeps his eyes wide open and faces the obscurity of what lies ahead. This does not mean that he counts upon events turning out in his favor, but rather that he counts upon his own ability to confront them without being overwhelmed. He knows there will always be a part of himself that will resist even the worst. The man of confidence is in this sense faithful to himself. Given over to the future, he puts his trust in his own strengths, even when they are as yet only potential.

Our contemporary has trouble trusting himself in this way. And that is why he makes such colossal efforts to eliminate chance. By fighting against the unpredictable, our era produces individuals who are vaccinated, bureaucratized, and insured against floods, madmen in power, and large families. The benefit of all these things is not at issue. But what price has been paid to acquire them? The value of life is proportional to what one is willing to risk for it. That is why it is not surprising that our contemporary's existence seems so narrow. By insuring himself against every possible eventuality, he deprives himself of the great joys that arise from having surmounted risks. When insurance pays off, he does indeed draw a certain satisfaction or contentment. But joy comes from having managed to go beyond one's established self-image, an image traced out by long-since proven abilities. It is these victories over oneself that allow one to develop one's potentialities. But one has to wager on oneself at the risk of being defeated and humiliated. And this wager, at least if it is not of the sort made by a careless Russian roulette player, rests uniquely upon self-trust.

The man who does not trust himself, through the obstacles that his fears build up over time, finally ends up with an existence that is both petty and, paradoxically, threatened. Petty, because it bricks itself into the narrow confines of what is clearly possible and certain. Threatened, because reality always exceeds the mind's full grasp, and this man, buffered against everything, is in fact ready for nothing. When a novel, unexpected event occurs, the distrustful man loses his bearings, struggles, and is finally overwhelmed.

Our ancestors, who did not know the kind of security we enjoy today, did know that the future held the unexpected within it. As fatalists, they knew to expect the twists and turns of fate, not being able to prevent them. Contemporary man's mistake is not that he has contained the difficulties and risks he faces, but that he has not sought to extend his limits, that he has become complacent about them and does not try to broaden the spectrum of his possibilities. He is like the family scion who is content to simply inherit the family fortune instead of using his material security to embark upon new, previously inconceivable projects. We may well be nostalgic about our fatalistic ancestors, who have left in their stead the narrow distrustful men of the present. The disappearance of the permanent insecurity in which our ancestors had to live could, however, leave open the possibility of undertaking brand new ventures.

CHAPTER 19
ON VIGILANCE

How can we then gain control over a world that seems so uncertain and seems to slip so easily out of our grasp? By arming ourselves with a different outlook and new concepts. Ecological uncertainties provide a significant example. Because of the growing difficulty of ensuring control over the environment, the concept of prevention is gradually being replaced with that of precaution in texts produced in international agreements. In other words, we are slowly moving from finding certitude in controlled technology—that is, prevention—to a mindset that recognizes that there will be ups and downs that can only be corrected along the way—that is, precaution. Otherwise stated, we are moving from confidence to carefulness. We have here a simple admission of our fallibility. And we are able to confess this fallibility without discouragement, able to take the reality of uncertainty into account without ceasing to fight against it. A lucid gaze upon the world's contingency is also a terrified one. How indeed can one tolerate an expectant wait for chaos? And yet freedom arises out of the storm of events. Cold rationality, as a mechanism with a single spring, is not equivalent to freedom. The concept of prevention, by requiring programmed and mandatory acts, belongs to the realm of technology, whereas precaution calls upon the imagination and an adaptive spirit. If our destiny does indeed hang in the balance, freedom and anxiety emerge from the darkness hand-in-hand.

There can be no stable system complete with definitive guarantees. That everything must always be redone is one of the consequences of tragedy, of the permanence of evil and uncertainty. The philosophy of progress, which forms the basis of contemporary thinking, supposes that any gains once acquired are permanent, and that each generation, without having earned them, benefits from all man's previous conquests. Thus, we are easily convinced that our victories over war, misery, or barbarity place our societies at a new height from which we can never fall, and beyond which future generations will have the calling to go ever further.

This conviction represents one of our most deep-seated errors, and is the reason for our most profound disillusionments. A characteristic example can be found in the terrible disappointment that has gripped us since the Second World War, a disappointment that Stefan Zweig (*After Babel*, 1975), George Steiner (*Real Presences*, 1989), and others have described so well, but which each of us also can recognize as his own. The systematic atrocities that the peoples of advanced culture have showed themselves capable of raises an immense doubt: What good is civilization if it cannot save us from our own barbarity?

One recalls that Hannibal, after a series of victories, saw his good fortune evaporate the day his soldiers indulged in the delights of Capua. In the twentieth century we fell victim to the Capua syndrome. We forgot that any conquest remains precarious and uncertain. One might well wonder why. The reason is the same one that explains why utopias can never exist: evil—as *diabolos*, or separation—is written into our very being. Thus, the victory against it is never definitive. Barbarity is always present, at times well-hidden, at times close to the surface. It lies deep within our humanity and can never be uprooted, but only reduced, repelled, or momentarily banished. The same is true of our struggle against poverty or inequality. Because we have forgotten the intrinsic fragility of republican equality, we have stopped defending it and allowed powerful interest groups and privileges to develop, which are now undermining it. We believed that the postwar boom represented a definitively acquired level of prosperity. That is why we have such trouble understanding the recent spread of social exclusion, poverty, and inequalities, in a country where everything seemed to indicate that these ills were destined to disappear. But how could they have "disappeared"? They had merely been pushed into the shadows, and to keep them there, it would have been necessary to maintain a constant vigil.

We will have to learn once again that everything must be redone. Not only in every generation, but, one might say, every morning. Life is like this in all its details, at least if one postulates the necessity of improving the world. Henrik Wozniakowski, for many years the leader of cultural resistance in communist Poland, defines culture as "the defense of creation." Culture struggles against destruction and, in a general way, separation. It is the product of an unceasing struggle against barbarity; equality is the product of an unceasing struggle against forms of selfishness, in the same way that love, on a personal level, tells the story of a daily battle against falling out of love. People are usually amazed at how easily hate seems to take the place of love following a divorce. In reality, that is not what happens. Love does not turn into hate. Love actually lives and grows in the face of the ever-present possibility of falling out of love, and constantly fights against it, while hate, which rises explosively to the surface in the heat of conflict, is nothing other than the revelation of an ever-present point of contention, which had remained hidden thanks to the perseverant combat of love. Similarly, barbarity remains latent, and smolders unseen beneath the bright surface of the most generous of cultures. After all we have come through, our contemporary becomes indignant when he sees groups openly flaunting their hate. These hateful people, however, do not represent a flaw or error in the civilized order of the world;

they represent our lack of attentiveness. We were wrong to believe that the civilized order is one that coasts merrily along thanks to the strength of its system; no, civilized order is the product of a permanent effort of vigilance.

Thus, the happiness of a society, like that of an individual, remains an earned and precarious blessing. It is not the assured result of social reorganization, as the ideologues of Progress would have us believe. Nor is it a momentary distraction of Fate, as the pessimists tell us. But rather, it is a moment of maximum watchfulness, during which evil and uncertainty have been surmounted, tamed, and controlled.

The question today is whether our contemporary, disabused of the idea of utopia, can still have hope. Icarus now realizes that he has fallen back into the labyrinth where the Minotaur—barbarity, misery, and separation—still lurks. Will this terrible disappointment discourage him from new undertakings? Is he now ready to fall on his knees, his eyes filled with tears? Surely not, for he cannot resist wanting to improve his lot, nor resist fighting the Minotaur. Yet just how will he fight, now that he has begun to understand the obstacles that make his struggle so uncertain? He must first grasp the depth of his previous errors and redefine the meaning of the struggle. It took a utopian spirit to believe in the radiant future of ideologies. But it was also out of a utopian spirit that he believed in the definitive guarantees of a humanist culture or in the happy society of the postwar era. In both cases this spirit considered its work to be an enterprise of reason or technique, and therefore securely established: the accumulations of technology are in theory never lost or called into question. We trusted the rule of law, the welfare state, and in France, the Republic, to maintain the level of happiness they were able to generate. But we were wrong to do so because we mistook the means for the end. Institutional structures are of course powerful means of attaining social well-being. But they can hardly be the *causes* of this well-being. In fact, they are nothing more than means in the hands of what might be termed vigilance. Social well-being and happiness in general are not only the result of rational undertakings, including various programs and organizations, but rather—and more than anything else—the result of an intrepid will to hope, together with a vigilance with regards to being, that is, reality. These two predispositions, when they do not weaken, remain steadfastly alert, always ready to readjust and even reinvent programs and organizations to serve their purposes. Having put too much trust in our instruments, we have let them stiffen and become distorted. And we have excessive confidence in them because, obsessed with rationality, we have forgotten that what is essential is to be found in hope and vigilance, not reason and technique.

So just what is this hope, which seems at first glance to be utopian and yet is really its opposite? While utopia refers to an impossible undertaking, the hope we are talking about here is one of hoping for the unhoped-for, yet possible reality, in the sense that Heraclitus had in mind when he wrote that "he who does not expect the unexpected will not attain it."[1] Utopia aims for the impossible in that it radically contradicts the essence of the human, and that is why utopian endeavors result in an inhuman world. But the kind of hope we are talking about consists of allowing what is most desirable in humanity to flourish, without however denying the reality of our condition. Was the rule of law, which subordinates violence to legal structures, not unhoped-for? The successful institution of the Truce of God in the Middle Ages, which limited wars to enviable proportions; the Edict of Nantes; the European peace projects since the fifteenth century, which today have given rise to the construction of Europe; the well-being of the postwar era; the fall of the Berlin Wall in 1989— were these not unhoped-for things? Hannah Arendt wrote, in reference to communist totalitarianism: "A decisive salutary change can only result from a kind of miracle," and added that we would have to "free ourselves from the prejudice that holds that miracles are purely and exclusively religious phenomena in which something otherworldly and superhuman intervenes in the process of human affairs and natural events."[2] The demonstrated human ability to make the unhoped-for come true must convince our discouraged Icarus that a world without utopia need not be a fatalistic world, devoid of promise and therefore devoid of inspiration.

Nevertheless, the incredible achievements and events that have turned societies in the direction of the "good," that is, towards conciliation and solidarity, are not the result of rational projects of transformation, ideologies, or utopias. They could never have happened but through the patience of an interminable will that would simply never give up. In all such cases it was essential to be always watching for the fractures through which malevolence creeps in, to seize the opportune moment to propose an otherwise impossible peace, to be watchful for the moments when the adversary let down his guard, or to use subtle trickery against those prepared for direct attacks. The work of an ant and a titan: of an ant because never discouraged or pretentious; of a titan because more determined and self-assured than any adversary.

All the great victories we have won over war, poverty, and oppression have in large part used the arms of reason, and yet they were made possible only through the perseverance to hope for certain ends that societies of the time did not seem to contain even in embryonic form. But this perseverance in battle is accompanied by vigilance for being, without which it really amounts to nothing. It is not enough to say no to evil and to concoct grandiose plans against it: this would be like thinking in black-and-white while fighting an adversary capable of seeing gray. One must say no, but with a patient and determined attentiveness to the reality of the world. For evil hides in tiny cracks and sometimes rises out of the good itself. If we have been victims of the Capua syndrome, it is not only due to the lethargy that comes so naturally to happy people, but above all because we erroneously thought that our organizations held the "good" in and of themselves.

The man of ideological utopia and the man of the utopia of Progress, who are twins split from the same embryo, found themselves in a position of expectancy. They awaited a radiant future and the resolution of our problems. Expectation implies that time alone will suffice as long as certain specific conditions are met. Our contemporary, however, realizes that expectancy will have to be replaced with attentiveness: he will have to become once again he who hopes, even if it is for the unhopeable, and arm himself with tenacious vigilance. This does not mean that the latter must act while the former was content to wait in the same way one waits for a train, even if it is true that there was something of that mindset in his blind confidence in History. The man of Progress found himself confronted with the work of clearing the land. He believed that it was up to him to root out Evil once and for all. The man of vigilance patiently waters a few seeds in his attempt to win the battle against the weeds. The man of Progress assumed that his expectations would be achieved through a calculating rationality, and in this respect he resembled the functionary who can go home at night without thinking at all about his work. For he could not imagine that reality might be playing tricks on his reason or that it might prove itself to be more intelligent than he. The man of vigilance, on the other hand, must stay on the bridge night and day and spend his weekends on the lookout. He cannot blindly trust institutions or authorities, or even himself, for every day he needs to verify whether the means correspond to the ends and are, in fact, in place. He has no guarantees, and must remain everwatchful. Now it might be said that this situation is quite exhausting. True. But it is the only way to obtain, and again with no certainty whatsoever, our hoped-for and sometimes unhoped-for happiness.

The man of Progress believed that future happiness was his due. The man of vigilance, on the contrary, knows that he owes a debt to the world. The attitude of vigilance contains the idea of a debt to be paid. And this is why our contemporary, who boasts of owing nothing to anyone, prefers to remain for as long as possible in the warm, closed world of utopia. The man of vigilance considers that he is the guardian of the world in both the present and future. He therefore answers personally for future peace and justice. He acts as guarantor of this future, as uncertain and as distant as it may seem. He willingly vouches for a promise, voluntarily carrying a debt, since one can watch over only what one has been entrusted with.

What then is this mysterious debt, the mere mention of which reminds us of the religious presuppositions we wish to discard? Does this mean, as Christianity for so long affirmed, that man is guilty of evil, and is consequently responsible for repairing it? No doubt he is as blameworthy of evil as he is credit-worthy of future perfection. He is, however, responsible for the betterment of the world, because he clearly feels that the world cannot remain as it is.

If we cannot be found guilty for what we have not done, how then can we be held responsible for what we have not initiated? The mindset of the watchdog of justice or the peacemaker can be understood through man's feeling of finitude. Because he is unhappy with imperfection and insufficiency, the man who acts demonstrates through his action that there is a promise to be honored. Because he holds within himself the points of reference for a better society, man feels an obligation to bring this society into being. An abiding awareness of "what remains to be done" in order for the world to be whole compels us to improve the world. For man is the only being capable of thinking as well as taking action, possessing both knowledge—or at least an intuition—of what is lacking, and the necessary tool to remedy this lack, that is, action. He is like the man in a crowd who alone perceives a danger and who alone possesses the necessary instruments to alleviate it. He has no choice. The situation demands that he act by virtue of his unique qualities, and thus invests him with a role. Man is a debtor before a future that is his alone—and which does not await a supernatural miracle, the providence of abstract History, or anonymous chance to come into being. It cannot be said that man was thrust into the world "just for this," in the sense that he is genetically programmed to transform the world or destined by some unknown god to perform his task, for he remains free from what he will not accomplish. But he is born with this blinding debt, and this debt is the basis of ethics.

If we can speak in this way of an obligation to the future, we must add that the shape and definition of this obligation change over time. There have been eras of injustice in which the man of vigilance found himself to a greater extent in charge of justice, and centuries of permanent war, when he found himself looking for ways to achieve peace. Every moment in history hopes for what it lacks. This is why we can speak of a specific role for each generation—in the sense, for example, that the current generation will have to rebuild the societies left in massive ruins by communism. This does not mean that every generation responds to its role in a satisfactory way. Yet each generation grows up faced with a project that beckons it and gives shape to its historic debt. It is in the magnitude of this work that each new generation can hope even for the unhopeable, that is, for a historic miracle, provided that vigilance is exercised.

We can no longer wait, as the ideologue was wont to do. For there is nothing to wait for in this sense: no radiant future will spring out of our rational projects. In fact, it is because we have come to realize this truth that we so easily find ourselves in the grips of discouragement. We will have to relearn the patience to hope, through vigilance and in uncertainty. And we will have to believe anew in the unhopeable, which is not a utopia. But this newfound attitude implies our condition as fundamentally incomplete beings. The debt that lies at the heart of a sense of responsibility for the world is constitutive, not temporary. Vigilance is the state of mind of care-givers who can never entirely heal, can never entirely eradicate illness and evil, but untiringly keep threats at bay. Thus, in order to finally lay utopias to rest and replace them with vigilance, we will have to accept the idea of our essential finitude. Even if we have tamed it, our world resembles and will always resemble a labyrinth, in the sense that nothing is guaranteed in advance—far from it. Our rediscovered and intimate conviction of finitude gives new significance to prudence, the very quality that Icarus in his labyrinth needs most.

This means that, by virtue of our need to understand our world and unceasingly try to improve it, we are confronted by the fact that not all situations are irreducible to one another. Naturally, science and social organization have permitted the construction of certain models—if this were not the case, our lives would seem chaotic and arbitrary. But the major error of our time is to believe that every situation can be fit into such models. This belief is precisely why we cling to models that are only means to an end, and that finally end up ceasing to serve the objectives for which they were created in the first place. The republican educational model, or the French model of public service, should be reconsidered in light of the passing of time and their inadequacy to serve the needs of a changed society.

By recognizing certain situations as irreducible, our aim is not to defend a "situational" logic, that is, to defend an arbitrary opportunism. It is rather a question of re-establishing the basis of human action in a contingent world, which implies replacing competence with prudence as the primary quality needed to know, judge, and decide, as much in the political as in the ethical realm. And this implies that we must rely on individual conscience, a faculty that has been too often forgotten.

Our time has lost touch with the advice once given to children: before you act, always ask yourself if what you are considering is right or wrong. Not that our contemporary always acts merely on the basis of self-interest or whim. If he is reasonably honest, he seeks to know whether his action contravenes a law, either civic law or the law of social consensus. But he does not seek to hear what his conscience whispers to him. He is not a cynic, for he does not confuse right and wrong, the limits of which are given him by the law. But generally speaking, he has forgotten that he has a conscience, in other words, the faculty to discern what is right even in contradiction with laws, and to discern the particular good in particular situations.

In the Eichmann trial, the witnesses observed with horror that they had before them the most conscience-less individual one could possibly imagine. Eichmann was absolutely impenitent about his crimes. It is not that he had replaced right with wrong and vice-versa. He was in fact ignorant of these categories. Or rather, he was aware of them only within the framework of positive law: he had simply obeyed the law of his government, nothing more. He could not imagine any other criteria for judging actions. Any individual who admits nothing but positive law as a criterion for right and wrong—or what amounts to the same thing, the law of social consensus as dictated, or rather suggested, by "correct" thinkers—finds himself deprived of a conscience, and runs the risk of making grave mistakes. Even those who recognize only the law of a church or moral institution are capable of serious error. Not that individual conscience is always right. But if it is wrong, it only concerns particular cases. There is nothing more dangerous than institutionalized laws or social conformism. For because of their authority, no one distrusts them. By gathering behind them the weak and undecided, they can lead whole peoples into the worst excesses in the name of a good that no one has ever dreamt of questioning. Nothing can replace the conscience: it is the only bulwark against the waywardness of authorities. Of course, Eichmann's crimes were so horrible that his case cannot be viewed as typical. But any loss of individual conscience carries with it great risk, even if it does not always result in horrid crimes. Our contemporary, who knows no other criteria for right and wrong apart from positive law and ambient conformism, unwittingly becomes vulnerable to the snare of unseen forms of perversity.

Because the objective "good," generally founded on religious grounds, had disappeared, modern thinkers, under the influence of Kant, have identified right action with action that is in obedience to the law. It can happen, however, that the law is bad. One might ask according to what criteria one can consider it to be bad, if there is no longer any such thing as objective right or wrong. But this raises another question: Why judge Nazi law to be execrable when several plebiscites were held that approved it, and when it eventually became the law of the triumphant state as well as the social consensus? Furthermore, how can we judge Nazi law when several decades of "scientific" thinking viewed eugenics indulgently or even favorably, and when anti-Semitism was so widespread? Do we hate Nazi law now because it is the law of the losers? Certainly not. Do we hate it in the name of a religious law, which would imply that we are playing the role of Antigone? Surely not. Could it be that we are following today's correct thinkers, who hate Nazism above everything else? We would again cry out "No!"—even against the correct thinkers, and even if we were ostracized by them, a normally constituted individual would revolt against such a criminal law. So why then? Because a normal person's conscience tells him that Nazi law is evil.

But while it may be the only bulwark against the possibility of law gone mad, individual conscience cannot seem to find its place in the sun. No one trusts it. And this is not just by chance. All the currents of recent history join together in scorning it.

In its struggle against casuistics and what has been called probabilism, modern Christianity has restored the authority of a moral law applied directly to particular situations. It did this to fight a situational morality that represented the excesses of the traditional prudential ethics inherited from Aristotle and Thomas Aquinas. By continuing this fight today it struggles against modern relativism, which is ultimately just another situational morality: the problematic is clear in the thought of John Paul II. But however just the reasons might be, individual conscience has had its authority withdrawn. Catholics have for a long time now lost the habit of judging for themselves: they merely find themselves confronted with the question of determining which law should be applied in any given situation. And this is what the hierarchy calls the conscience: the faculty of recognizing the law and applying it, while it should actually be the faculty of interpreting the law in particular cases, and even judging it. At the point where the individual, sovereign in a world without criteria, is in such great need of his ability to judge, he finds himself robbed of it by tradition. Religious law is no longer adequate, and the kind of individual reflection it has helped to erase is no longer there to compensate for its absence.

Modern ideologies have not honored individual conscience to any greater extent. They required passive obedience to predetermined doctrines and to its minions, that is, the party authorities. Here again the individual lost confidence in his own capacity for moral reflection. And so contemporary man, disabused of ideologies, can no longer even form for himself an intrinsic vision of the good. This is undoubtedly why, in the West as in the East, the apparatchiks who have lost the faith fall so easily into corruption: not only because the former ideology was embodied in a morality as well as a social system, but also because it destroyed the habits of individual judgment.

Our old beliefs, as if they had employed a scorched-earth policy, have left only emptiness behind: a naked and shivering subject deprived of judgment and independence of spirit. And we only perpetuate the situation: our fear of irrationality, which keeps us from adopting an attitude of prudence, at the same time prevents us from taking individual conscience seriously.

The disappearance of objective points of reference gives rise to terrible distress when there is action to be taken. For even if complacency eventually guides his decisions, the individual, especially in difficult circumstances, clearly feels that right and wrong must be out there somewhere, even if he feels incapable of discerning them. Having become so unaccustomed to exercising judgment within his conscience, and being so used to guidance by undebatable exterior laws, valid for each and every case, he naturally seeks out authorities capable of dictating to him the criteria for good judgment. For him, legislative decisions serve as the arbiters of moral law, and anything that is legal becomes by definition morally acceptable. Legislators in turn call upon committees to define morality. These committees replace not only the long-gone religious or ideological laws, but also the individual conscience that religions and ideologies had erased. The individual longs to have answers without having to ask questions, for he no longer knows how to ask himself the right questions. The existence of the committee, not legally sovereign, but ultimately sovereign by virtue of the authority with which it is entrusted, leads us to believe that ethics is a sort of science of limit-situations, however contradictory these two notions might be. Of course the people who are appointed to these committees are called "wise," which would seem to indicate the institutionalization of a collective prudence while prudence is lacking in the individual. But collective prudence means precisely nothing: prudence is either individual or is not at all, since it applies to specific cases. The "wise men" themselves are not mistaken, because they cite their scientific competency in order to convince others of the validity of their judgments. And it is quite natural that science should be brought into the picture in this way, since it offers objectivity where an objective "good" is no longer clear. However, the objectivity of science applies only to scientific knowledge, never to moral judgment, and the surreptitious blurring of one area into another is deceptive. Furthermore, it risks becoming extremely dangerous. We know from experience just how tyrannical moral law can become when religion, even when it does not hold political power but wields social authority alone, dictates that this law is applicable to limit-situations in their particularity. A moral law proclaimed from on high in the name of science would tyrannize to an even greater extent, by virtue of its universality and its unquestioned objectivity: one can always reject religious truth, but who would dare question scientific truth, unless one wished to seem mad? One shudders to think that the issue of euthanasia, which touches individual consciences in the secret of their hearts, and which hinges on decisions made by families in tragic situations, could be settled by the scientific oracle raised to the level of Inquisitor.

The citizen, because he votes, is considered capable of consciously ruling on issues of general democratic interest, issues concerning the fate of society, but he is witnessing the decline of his capacity to rule on the issue of the individual good, which seems paradoxical. But not entirely, however, for we count above all on technicians to take care of politics. Led as much in politics as in morals by those who are "competent," and who think in his stead, the modern individual is undoubtedly much less sovereign than is believed. The authorities he turns to in his moral distress will not fail to reinvent precisely the type of oppressive truth from which he wanted to free himself. And it is easy to see just how helpless the individual is before conformist thinking, before the truth of consensus, to which he submits unawares. If he does not wish to be yet again faced with systems of seductive and demented thinking, and if he wants to be able to resist the excesses of the law whatever its origin, he will have to rediscover his moral conscience. One might object by saying that to constantly be asking questions of right and wrong is nothing short of an exhausting task, and that in restoring this atrophied faculty, peace of mind will necessarily be sacrificed. This is probably true. But the grandeur of man lies in his ability to judge situations in the midst of the disorder he necessarily finds himself confronted with. And it is odd that an individual whose most diverse rights we claim to have guaranteed should not be treated as an adult. As soon as we speak of allowing everyone to judge according to his conscience, voices are raised in protest of the danger that decisions would become arbitrary. Naturally, individual conscience can widely and frequently be wrong. But do the official authorities, bearers of the image of what is right, not also often make mistakes? Their historic errors need no retelling. "Scientific" authorities will err in the same way, and will impose their follies on an initially consenting people, who will have to endure the inevitable catastrophes before they finally open their eyes. For the heart of the individual conscience is stirred, all too late, by disastrous events.

How then can a way be found to personally judge the law of the state or the consensus of correct thinkers, if no other norm exists? History teaches us that a moral conscience will find its way without the help of any extrinsic authority or any objective "good." The prudential ethics of Aristotle emanates from such a conscience, deprived of recourse and assurance. The ancient Greeks were unaware of anything like the Ten Commandments; they never thought that political law was sufficient to express the good. In this sense, they were completely unarmed. Man as described by Aristotle knew no universal ethical models, but that did not stop him from seeking the good. Nor did it lead him to expect a god to identify it for him. His conscience gropingly defined the good, without any moral code having been imposed upon him. Where, then, did he find his bearings, since they were not prescribed? He perceived them in the uncertain world and in fragile experiences. Perhaps he once saw a man who seemed to him to be wise, one whose life-work would be crowned with history's laurels. He then had in his mind's eye a path of life that made for happiness. He listened and collected knowledge, but he was not restricted by *a prioris*. He knew how to wait and observe. He drew lessons from everything. He neither imitated nor obeyed. He was inspired. He navigated more than he forged ahead. He knew intuitively what he was looking for, but did not know what it looked like.

We would gain a lot if we acquired the inward freedom of such a man, if we were able to step back, as individuals, from conventional ways of thinking. This inward freedom presupposes choices rooted in individual conscience, a re-organization of common criteria. As such, it is a much different thing from mere whim or errant thought. But it differs at least as much from the kind of freedom that the philosophy of rights confers upon us. We have a tendency to believe that freedom can be summed up in a catalogue of rights. But as Marx rightly recognized, rights mean nothing if they are not coupled with the means to exercise them. What does freedom of information mean to an illiterate? Other conditions must be added as well, not concrete social conditions but those concerning receptiveness to the truth. What do rights, the outward manifestations of external freedom, mean without inward freedom? What is freedom of thought worth if we are expected to echo the thoughts of the politically correct? What value can suffrage have if there is only one "politics," so-called scientific and objective, all the rest having been marginalized as "protest movements"?

We aspire with all our strength to an independent existence, and are unaware of what it means to have an independent mind. Yet independent thinking is precisely what is required. Contemporary man does not want to depend on anything or anyone, which is impossible, for society is no more than a structure of bonds, and the individual dies if he cuts himself loose—indeed, we are forced to manufacture artificial bonds for those individuals who have either drifted away from society or who have been marginalized. Still, the personal thinking of contemporary man is generally no more than an echo of common thinking. This is true even though he is in great need of independence of mind, although this need does not occur to him. It was through this sort of independence that Socrates said he would rather agree with himself against the rest of the world rather than agree with the world at the cost of disagreement with himself. Schindler acted against official thinking and against the authorities, even against the safety of his own family. But he acted according to what he believed was right. The internal judgment of such unorthodox men naturally does not carry the guarantee of being right. But it increases their chances of being right, if only because it involves questioning and reflecting on what is right. We have no way of always avoiding error. But we risk falling into collective error, disguised as collective truth, if we neglect to question the so-called self-evident truths. We must constantly be on the lookout for the disguised presence of Panurge.*

* Panurge is a character from Rabelais's *Pantagruel*. A debauched, cynical coward, he is the constant companion of the novel's main character, Pantagruel. In English literature, Iago comes to mind. *Trans.*

CONCLUSION

Icarus could defy his human condition, but he could not deny it in the end. Having attempted to transcend his own condition, man is experiencing a separation analogous to that of an exile and lives without fervor in a land that is not his own. His efforts, even when they are monumental, remain useless. His failures are unexplained. The contemporary age will have to try to learn how the individual can reappropriate his surroundings. However—and here is where the difficulty lies—the individual is not the storied exile, happy to be back home, but rather he must be seen as a repentant magician forced to return home, back to reality, where rabbits can no longer be pulled out of hats and spirits can no longer be called upon. This return home is thus made in suffering. We find our surroundings confining, at least in the light of our past hopes. Any "condition" takes the shape of an enclosure that cannot be escaped. But above all, man's suffering stems from disenchantment, from the feeling of disappointment at having tumbled back down to earth.

Two dispositions hold us in their grip: a relentless resentment towards our own errors, tied to our will to expiate our historical sins; and a boundless disappointment at not having been able to make destiny submit to our hopes. For the time being, neither this resentment nor this disappointment has reached its limits. We are blindly subjected to them. And we spend our time either rehashing the catastrophes from which we have emerged or weeping over our dashed expectations.

We find ourselves at a point in our history where we no longer have a very clear idea of who we are, nor of what we can hope for. And yet our distress itself provides us, without our being aware of it, with all the necessary means to answer these questions, and to do so more soundly than before.

All traditions having been rejected, all certainties revoked, we no longer know anything in advance. Our situation resembles that of the first astonished minds of our history: the pre-Socratics. We are waking up under an ancient Greek sky. Still, our memory is encumbered by everything we no longer wish to see.

This unprecedented conjunction of a heavily charged memory and a virgin spirit may actually give rise to great hope. For our astonishment has left in its wake great quantities of superfluous baggage and incredible doctrines, in which the old civilizations ultimately became too mired. But our memory, haunted by images of the unacceptable, has erected barriers at the edge of the abyss and will not fail to subject each new certainty to its demands.

From the modern project we have learned that our "condition" cannot be summed up in any definitive dogmas. For we have, for better and for worse, visited places other than those assigned to us, and we have managed to escape all definitions. If any religion again claims to have a complete understanding of man, we will recognize that claim as being pure vanity. We will no longer let any orthodoxy define our limits from atop an uninhabited realm.

What this means is that any new anthropology will have experience alone as its starting point, and probably, initially, only negative proofs. We will learn about ourselves by identifying what makes us unhappy. And because that entails making judgments, moral conscience, as well as experience, will be necessary.

At what price, and under what conditions, will experience be able to reveal anthropological truths? For experience does not teach on its own. It has to be decrypted by clear vision. Prejudices confuse it. Today, our way of looking at social phenomena remains encumbered by former certitudes, which have grown out of the ideologies we in principle have rejected. We remain heavily under the influence of what we believe we have left behind. This situation is understandable, for we have abandoned systems because of their excesses and in order to flee their perverse consequences, but without having analyzed their poisoned logic or foundations. Thus, our feelings still bind us to their generous illusions. Moreover, our minds remain stuck within a particular individualistic interpretation of human rights that we are unable to consider with a critical eye because we are convinced it is the only correct interpretation. Furthermore, we are unconscious followers of the ideology of the apostate, which leads us to make judgments out of resentment, out of blind passion. If we really want to learn from our experiences, we will have to acquire a spirit of independence and patient attentiveness to reality. Any certitude will have to remain subjected to the attentiveness that judges its consequences, and it will have to accept being called into question. The son of Icarus will have to become a watchman. Being attentive to reality, an attitude so neglected by our contemporary, does not call for disinterested or fatalistic contemplation, nor does it call for cynical acceptance of everything that happens. It rather calls for an active consideration of reality, including ethical reality. Attentiveness means not only having one's eyes wide open to the real or true, but having a conscience attuned to the good that is part of reality: that is, there exists both a good and an evil that spring up of themselves and indelibly color reality. There are norms that are simple givens. We can no longer claim the contrary, since we recognize what is in itself unacceptable. We will remain on the lookout for misfortune or obvious happiness, neither of which spring from standard repertoires or dogmas, but from experience enlightened by moral conscience.

Every political action will have to be based on a reflection upon happiness and its conditions. It will have to distinguish between temporary well-being and the kind of happiness that integrates time and space. It will have to recognize the limits beyond which the quest for happiness gives rise to certain unhappiness. Our history has not accustomed us to this indefinite quest for an anthropology. The Christian era defined man in advance in the light of tradition and sacred texts. The ideological era held that man was infinitely plastic and therefore rejected any anthropology. Contemporary "correct" thinkers proclaim with the confidence of theologians that an individual can be happy in the short-sightedness of complacency. We have to return to the ancients to find a sort of innocent, open questioning about the nature of man and his happiness. Or perhaps to the Renaissance, when various adventurous minds dared to rethink man's nature without using the dominant categories. That is why we have so much in common with these two moments in history. Anthropology will never again be triumphant or sure of itself; it will forever remain in self-doubt. A difficult proposition, because the mind seeks repose in certainty of thought, and tends to linger there.

The coming era will seek to know the human world in order to be able to make it better. We will then perhaps witness the rejection of the absolute primacy of action over contemplation that is proper to modernity. Contemplation, as a gaze cast upon the world, became useless once the prospect of recreating society arose. Since one of the aims of modernity consisted of replacing the labyrinth, there was no further need to become familiar with its intricacies. The time that is now dawning will see the reappearance of the necessity to seek the truth about the human world, or what amounts to the same thing, it will see the reappearance of the idea of "truth" as an adequate account of the real, while the previous era saw truth as the creation of the future, identifying it with the negation of knowledge and the primacy of the will.

The present tendency is to live in unreality, or in the disharmony between what is left of utopia and the reality of ordinary humanity.

We have not yet identified all the black markets through which our condition is reasserting itself. Nor have we yet really come to understand by what trick of fate all of our brilliant inventions— sovereign individual liberty, individualistic democracy, the murder of God—have given rise to certain unfortunate consequences. We do, however, realize that egalitarianism creates inequalities beneath the surface; that rights viewed as sacred harm even their benefici- aries; that well-being can be a contradiction of happiness; that instinctive emotion is not sufficient to fashion a coherent ethics. And our clear-mindedness grows with the ever-widening gap between reality and discourse, between daily life and the projects that go out of their way to deny it. The man described by Kierkegaard who builds a sumptuous castle and then lives in the gatekeeper's quarters, or even in the doghouse, will some day gather about himself all that remains of his wisdom and will draw up the plans for a house of truly human proportions. The children of Icarus will no longer demand bread, as was the case two centuries ago, nor dreams, as they did a century later, but rather truth. Truth is the only foundation upon which an indispensable ethics can be built. For no one can seek the good without defining it. All hope rests on knowledge. And no society can respect man without knowing what is specifically human.

The son of Icarus will have to live with his questions and accept his tragic condition once again. He will know that complete fulfill- ment is beyond his reach: only God is self-sufficient. He will have to live in a world where evil and death are lurking, where uncer- tainty impertinently provokes reason, and where war is always waiting in the wings of peace. He will know that he is not destined to witness the disappearance of oppression and war in order to one day find rest in his warm and cozy home. He will discover a home- land that has flexible conceptions of justice and liberty. And he will stop cursing this incertitude when he has finally understood that the tragic is a bearer of meaning. Life has value in the antinomies among which it struggles. The man of vigilance is a perpetual guarantor of meaning and as such will always have his place in the world. He is indefinitely worthy because he alone maintains the presence of a precarious "good" apt to disappear if ever he should lower his guard.

What this means is that the son of Icarus, aware that the presence of the Minotaur is ineluctable, will meditate upon death, conflict, and human selfishness in order to attenuate their effects and soften their harmful blows. By doing so, no matter what he believes, he will be more efficient than his forefathers, for one advantageously engages in combat only what one first recognizes is present. He will ceaselessly seek out the reasons for his most intimate certitudes. He will rebuild the morality that the utopias had dismantled by putting themselves in its place. He will refashion the otherness that egali-tarianism had tried to dissolve. He will invent safety mechanisms to keep his truths from becoming oppressive. The great difficulty will be to defend the gains of modernity while at the same time strug-gling against its excesses. For taking a simplistic approach is always the first reflex, and the great temptation of this disappointed era could easily be an overall rejection, a return to the besieged cocoon of *a priori* certitudes, or purity-seeking fundamentalism, which is just another form of utopian delirium.

The son of Icarus will not be ashamed to admit that the absolute remains the missing piece of the puzzle, and that certain mysteries still weigh upon him. For he will know from his successive adven-tures that life is also nourished by what it is missing.

NOTES

CHAPTER 2

1. *L'Essence du politique* (Sirey, 1965), pp. 4–5.
2. *Du Principe fédératif* (Marcel Rivière), p. 521.
3. (Hachette, 1867), p. 368.
4. (Guillaumin, 1877), p. 209.
5. *L'Esquisse d'un tableau historique des progrès de l'humanité* (Flammarion, 1988), p. 294.

CHAPTER 3

1. A. Glucksman and B.-H. Lévy, for example, have recently rediscovered two obvious truths: the imperfection of the world is irreducible (*Le Onzième commandement*, Flammarion, 1991) and utopia engenders terror (*La Pureté dangereuse*, Grasset, 1994). New currents of thought are re-legitimizing politics as conflict (Chantal Mouffe, *La Politique et ses enjeux*, La Découverte, 1994). What is interesting about these analyses is not so much their content, which has long been known, as it is the fact of their open manifestation. It must not be forgotten to what extent this point of view was for a long time considered heretical, and marginalized when it did exist. Julien Freund recounts, in the excellent book by Charles Blanchet, *L'Aventure du politique* (Critérion, 1991), how Jean Hyppolite refused to oversee his thesis, according to which politics was irreducibly linked

to conflict; and how during the final defense of his thesis, ultimately written under Raymond Aron, Jean Hyppolite, a member of the jury, cried out while the argument about conflict was being made, "If the world is like that, all that's left for me to do is commit suicide. . . ."

CHAPTER 5

1. *Aurore de la raison historique* (Klincksieck, 1989), pp. 221–22.

2. Conceptualized in particular by American pragmatism from John Dewey (1859–1952) to Richard Rorty.

3. C. Viola speaks of "the invasive aspect of truth . . . which presupposes, in the subject himself, the existence of passivity . . . ; the knowing subject realizes the fact that he is not the absolute master in the strict sense of the term, that is, he does not fully exercise his liberty." *Les Dimensions de la vérité* (Villejuif : CNRS, 1994), p. 15.

CHAPTER 7

1. (Gallimard, 1970), p. 113.

CHAPTER 8

1. Conclusions of the National Ethics Committee, December 1994.

2. "Faits et méfaits de la pensée correcte," *Le Débat*, no. 81, 1994. In this matter, what is true in the United States is now also applicable to Europe.

CHAPTER 9

1. For example, F. Magnard in *Le Banquet*, no. 1, 1992, pp. 160–61: "Until very recently, political thought has involved the search for a theoretical foundation for action. That period, which began with Plato, has come to an end. . . . Today, the only project worth undertaking—autonomy—is not founded; it is projected into the future."

2. *Theory of Justice*, pp. 595–96.

3. In a speech given when he was received by the French Academy of Moral and Political Sciences.

CHAPTER 15

1. *On the Republic*, I, XXXII: "From the domination by kings and by the great, there is usually a phase of a free popular state, while free peoples do not return to kings, nor do they clamor for a rich and powerful elite."
2. (ŒIL, 1984), pp. 96–97.

CHAPTER 16

1. Cf. the study of Schicksanalyse by L. Szondi, in H. Niel, *L'Analyse du destin* (Desclée de Brouwers, 1960). For Szondi, mental illnesses were actually illnesses of destiny.

CHAPTER 17

1. *Les conséquences du pragmatisme* (Le Seuil, 1993), p. 22.
2. *Platon et l'Europe* (Verdier, 1983), pp.10–11.
3. *L'Esprit européen* (La Baconnière, 1947), p. 276.

CHAPTER 18

1. *Esquisse . . .* , p. 296.

CHAPTER 19

1. Fragment 66.
2. "La politique a-t-elle finalement encore un sens?" in *Ontologie et politique* (Tierce, 1989), p. 165.

INDEX